D1242257

HISTORY

OF

PHARMACY

and
Pharmaceutical Industry

All rights reserved
in the whole world
for Asklepios Press,
Lussy-s/-Morges, Switzerland

ISBN 2-88095-093-2

Distributed in the United States, Canada, Central and South America by THIEME-STRATTON INC.

381, Park Avenue South
NEW-YORK, NY 10016
Phone : 212. 683.50.88.

HISTORY

OF

PHARMACY

and

Pharmaceutical Industry

Honorary Head Librarian
of the City of Paris Library

Henri BONNEMAIN
General Secretary of the French Society
of the History of Pharmacy,
Member of the Academy of Pharmacy

Frank J. BOVÉ
Ph. G.B.S. Fordham University New York City
M.A. Ph.D. Basle University,
Member of the National Association of Scientific Writers

First part :
original text in French, translated into English by
James Desmond NEWELL, B.A. (HONS) of the Queen's University, Belfast

Second part :
(from "Impacts on two fateful centuries" on . . .)
original text in English
by Frank J. BOVÉ

ASKLEPIOS PRESS

PARIS — LAUSANNE

FOREWORD

As President of the International Association for the history of pharmacy, I was asked by the publisher to write the preface to this book—and so I have happily accepted. An earlier, most succesful edition, written by Patrice Boussel and Henri Bonnemain, presented the various periods of development of classical pharmacy. This revised edition includes an additional section, History of the Pharmaceutical Industry by the American historian Dr. F.J. Bove. This section fulfills the publisher's intent to provide an international edition for experts in this field. The science of pharmacy, the profession of the pharmacist, and the areas of application have become so internationalized that demand has increasingly grown for a detailed analysis of the history of international pharmacy. F.J. Bove's work is extremely significant as it shows the pharmaceutical industry to be an integral component in the 7000-year-old history of service to mankind.

Until the middle of the 19th Century, the pharmacist prepared his own medicines. However, the development and technological evolution of the natural sciences—in particular, chemistry—and the changing economic and social structures of the era led to the expansion of small pharmacies into industrial undertakings that later grew into factories. Certain pharmaceutical enterprises sprang from dye producing companies as organic dyes and synthetic medicines revealed a similar chemical structure. The pharmaceutical factories not only manufactured the basic substances but also the finished products which could then be used for therapeutic purposes. This resulted in new production processes that transferred the primary function of the traditional pharmacist, the making of medicines, to the more efficient factories. Thus the pharmacist lost his privileged position as others such as chemists, biologists, and engineers added their expertise to the field.

Among the pharmacists were a few who quickly realized that the increasing demand of a steadily rising population could no longer be met by conventional manufacturing in small workshops, thus necessitating large-scale production in pharmaceutical factories. In addition, the production of numerous medicines was neither technically feasible nor economically profitable for the individual pharmacist. As all jobs and professions undergo change, so too has this profession; all the applications of its art have been modified by the passage of time. Yet the goal of service to mankind has remained constant throughout the 7000 years of pharmaceutical practice. This has not merely included healing, but also the prevention of disease. Taken together, these have maximized care for man's physical, mental, and social welfare as well as extended his lifespan.

HISTORY OF PHARMACY

To realize this goal of service, natural development in the industry has brought about drastic changes in the thoughts and insights of practitioners both in pharmacies and in the industrial laboratories. Whereas the work of the industrial pharmacist is based on his scientific, technical and administrative knowledge, the pharmacist who works in a pharmacy or hospital must have a thorough working knowledge of biology and medical therapy in order to understand the medicinal-therapeutic work of the physician and to inform and advise the public accordingly.

It is my opinion that this industry, which began in the 19th century, and which has advanced considerably in the 20th century, has given new impulse to the profession, the science, and the practical application of pharmacy. Time hastens relentlessly towards the turn of the century and questions arise as to what will be the further development of our profession. We, the pharmacists, should also participate in the shaping of future trends. 7000 years of knowledge can be of great help; thus the study of this book may well contribute to the progressive advancement of pharmacy.

Budapest, 1982
Prof. Dr. (pharm.) K. Zalai
President of the International Association for the History of Pharmacy
Member of the Academie Internationale d'Histoire de la Pharmacie
Vice President of the Fédération internationale pharmaceutique
President of the Pharmaceutical Society of Hungary
Professor of medicine at Semmelweis University, Budapest

INTRODUCTION

History, formerly a literary genre and for some an insignificant conjectural science, has since evolved by means of accumulation of studies carried out, discoveries made, and perfection of methods of approach and adoption of a global perspective. The history of the history of the sciences represents no sombre museum of dead theories and outdated explanations but a vivid chapter in the account of the general history of human thought, outlining, as Lucien Febvre said, "the intellect's adapting to the concrete and man's taking possession of his environment."

No longer is the history of pharmacy simply that of drugs. It now includes the history of physical and natural science, medical principles, and techniques and instruments, as well as the people who had to choose and prepare the medicines, their relationships with the public, the related professions, the economy of a particular period and country and history in general.

To recognize any deterioration in health implies knowing "what a sound state of health is." How a healthy constitution can be impaired varies according to civilization, social class, level of education and age. For example presence of intestinal worms, a "disease" according to the doctors of the western world, is the sign of good health in certain South American tribes. Not having worms becomes for them a pathological case. Society (most frequently the doctor, the word 'doctor' being used in the widest sense) determines the nature of the illness, its gravity and the patient's responsibility. To ascertain the existence of certain "fashionable" diseases is banal, but some diseases are disproportionately rife according to country and period. Some disappear while others emerge; they, too, like mankind, have a history.

Doctor Cabanès liked to distinguish between medical history and historical medicine, the aim of the former being to shed light on the clinic of the past with the knowledge of the present and to confront the pathology of bygone ages with that "professed by our contemporaries." The domaine of the latter, on the other hand, is the compiling of texts and archives set down according to the methods of historical criticism in order to appreciate and interpret them from a biological point of view "finding the pathological factor and especially the mental element in the decisions of those who direct events or in the events themselves." The history of medicine, therefore, becomes a comparison of historical data to contemporary science, the latter naturally being of greater importance, enabling us to judge errors.

HISTORY OF PHARMACY

Certainly the dangers of such a procedure and the deformation of historical fact caused by such a comparison is better appreciated today, but the confidence placed in science, which is always progressing, still leads us to believe that all great doctors, all great pharmacists, all schools of therapeutics prepare the way for their successors the method used by all being, if not the same, at least the same in nature. Thus, the history of medicine or pharmacy is traced by precursors, heroic victims created by historians. A presursor actually delivers a message that is not understood in contemporary times, but is later confirmed, enlarged and set down as truth. The precursor is condemned to failure by the historian for the simple reason that the latter retains in the work of the past only that which he finds analyzed, developed and concluded in the science of his time.

Since the age of antiquity, hypotheses on the atom were proposed to explain the composition of matter. Long before Pasteur, different writers believed that contagious diseases were caused by the transmission of animalcules invading the organism. However, the setting in which these ideas were put forward was much different from the one in which the first scientist worked to become recognized today as an inventor and not as a precursor.

Putting aside the notions of the precursor and coincidence, why not admit the existence of a structure in the scientific spirit, of a permanence in this thought process, that would explain the return of certain hypotheses that were considered to be without relation among the different doctrines? In addition, this constancy in very general schemes does not imply the use of any one scientific method—the modern experimental method for example—on the part of the different scientists. Today's ideas on experiments and experimenting are not those of Hippocrates.

The history of pharmacy, therefore, cannot be limited to an account of the progress made in the art of choosing and preparing medicines, which would turn out to be the story of successive failures endured until the triumph of the present day. The historian of pharmacy should equally research the successes of each period and try to understand why they were judged successful in the scientific context of the period before condemning them as the contrary seen from the scientific perspective of his own time.

Such an attitude has perhaps become possible with the recent fundamental transformation of pharmacy, the very nature of medicines, their preparation, packaging and sale, and equally with the training for and practicing of the profession and the pharmacist's relationship with his clients. Only yesterday, the history of pharmacy was approached from the pharmaceutical and not the historical point of view. Claude Bernard could scoff at the theriacum, but he had collaborated in the preparation of this miraculous remedy in his youth. The pharmacopoeia of Galen, Salerno or Charas could be opposed, but they remained important for their readers. Why should things in pharmacy be different from those in medicine? In 1804, Laënnec, pioneer of modern clinical medicine, compared in his thesis the doctrine of Hippocrates with that of Xavier Bichat, treating them both as contemporaries.

The sacrifices made by our forebears on their laboratory benches in the second half of the 19th century provided the 20th century with new historical knowledge of these authors, who, for the first time, could be put back into their own milieu, insofar as this is possible. Certainly, modern specialists know more than their counterparts of a century ago about the great Greek, Latin and Arab authors or simply those of the Middle Ages, though there is a certain difference of opinion among them that did not exist before and that has encouraged a new concept of science in the past, of the Athenian and Roman drug-seller's art and of the apothecaries of the 16th or 17th centuries.

The science of pharmaceutics having been created by man for man, and given that at different times and places, scientist and patient have not always seen things the same way (the aim of the former always being to relieve the suffering of the latter and restore him to health), the historian of this science should call on everything the other historic disciplines have been able to discover about each of the periods studied. The history of pharmacy will take man, whether pharmacist or patient, into consideration inasmuch as both are affected by medicines.

"The history of the apothecaries, as it exists today, only consists of isolated pictures or fragments buried in piles of scientific collections; it resembles, in a word, a great, mutilated body whose members are lying about here and there on the ground, all at a great distance from one another."

Since 1852, when A. Philippe wrote these lines, the bibliography of works dedicated to the history of pharmacy has greatly increased in importance. The creation of university courses in the history of pharmacy

10

and the development of important societies of research scientists has considerably widened knowledge in many countries. In France, the collection of works published since 1913 by the Society of the History of Pharmacy, the impressive list of works and scholarly articles by Maurice Bouvet, the monumental publications of François Prévet, the numerous theses written on the local history of apothecaries, the history of the chemist's shop, of patent medicines or of packaging, adequately bear witness to the interest shown in the profession's past. The edition of Maurice Bouvet's great *History of Pharmacy in France from its Origins to the Present Day,* published shortly before the last war, is sold out today as is our *Illustrated History of Pharmacy* edited by Guy Le Prat in 1949. That alone would surely justify a second edition, but while in the course of the last twenty years the very concept of the history of science has evolved, a veritable revolution has taken place in pharmacy, affecting simultaneously pharmacology, industrial production, the retail trade and professional training. Thus, we deemed it necessary to take up our *History* again and complete it.

The text of the first edition was written under the benevolent supervision of Maurice Bouvet, and with his consent, the history of the profession was linked much more to history in general than was the case in his own work. So we believe that the one complemented the other. Distinguishing among three great periods in the evolution of the profession—i.e., the origins, the time of the guilds and the regime of the Germinal law—the president of the Society of the History of Pharmacy methodically studied in each of these periods the professional training of the person who makes up a prescription and his entry into and performing of the profession (the internal services such as shop, personnel, contact with customers, and the external functions such as contacts with colleagues, other guilds and public authorities).

The very existence of this work demanded a survey of the history of the profession, which was both more chronological and no longer confined to the national scene. A new look is now being proposed to the reader, and though Maurice Bouvet is no longer here to supervise it, paradoxically his presence will be felt all the more intensely since Henri Bonnemain has authorized, in the name of his heirs, the enrichment of the text with much borrowing from Maurice Bouvet's major work. We would have preferred to use all of it. The dimensions of our book have made a delicate choice of extremely rare fragments necessary.

Patrice Boussel

I

PRE-SCIENCE AND THE SCIENCE OF PHARMACY

"INSTINCTIVE" PHARMACY

Lesions have been found on plant fossils. Dinosaurs suffered from bone tumors and plesosaurs, victims of misfortune, remained crippled. However, such victims of disease no more showed the symptoms of their ills than the neat angles of a crystal prove that geometry exists or falling apples the existence of physics before man created science. The dog, eating laxative-like grasses, the ibis performing an enema, seem like the practicing of the pharmaceutical art to us. Yet it is little proof that pharmacy existed before man.

Given, on the other hand, that the expression "prehistoric times" does not necessarily mean an arbarous and uncultured period, and that the word "primitive" serves only to describe a certain number of civilizations different from ours and in which writing, as we understand it, is unknown, it is possible and even necessary to believe in the existence of prehistoric and primitive therapeutics.

Palaeopathology enabled the signs of prehistoric man's many diseases to be found. Skeletons with deformed joints indicate the frequency of rheumatism, and historians of this period put this down to insufficient nourishment and a cold, extremely damp climate. On the other hand, rickets was practically unknown and could be classed among the "diseases of civilization." Tuberculosis was extremely rare and of the thousands of bones exhumed, only eleven cases, some of which were supsect, were found for all France's prehistoric periods. The question of syphilis is very complex, since the lesions on teeth and bones could not be attributed with certainty to this disease. We could agree with the words of A.V. Vallois: "Syphilis is an endogenous disease for us and existed in prehistoric times, but only in very localized areas." It is equally possible to suppose that syphilis appeared in a different form, rarely attacking the skeleton.

The significance of cranial surgery and the skill of prehistoric "surgeons" have long been the subjects of studies. The examination of certain bones has also proved that voluntary operations were performed after war wounds or accidental fractures. It is more delicate to speak of prehistoric pharmacopoeia since the remedies, if they existed, have left no traces. Is it absurd, therefore, to maintain that prehistoric therapeutics existed, perhaps in complex forms? The technique of prehistoric trephination, as far as can possibly be reconstructed, has been found in certain primitive populations of Africa and South America. Numerous rites, such as entering a hole in a rock or a tree, rubbing a rock, scraping a stone and drinking its dust, etc., are mentioned and described both by folklorists studying the popular medicine of the present day and by prehistorians. Sorcerers and healers seem to have used comparable therapeutic procedures both in our country regions and among our so-called primitive populations. In addition, "the fetishists of primitive peoples always had quite an extensive knowledge, at least in the use of the properties of simples, a knowledge secretly handed down to them by their respective masters. Thus, they were acquainted with emetics, effective purges, diuretics, vermifuges and drugs against the various types of enteritis, etc." Could not these words, written by Doctor Stephen Chauvet about primitive peoples, be applied to prehistoric peoples? Perhaps it may still be said that present-day "primitives" have, like ourselves, a long past, that their ancestors, like ours, must have taken advantage of the lessons of experience and consequently, that it would be more logical to consider these primitives as people whose history is in regression, rather than to regard them as the last representatives of prehistoric ages.

With much humour, G.K. Chesterton observed that "second childhood is not the exact image of the first; a new baby is as bald as an old man, but he who has never seen an infant would be wrong in deducing that the baby has a long white beard. Similarly, even though the old man and the baby experience the same difficulty in walking, whoever hopes to see the old gentleman consoling himself by rolling on the floor and sucking his thumb, will certainly be disappointed."

There is, therefore, an undoubted danger in considering as originals social types who are an end-product, the result of a regressive evolution, societies with a very long history behind them.

Taking this argument further, we conclude that the Greek and Latin poets were perhaps not entirely wrong in evoking the golden age forever past. The first prehistorians rejected this hypothesis. Pierre Braun took it up again placing this age in the neolithic era, the period of polished stone: "We know that after disappearance of the last glaciers corresponding to the Würm glaciation, the climate entirely changed. This climatic optimum went hand in hand with a biological optimum and an extraordinarily rapid progress which changed radically the life of mankind. The transition from an economy based on hunting and the picking of natural food to one based on the production of foodstuffs, i.e. the cultivation of food, represents a revolution in the history of humanity. The division of labour is one of its most important consequences. The effects of this neolithic miracle were immense: it has often been emphasized that they have influenced all the ulterior development of civilized peoples. With few exceptions, our world benefited from neolithic conquests until the invention of the steam engine."

Since we are ignorant of practically all prehistoric therapeutics, can we not imagine that they were, at least in the neolithic age, complex, skillful and effective? Consider, after all, that both explorers and ethnologists agree that astonishing results have been achieved by sorcerers, shamans and fetishists, and that folklorists admit that strange cures have been brought about by the use of popular remedies.

The human body seen astrologically; drawing illustrating a synopsis of the *Qanun* of Avicenne. B.N. Hebrew MS, 1181, fol. 263 V°.

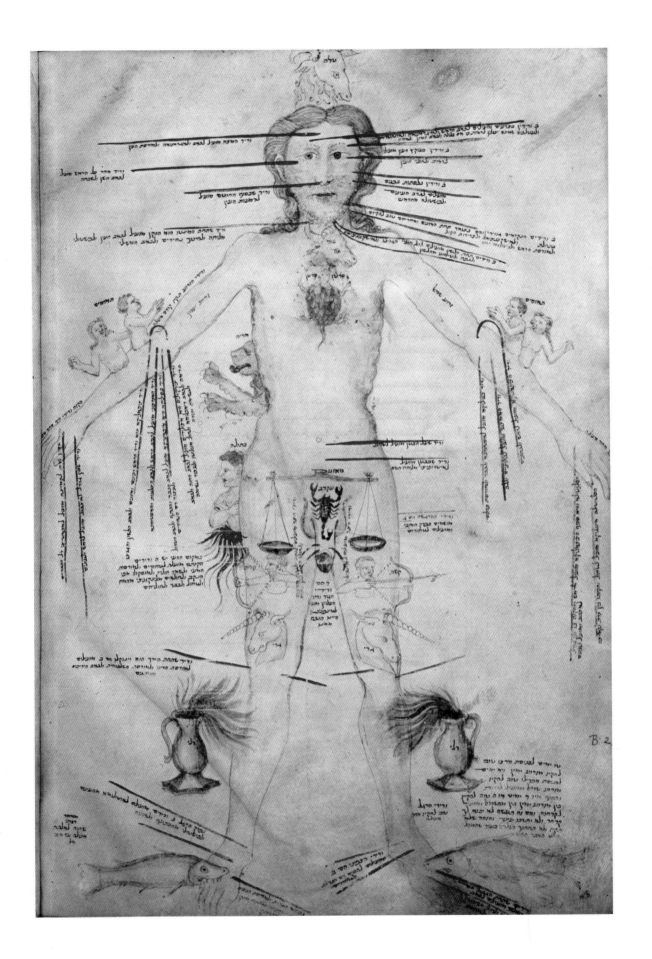

de balsamo siue opobalsamo &c

Balsamus arbor est ut qdam dicunt ul' fructex qd uenus est atestante dya=
scoride 7 etiam illis qui derut qa nuq
amplius nisi i qntitate duox cubitox ad plus.
circa babilonia repit i quoda capo i quo sut
septe fontes. Si aut alias trassertur nec flore=
nec fructus faceret. i tpe aut estiuo icidut rami
aliqntulu cu cultello. no penitus psa guttatim
emanas. colligit i uase uitreo fassure suspe=
so. In uno anno colligit xl. libre illius succi q
dicit opobalsamu. frutex di balsamus. psa
rami i casu aliqntulu dsiccant. 7 colligut. 7 dicit
xillobalsamu. fructus q i fructuce repit di capo
balsamu q no pot suari ad plus. ii. p. iiii. annos
postea eis icipit putrefie. Est ergo illud bonu
qd recens est. ul' qd no sit pforatu. licet no sit uetus.
si aut e pforatu significat uetustate esse osup=
tu. xillobalsamu p duos annos suat. postea
icipit putrefiei. At ergo eligedu q cu fragi=
tur aliqd glutinositatis hit iteru q sit etia
solidu iteru 7 no puluificat. qz si hoc e significat
uetustate ee osupta. et ista .s. xillob 7 capob.
uirtute hit calfaciedi 7 pfortandi. Opob=
samu potissima hit uirtute. qz ca. e 7 sic. i ho.

gdu. si qa carissimu e multis modis soph=
sicatur. aliqd uendut terbetina p opobalsa=
mu. qda amiscet pix balsama 7 terbetine 7
ita habet odore balsami 7 similitudine. alii
accipiut sucu limocelli ul' folioz citri 7 ad=
miscet terbetine addito croco orietale. alii
admiscet oliu nardinu eletine. Qda aucto=
res dicit q sic discernit. qz si ponat i stilli
picea 7 accedat ardet. Similit q terbetina
dyascoz dicit. q si gutta opob. ponat i lacte
caprino. lac coagulat et gutta discendit. ad
fundu. sz sut multa alia coagulantia. Alii dicut
q pan' subtilissimi madefactus opob. 7 ablut.
si i nulla pte remanet isectus puru fuit opob.
est citrinu 7 multu clar. Dignoscat sic a sophi=
sicato. si cu stillo ponat suauiter i supiori pte
aque. ibi remanet. si i medio 7 ibi remanet. Et
alia pbatio poit aqua i aliquo uase 7 nulla
i illa aqua poat opob. poit moueat cu aliquo
ligno. si sit sophicatu ul' eletina turbat. si uo
sit pur opob. no turbat. Alia pbatio. ablue ma=
nus tuas p optie. psa pone opob i pano sbtilmo
7 mudissimo pudicato tu pus opob. postea ab=
blue i uase argeteo mudissimo. ul' alio uase
cu aqua mudissima. qd puru e ad una pte
agregabit. uelud uiuu argetu. Si aliqd gui
ibi fueit remanebit. i alia pte. Vl' si aliqua so=
phicatio ibi afueit. panus ificiet. Et etia ent
cidz podiis cu prius fuit. Alia pbatio. podret
priu opob. i aliquo uase. 7 psa opdat 7 postea
poat. 7 psa podret eletina i eodez uase. ul' simili
si fueit opob puru. podrabit i triplo. plus q ter=
betina. Siut aut no plus ul' par plus qua ele=
tina ostat ee sophicatu. dicit 7 qda q si ponat
i uola manuu penetrat uolas. q falsu e. sz pu=
ru opob. poat i palato. cerebru calfacit. q uidetu
succendi. Virtutes hit dissolueti 7 atraheti
Opobalsamu .3.c. dat cu uino matric supsflu=
itates mudificat fetu mortuu 7 secudina edu=
cit. menstrua q puocat. i opob. lobice iteeta et
supposita.   Ualet striguria 7 dissuriu. ul' lapidez
uessice. Et si q opilatio fueit certo hu. otu cum
uino. ul' uinga psa erecta. 7 ex aqua cala iniciat
cu olo miscelleo. p siriga. Ungat q exteri opob.
ul' muscello. ul' nardino. Ot dolore yliacu

bolus

THE GREAT EMPIRES

ASSYRIA AND BABYLON

Between the end of the neolithic age and the dawn of history, in that dark time called protohistory, there existed systems that archaeologists were later to discover, classify.

Here, we are dealing with peasant civilizations in the fifth millennium before Christ in Western Asia; the excavations carried out in the Tigris and Euphrates valleys bear witness to the Sumerian invasion in Babylon, the foundations of important towns and the construction of giant temples. However, three thousand years had to pass before documents could be found that revealed Assyrio-Babylonian therapeutics. We can say that the medical practices and the remedies prescribed are the heritage of a distant past and we can therefore, assume that what is known about the fifth millennium before Christ is also valid for the fourth, something which presupposes considerable intellectual audacity.

Yet, the therapeutics revealed by known medical tablets which are less than three thousand years old is extremely interesting for several very different reasons: it is both strange and strangely near us, both magic and common sense and is at the same time barbarous and modern, absurd and rational.

Certainly, Herodotus was exaggerating when he recounted that the inhabitants of Babylon carried their sick in the streets so that passers-by could advise them on the best treatment to follow in the event that the passers-by had already suffered from the same diseases, or that they had seen one of their family suffer in the same way. They, too, had their doctors, but today, instead of looking in the street for supplementary details that the doctor either neglects or refuses to give, we content ourselves with information (often abundant) provided by friends, relations, neighbors, the landlady, the press and the radio.

Three thousand years ago, the inhabitants of Western Asia naively believed that the sick were possessed by demons. Therapeutics, therefore, was a matter of identifying the demon and finding a way to cast it out, the simplest method being to make its dwelling place as unpleasant as possible. As the idea was that what the patient found disagreeable, the demon would also find disagreeable, a particularly varied choice of

---

Naive portrayal of Babylon and its ramparts with the seven fountains in whose vicinity the balsam tree was said to be discovered, by Manfred de Monte Imperiale (14th century author, perhaps from Kayserberg), Liber de herbis et plantis... B.N. Latin MS, 6823, fol. 25 V°.

bitter and revolting medicines was used. It would be particularly unjust to accuse parents of having forced their children, until a short time ago, to ingest cod-liver oil simply because they imagined that whatever tasted as bad as that should be good for them. It would be even more absurd to suggest the slightest relationship between demons and microbes, viruses, etc., which, once identified, one tried to fight.

No longer do we take seriously the sin-sickness idea and the possibility of sins being committed unwittingly (to the extent that on the eve of great public celebrations, the Babylonian clergy had an expiatory service to atone for the lapses in the ritual committed the following day). The divinity no longer interferes today, but only it and the psychoanalyst know the mistakes made or crimes committed by the child in his cradle, if not before birth. He still has to pay. With this pessimistic conception of existence (i.e., the Assyrio-Babylonian) went a developed spirit of observation which enabled the Babylonians to draw up an extremely detailed medical system and use a pharmacopoeia comprising about two hundred and fifty plants, the mineral sulphur, and animal products such as cow and goat milk, honey and wax, lion fat, castor and also human excrement and the urine of cattle.

As far as plants are concerned, the Sumerian-Akkadian pharmacopoeia used the seed, roots, stem and sap of young shoots, leaves and fruit, distinguishing among the herbaceous, woody, aromatic and resinous. Their pharmaceutical technique enabled them to prepare macerations, decoctions, poultices, liniments and suppositories. The beer or wine from the palm tree was used for taking medicines. So for example, it was prescribed:

"If a man's stomach is inflamed, pound together mustard, hellebore, salicornia, *Acorus calamus*, fennel, andropogon gum, nitre, fir turpentine; he drinks this in beer on an empty stomach and he recovers."

For an inflamed stomach, enemas were also recommended. These contained *Acorus calamus*, *assafoetida*, dates and fir turpentine, all of which were pounded together, pressed and macerated in beer, then strained and cooled. Barley and rose water were added.

The recipe for a suppository was as follows:

"Should a man suddenly have stomach pains, if his thighs and genitals are sore, this man will have pains in the anus whenever he walks. To cure him, grind together ammi, pine turpentine, opopomax, fir turpentine and roses; mix fat in equal proportion; make a suppository out of it and grease it with cypress oil, insert it in his anus and he will recover."

When the lungs are affected, "sprinkle tar dust over burning thorn bushes. Let the smoke enter his anus, his mouth and nostrils and he will begin to cough. Rub him with a lotion of chaste tree water, anoint his body from top to bottom with purified butter, grind grains of flax in milk. Make a poultice from this and leave it for three days. Let his tongue taste honey and fine oil and he will get better."

Even the use of anaesthetics was not unknown: "If a man cannot urinate when he wants to, let him drink some poppy grains in beer. Boil in oil and galbanum resin, filter and blow it into his ureter with a bronze tube."

EGYPT

At the beginning of his study on religious life in ancient Egypt, Sainte Fare Carnot depicts "the ancient Egyptians, as can be seen in their literature and monuments, as an affable and optimistic people, hostile to disorder and excess of any kind. This is confirmed by their history where they appear enterprising but peaceful, better given to the arts of peace than the ways of war with a passionate zest for life." This attachment to earthly things and this taste for moderation had its effect not only on religious beliefs, but also on the practice of therapeutics.

While a very keen sense of observation enabled these people, who lived on the banks of the Nile to use, from the most ancient times, medicines judiciously chosen and which often seem mild to modern doctors, their optimistic philosophy of life was a support against sickness, suffering and death, with its creation of helpful and sympathetic gods, its idea of human survival, and the intuitive feeling that the morale of the sick person was of equal, if not greater, importance than the body, an idea justifying the use of incantations.

It was the gods themselves who dictated to men the prayers accompanying medical care and the ingestion of drugs prescribed by doctors; and it was a doctor practicing under the reign of Ramses I, founder of the 19th dynasty (1314 B.C.), who formulated this precept: "Incantations are excellent for cures and cures are excellent for incantations!"

With magic formulas making medicines more effective, the Egyptians naturally had at their disposition a great number of formulas, some general, others adapted to each particular case. Thus, to make a

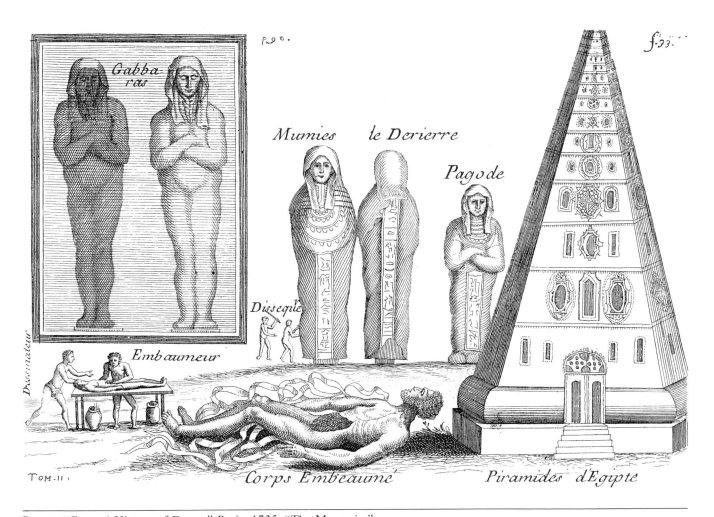

Pomet, "General History of Drugs." Paris, 1735, "The Mummies"

purge more effective, one repeated while drinking: "Oh, male hena, of female hyena, of male and female destruction!"

To help a cure get rid of a tape-worm: "Let these words stop the teeming progression of the one who fills my entrails! It is a god who created this enemy: let him be destroyed by this charm and the disorders he is causing in my stomach be banished!"

Anybody who reads, uncomprehending, but with undeniable satisfaction, the printed text that goes with a medicine will easily understand the interest of such a practice.

Of 5th century Egypt, Herodotus wrote: "In Egypt, medicine, like oracles, was specialized. For every sickness, there was a doctor, and there was no such thing as general medicine. Everywhere, three was an over-abundance of doctors: While some were eye doctors, there were specialists for the head, the teeth, the stomach and internal disorders." Since ancient times, doctors were extremely numerous and effective, since the Egyptians, with the Libyans, were known to be men in the best of health; but the specialization mentioned by Herodotus and which, to a certain extent, testifies to a scientific spirit, must have been less developed in earlier times. According to the most ancient documents, not only did doctors appear to treat all kinds of diseases, they were also magicians and priests. It is also appropriate here to add that they were also pharmacists and that they remained so even after specializing.

Life, they believed, was a breath of air which entered the right ear, and death a breath entering the left ear. Internal diseases were explained by "a god or goddess, a dead man or woman, a male or female enemy" interfering with the body, and the doctor acknowledged that he was not always able to save the "possessed" patient by his own means.

The legend of the "Princess of Backtan" tells of a doctor admitting his helplessness. The princess was suffering from an unknown disease. Her father implored Ramses II to send him an Egyptian "scientist." After the latter had examined the patient, he diagnosed that she was possessed by an "enemy against whom she should fight." Thus, it was possible to save the young girl, but he needed help. So he asked the Theban god Khonsou for help. The statue of this god was transported to Backtan and the evil spirit was driven out. A second case shows a doctor invoking the divinity on the one hand, but playing the role of sorcerer and healer on the other. According to the Egyptologist Gustave Lefebvre, the invocation to treat burns was as follows:

The messenger: Your son Horus is burning on the desert plateau.

Isis: Is there water there?

The messenger: There is no water there.

Isis: There is water in my mouth and a Nile betweeen my thighs. I have come to extinguish the fire.

This formula was to be recited "over the milk of a woman who has given birth to a boy, sweet-smelling gum and the hair of a goat, all of which was to be placed on the burn."

By naming the goddess, one forced her to react in a beneficial way; using goat hairs, the witch doctor performs magic. In using milk and gum (acacia resin), the doctor assumes the role of healer.

A long tradition, which was not only Egyptian, claimed that human milk was superior to that of animals, the most preferable being that of a woman who had given birth to a boy.

In a third case, an Egyptian doctor simply appears to recommend a remedy whose effet he knows by experience to be beneficial. So, in order to treat hemeralopia, an ailment of the retina, which makes one blind at night, he advised pouring on the eyes the extract of "ox-liver which has been placed over a fire of wheat or barley shoots and steamed in the vapour thus given off." Raw liver, liver extract and cod-liver oil are still used today in the treatment of hemeralopia.

The indications given to relieve a constipated child seem strange: "Boil an old book in oil, applying half of it on the stomach to start evacuation." However, old books being made from papyrus must have had virtues comparable to those of linseed meal poultices, once boiled in oil. While mentioning this treatment, the doctor Naguib Riad observed that if the doctor recommended the choice of an old book, it was simply for economic reasons.

Thus, therapeutics was to evolve from magic to experience, and for evidence of this one only has to be reminded that the ancient Egyptians, from very early times, used cures that were simple, natural, adapted to the patient, and that acted according to their inherent properties. Quoting Gustave Lefebvre, "Let us suppose the case repeated itself a certain number of times. The non-initiated remembered the formula for the cure, precisely making out the potion formerly prescribed by the magician and avoiding the incantation, which was always difficult to remember or recite correctly. This did not compromise in the slightest the patient's recovery and in the end, the treatment itself gained in credibility, i.e. the cure became isolated from its magic formula."

Thus, positive therapeutics was the logical successor to the magic therapeutics of the Egyptians. It is helpful to know that the Pharahos gave Egypt the name "Chim", meaning "the black land", from which our word "chemistry" derives, the Egyptians having been the most advanced in the knowledge of the nature and properties of simple bodies. The word pharmacy is of Egyptian origin, "Ph-ar-maki" "that which brings safety", designating the god Thot. Other words originating from the banks of the Nile are "migraine" (in Egyptian, half a head, giving in Greek, *hemikrania,* half of the head, migraine), "ebony," "gum," etc.; and the eye of Horus, the Eguyptian god of the sun and health gives us the origin of the medical convention of "recipe" (formerly a prescription). The eye, lost by the god in the fight against Set, later to become the sign of Jupiter for the Romans, resembled an "R". According to Doctor Naguib Riad, historian of medicine at the time of the Pharaohs, the letter p was supposedly added at a later date, giving the "Rp": "Recipe", i.e. receive and make up the prescription.

The role played by the Egyptians in the origin of medical, surgical and pharmaceutical science has only begun to be known. A century ago, before the Ebers papyrus, the first medical work discovered in a tomb, was published, historians had to be satisfied with Homer's account of the excellence of this "fertile land, which produces an abundance of drugs, some beneficial, others harmful and where the doctors were the most skilful of men."

This account, confirmed by Hippocrates and Herodotus, Aristotle and Galen, was finally completed by documents provided by the Egyptians themselves. After the Ebers papyrus (dating from the beginning of the 18th dynasty, in approximately 1580 B.C., published in 1875), came the Edwin Smith papyrus (same period published in 1930), the Berlin papyrus (19th dynasty, 1314 to 1200 B.C. published in 1909), the London papyrus, the Kahoun, the Carlsberg Number 8 and the Chester Beatty papyrus.

Only eight works, and in these works we find truncated texts, obscure passages and words impossible to translate; it is still not very much to give us any clear impresson of the therapeutics of a people through out several millenia. The specialists reassure each other by attributing to the Egyptians a liking for the collecting of documents and by admitting that those found are only copies of older texts faithfully reproduced. They quote Diodorus Siculus who wrote: "Egyptian doctors set down the treatment of the sick according to precepts written, edited and handed down by many great doctors of the past. Should they, while following the precepts of the sacred book, not succeed in saving the sick person, they were found innocent and exempt from reproach. If, on the other hand, they acted in breach of the precepts, they could find themselves convicted and condemned to death, since the lawmaker esteemed that few were capable of finding a better means of treating the disease than that observed for so long and set down by the most accomplished men in the art."

Strange as it may seem, the Ebers papyrus, the oldest one known, was responsible for the role of magic in Egyptian therapeutics being over estimated. The Smith papyrus seems much more scientific in inspiration. Now, according to the grammatical analysis of the document, the original of this collection of medical recipes or prescriptions (the copy of which is contemporary with the Ebers papyrus) could go back as far as the 28th century B.C.

Despite the astonishing richness of Egyptian pharmacopoeia, the doctor seemed, in the first place, to want to cooperate with nature, so he starts treatment with the diet. In the second place, medicines for external use seem to be more important than internal medicines.

Thus, headaches are treated with ointments, massages and bandages only. An ointment made up of reed stems, juniper, pitch pine, laurel berries, terebinth resin and fat can be applied. For afflictions of the scalp or simply for hair care, castor oil is recommended. It is still used as an excipient in creams for skin and scalp diseases. To treat coryza: fill the nose with palm wine. For earache: a cream made from melilot and labdanum (the resin of *Cistus ladaniferus*); for toothache; daily cleaning with a potion made from colocynth, gum, anise, the notched fruit of the sycamore (not the plant we know today by that name but the *Ficus Aegyptiae*), and a plant called "Qebou" in water; fillings and certainly extractions.

The cure for blepharitis was a cream made from aloes, borax, colocynth flour, acacia leaves, ebony bark, all mixed into a paste, dried and then pounded in water. A cream prescribed for cataracts was made from lapis-lazuli, borax, balsam sugar, galena and crocodile droppings.

Women's diseases preoccupied the Egyptians greatly and multiple remedies, internal and external, were proposed. The doctors also imagined diverse procedures for estimating the fertility of women and predicting the sex of expected children. On this subject, the Egyptologist Gustave Lefebvre indicates an investigatory method which is based on the action of the woman's urine on different grains: "We could liken it to modern theories on the role of the hormones, expecially oestrone and pregnadiol. It has been noticed, for example, that oestrone extracted rom the urine of pregnant women can, when added to the watering of certain plants, hasten their flowering." Another method appears not to have any modern equivalent. It consists of fumigating certain parts of the woman using hippopotamus excrement: "If she vomits immediately from her mouth, she will never give birth. If she immediately lets out wind from her behind, then she will give birth." It is true that the raw material for fumigation is difficult to find in Europe.

Egyptian doctors were definitely the first to recommend inhalations against coughs. First, myrrh had to be pounded with an aromatic resin and date pulp, then "you fetch seven stones and heat them in the fire. Then you take one of them and put some of the medicine on it. Cover it with a new vase whose bottom has been perforated. Then put a reed stem in this hole and put the stem in your mouth so that you swallow the vapour emitted. Do the same thing with the six other stones. After that, eat something fat, e.g. meat, fat or oil."

It would be easy to give many more examples. In conclusion, let us quote the treatment, which, in the Smith papyrus, enabled an old man to become young again: "Take some fenugreek pods, take out the grains. Then, mix in equal measure these grains with little pieces of emptied pods. Add water and heat the paste thus obtained in a new cauldron. Removed from the fire, it is allowed to cool, and is then washed in the river and dried in the sun. It is then beaten in a millstone, reheated and mixed with water. Heating is stopped when small layers of oil appear on the surface. Once removed with care and then filtered, this oil is decanted into a container made from hard, precious material, from which one takes it to anoint old men who want to be rejuvenated." (G. Lefebvre).

More than 500 substances taken from three reigns appear in the medical papyri discovered. The Egyptians used potions, herb teas, decoctions, macerations, mixtures, pills, boluses, lozenges, electuaries and, for external use, poultices, ointments, eye lotions, plasters, creams, inhalations, fumigations, suppositories and enemas.

Imhotep, who was architect, astrologer, sacred reader, magician and doctor to King Zoser, second Pharaoh of the third dynasty (about 2800 B.C.), before becoming god of medicine and consequently ancestor of Aesculapius, had learned disciples, and if they venerated their ancestor, those who prepare the prescriptions of the 20th century A.D. may also feel a certain respect for their "elders" who lived on the banks of the Nile some three thousand years ago.

INDIA

The historical importance of Indian science is comparable to the Greek. The former was adopted in Tibet, Central Asia, Indo-China and in Indonesia in certain Chinese and Japanese milieux. The latter served Christianity and Islam as a model. Leaving aside the domain of the Chinese (which had a wide but limited influence often encroached upon by India), they dominated the world until the development of modern science, which can be considered as the emancipation from the Greek scientific tradition.

Numerous chronological problems have arisen and certain writers thought they discerned the influence of one science on the other. In fact, it is possible to envisage the two medical traditions, Indian and Greek, developing on parallel lines. As M. Jean Filliozat wrote, if "the special treatises of Indian science which have survived are relatively late didactic works, they are generally neither innovatory nor original, but school manuals which success has made traditional and which, for that reason, have been kept in preference to older ones, which they, to a greater or lesser extent, copied. Their date of compilation is of secondary importance and is valuable only insofar as it dates the period of the doctrines they contain. »

The oldest Indian classical medical treatises are the "Samhitâ" or "Corpus" said to be written by Bhela, Charaka and Susruta, all three transmitting the same tradition, namely the "Ayurveda," science of longevity." We know, according to Ctesias (4th century B.C.), one of the first Greek doctors to mention India, that Indians suffered from few diseases and could reach the age of two hundred.

In the beginning, magic in India, as in Egypt or China, had an important place in therapeutics, and numerous incantations to demons are known either for healing or for causing illness; but with the evolution of the "Ayurveda" tradition, the doctor was no longer a sorcerer but a practitioner and scholar. He took the data of experience into account, organizing them according to a general theory of mankind.

In the treatise attributed to Susruta, we read: "The doctor, the patient, the remedy and the nurse are the four pillars of medicine on which recovery rests. When the last three of these pillars are as they should be, then with the help of the first, i.e. the doctor, recovery will be complete and the doctor will be able to cure a serious illness in a short time."

The same text goes on to give this definition:

"For a remedy to be considered a real pillar of medicine, it should be composed of plants grown in excellent soil, picked on a good day, and should be administered in the proper dose at the right time."

The legendary story of Jivaka, the doctor, illustrates the richness of Indian phytotherapy. Jivaka learned his art from Pingala. After seven years, the pupil asked his master if his training was complete. Pingala replied by asking a question. He asked Jivaka to enumerate all the plants in a given region which he considered to be of no medicinal use. Jivaka found himself incapable of naming any plant devoid of any curative power.

"Go," said his master, " from now on you possess all medical knowledge! Up to the present, I have been the only one to possess it in all Jambuddipa. After my death, you will be my successor."

Jivaka healed all sick people. "Sometimes he treated all diseases with a single plant and sometimes he used all plants for one disease. Among all the herbs of the whole universe, there was not one that he could not use; among all the sick people of the universe, there was not one that he did not cure."

Among the most frequetly used medicinal plants, we may list garlic, myrobalan, pepper, ginger, *Acorus Calamus, Bela* (anti-dysenteric), ricin (a purge and cutaneous disinfectant for leprosy), lycium (a kind of rubber still used today in India for ocular infections), tamarind, hemp, cardamom, Mudar bark, aconite, etc. The Indians used animal products like bezoar, adder, cow urine, and minerals such as iron sulphate, borax and alum. Mr. Bouvet found in the text attributed to Susruta proof of the fact that in ancient Indian therapeutics, infusions, macerations and decoctions were used and that they knew how to prepare powders, pills, ointments and liquids used as eye lotions, enemas or liniments.

The therapeutics followed by Susruta in his text for the treatment of consumption can be compared to that of phthisiologists a hundred years ago; this comparison enables us to have quite a clear impression of the experimental level attained by Indian doctors more than two thousand years ago. Susruta ordered baths, sprinkling, massage, a diet becoming progressively stricter, milk and grapes, plants which stimulate the appetite, digestants and laxatives, febrifuge substances, a very varied meat diet, wine of the vine and its alcohol, and finally staying in cowsheds in very high regions.

CHINA

For more than two thousand years, scientific medicine has existed as handed down by dated and catalogued texts. It is closely connected to philosophy, religion, magic, and in a very general way, to a certain view of the world. All the specialists agree on the extreme richness of Chinese medicine. This can easily be seen by quoting some figures. In his treatise known under the name of *Pen ts'ao kang mou,* the pharmacologist Li Che-Tchen (1518-1593) studied 1871 substances, 1074 of which were vegetable, 443 animal and 354 mineral. This author selected 8161 recipes in earlier medical works and arrived at nearly 16,000 prescriptions. Quoting these figures, Doctor Pierre Huard also observes that of the 1871 substances described, 374 were new.

If that is an illustration of the science of Li Chi-Tchen, it also proves the astonishing abundance of traditional remedies at the disposition of Chinese doctors. It also tends to indicate that Chinese knowledge could evolve. Certainly, the primary task of scholars was to maintain the knowledge handed down by ancestors; yet on certain points they broke new ground.

Shen-Nung, "the divine labourer" and fire god, who, using fire, transformed the jungle into arable land and then taught the people the use of the plow, was also the god of medicine and pharmacy. Legend has it that his knowledge of medicinal plants permitted him to write the *"Pen ts'ao"* or book of medicines. He experimented with poisons, discovered addiction and had some ideas on posology. Shen-Nung's successor, Honang Ti, "the yellow emperor", was according to the same tradition, author of a medical treatise called "Noi Tsing." Here one reads:

"I miss everything my people, who are struck down by disease, do not pay me in taxes and fatigues. I want them to be given no more medicinal poisons and to abandon the use of the old stone bodkins. I want only the mysterious metal needles which direct energy to be used."

Despite the wishes of this emperor, who lived several centuries before Christ, and the respect the Chinese have shown him since then, and despite the fact that as Doctor Huard wrote, "the most distant medical past remains in certain respects extremely near and familiar and constitutes what has been called the uniqueness of the Chinese," acupuncture was not the only treatment used in East Asia and vendors of medicines or "pharmacists" have always been of great importance.

A description of their shops, which is only a hundred years old, but which is good for two thousand years if one accepts the Chinese dislike of change and the excessive veneration of tradition, evokes in bizarre fashion the shops of the apothecaries of the Middle Ages in Europe:

"The premises of a reputed pharmacy are generally divided into two compartments, one for receiving clients, the other reserved for the pharmacist and his pupils. These two compartments are separated by a counter running the whole length of the pharmacy.

Dried medical substances are all closed in drawers one below another panelled in wood around that part of the premises not reserved for the public. The upper level of this panelling is reserved for oriental and other glass or porcelain vases in which preserves, electuaries and pharmaceutical powders are kept.

Depending on the affluence and fortune of the pharmacist, the panelling is made from oak, pine or sometimes rosewood. The surface is often painted and varnished. Red or yellow paper labels are stuck on the front of each drawer to indicate its contents...

In the pharmacies of the small coastal towns and the interior, medicines prepared in advance in a room adjoining the pharmacy were given out to sailors, travellers and natives. These medicines were for the most part infusions, decoctions, medicinal wines, electuaries, preserves, pills that the patient takes himself either at his own request or according to indications given by the pharmacist."

The importance of the so-called "signature" medicine has been illustrated by Mr. Bouvet. Remedies green in colour and of acid taste are good for the liver, composed as they are of wood which corresponds to the liver, according to the traditional philosophic system. The higher parts of medicinal plants (buds, blossoms) were used to treat the top parts of the body, while the roots were used to treat the lower regions. Glow worms are found in the composition of eye lotions, beans healed the kidneys and yellow saffron was used against jaundice.

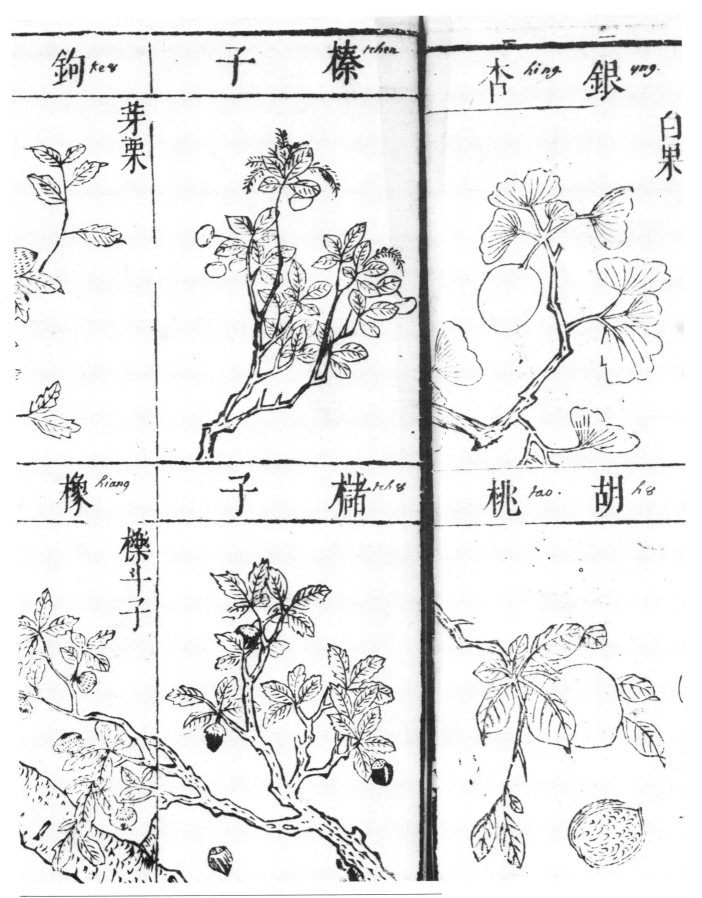

Treatise on simples (Chinese manuscript), B.N. Chinese MS, 5280. pp. 186-187.

25

Of course, important medical powers were attributed to precious stones, just as they were in Europe up to the 18th century. Jade and pearl seem to have played quite a particular role in ancient Chinese pharmacopoeia. Doctor Huard tells us that venereal ulcers were treated with calomel. Goiter was treated with seaweed (iodotherapy), *Ephedra sinica* (*ma houang*) was used to treat respiratory ailments as early as the second century A.D. (ephedrine having been discovered only at the end of the 19th century). Datura, rhubarb, rye ergot, ginger, camphor, cinnamon, pepper, betel nuts, etc., all figure in the numerous pharmaceutical preparations of antiquity.

The doctrine of signatures enables us to understand why medicines of animal origin were of such great importance in Chinese pharmacopoeia. This or that part of an animal's body should necessarily heal the corresponding part of the human body. But was it not preferable to use human products to heal humans? The placenta, the urine, feces, scabs, sperm, a young woman's milk all have their part to play. Human blood sucked from the living vein by the patient was considered a very effective remedy against consumption. Too little time has passed since the days of going to the abattoir to drink fresh blood for us to condemn such practices.

"Take the gall of *a man recently killed,* add mercury sulphide, arsenic trisulphide and gum, beat into a powder and use pills covered in coarse silk and apply on the right side of a man's stomach or on the left side of a woman's. Recovery will not be long in coming."

During the last century, many a fine story of medical cannibalism was brought back by travellers and certain of these were linked to the cult of the ancestors: to save an old man, his son or grandson cuts off a piece of his arm, cooks it, coats it in batter and serves it hot. The patient must have no suspicions as to what he is eating and, in addition, the remedy is never of any value to descendants. It cannot be prepared by a husband for his wife or by a father for his children. In China today, traditional medicine is studied scientifically, this discipline taking the name of "pents'aology." It is doubtful, however, that the chemical and pharmacological studies of the pents'aologists focus on this aspect of ancient Chinese opotherapy.

The emperor Shen-Nung, author of *Penn-Tsrao,* who, according to Chinese tradition, was the father of agriculture, medicine and pharmacy. B.N. Chinese MS, 1236, fol. 2.

PERSIA

Geographically, Iran corresponds to the "Perside" of the Greek and Latin texts, that immense platform situated between the Tigris and the Indus, whose northern seaboard is the Caspian Sea and whose southern border is the Persian Gulf and the Gulf of Oman. Though the name of Iran figures in the "Avesta," the term Persia remains preferable from the historical point of view and to use it here presents no problem since in antiquity Persia and Iran mean the same thing.

Archaeologists have discovered that men were living in this part of the globe as early as eight to ten thousand years before Christ. They lived in moutain caves. It has been proved that the plateau saw its first settlers about 5,000 B.C. A civilization evolved whose principal characteristics have been discovered through recent excavations. We know that there were clashes between these populations and those of the rich plains of Babylon 3,000 years B.C., and that a brilliant Elamite civilization existed a few centuries later. We are aware of the great Indo-European immigration at the end of the second millennium before Christ and the creation of a great Iranian empire in the first half of the first millennium. Since the 8th century A.D., we know more about the succession of the Achaemenid kings. But it is possible to make only suppositions regarding the manner in which the different populations fought against sickness until the arrival of the Arians, the Aryans or even Iranians, since Iran owes its name to *Ayryana Vaejô* (literally the origin of the Arians). As far as ancient Iranian therapeutics is concerned, the only access available is found in the holy Iranian book, "Avesta." This text, which is supposed to be no older than the 7th century B.C., has come down to us mutilated but enriched by much more recent fragments.

A Parsee tradition attributes the "Avesta" to Ahura-Mazda. He allegedly gave it to the prophet Zoroaster, and the latter is supposed to have lived in the 7th century B.C. Alexander had it partially translated into Greek and burned the rest. It was at a much later date that other sovereigns began to restore it, to be completed in the second half of the 3rd century A.D. The "Avesta" is, therefore, a late compilation of heterogenous elements, with Greek and Hindu borrowings. And a certain intellectual audacity is required to place the origins of Iranian medicine in the third millennium and in the eneolithic civilization recently discovered in the Indus valley, as Doctor Assad Ghavami has done.

The "Avesta" distinguishes between three different kinds of therapeutics, which are not all equally effective: the conjuration or incantation, medicinal plants and surgery. It is appropriate here to add that water is of the greatest importance which comports well with the ancient vedic literature of India. On this subject, Doctor Assad Ghavami wrote that, the Gaokerena tree. It really is annoying not to know what tree it is.

Different species were named one by one: *Asclepias acida, Ephedra pachyclade, Sarcostema viminalis, Ephedra distachya.* Doctor Ghavami maintains that it is a tree giving latex. The *Ficus religiosa,* the fig tree of the Indian pagodas, Buddha's tree of illumination, cannot, unfortunately, be considered since it is particular to India. The description given in the Avesta offers little help to those seeking the tree's identity:

"Homa is good, Homa is well made: it is made right and good and is a healer. It is handsome, wants to do good and is victorious. Gold in colour, of flexible stem, it is excellent to drink and is the best food for the soul."

Our disappointment grows with the knowledge that around this prodigious tree, medicinal plants grow "in their hundreds and thousands, in myriads." In fact, there are as many of these plants as there are diseases: 99,999; Discreet, as always, the Avesta never names one.

However, the Iranian medical tradition was maintained throughout many centuries, and was annotated and a 9th century compilation, the "Dênkart", analyzes those parts of the text that have come down to us. One chapter is dedicated to diseases whose primary cause is always the evil spirit. They are 4,333 in number and to treat them, 70 categories of remedies exist, all derived from plants. Among these plants are some that are poisonous. Are they enumerated? Again the answer is no.

We should, therefore, be very grateful for the Greek accounts of Persian therapeutics despite their partiality. Through them, we know that King Kalbûjiya (Cambyses II, 529-522 B.C.), son of Karack II (Cyrus the Great, 559-530 B.C.), and grandson of Kambujiya (Cambyses I, about 600-559 B.C.), led a campaign against the Pharaoh Amasis, besieged Gaza, took Memphis, deported the new Pharaoh, Psammetik III, the son of Amasis (who had since died), to Susa and sold him ointments that he prepared himself. He is also said to have derided the Egyptian religion and wounded Apis, the ox, with his dagger, which, according to R. Ghirsman, can only be explained by an epileptic fit.

Herodotus drew attention to the great number of foreign doctors in Persia and tells the story of Darius I (Dâryav, 521-486 B.C.), and the foot he sprained jumping from his horse. The sprain was so bad that the ankle was dislocated. Darius had in his court doctors known to be the best in Egypt. After he put himself at their disposal, they turned his foot with such force that they only increased the pain. Such was this pain that the king passed seven days and nights without any sleep: "In the end, he learned of the presence in his kingdom of Democedes of Crotone; he summoned Democedes, who treated him in the Greek way and by alternating gentle and harsh remedies, he managed to get Darius to sleep and after a little while he recovered." Again it was Democedes who is supposed to have healed Atosse, Darius' wife, of a breast tumor.

In the Bible's book of Esther, we read that before entering King Assuerus' harem, the young girls "used an ointment of myrrh oil during the first six months and aromatic perfumes during the last six" to make themselves more desirable.

Democritus of Abdera, according to Strabo, stayed with wise men in Persia and brought back many recipes to his own country. Persian doctors themselves borrowed remedies from Mesopotamia, Egypt and India that they judged useful. In this way, they imported from India in the reign of the Achaemenids, the lemon tree or the apple tree of Media, whose pulp or seed was used in wines against poisons. Mr. Bouvet notes that the Persians also knew the properties of hemp, rhubarb, manna, camphor, different gums and gum resins (tragacanth gum, sarcocolle, asafoetida, galbanum, opoponax, etc.) and that they used numerous vegetable oils (roquette, castor oil, sesame, etc.).

In the 3rd century A.D., a new dynasty, the Sassanides, came to power in Persia. Chahpuhr I (or Sapor I), "King of the kings of Iran and Outer Iran," fought against the Roman Empire, reached Antioch, and in 260 took Valerian prisoner near Edessa. He was interested in philosophy, astronomy and medicine, and had numerous Greek and Indian works translated. His great grandson, Chahpuhr II (Sapor II), was also a great king. He imposed his authority on the whole empire, stopped the Huns invading from Central Asia, repulsed an attack from the Emperor Julian in 363 and consolidated the allegiance of Mesopotamia and Armenia. He is of interest to us because he gave his name to apple syrup, or syrup of Sapor, and he summoned to Gundi-Sapur, his capital, the Greek doctor, Theodosius.

In the 5th century, the Persians used new medicines under the influence of Greek doctors banished from their schools in Edessa. The Nestorians also gave them access to their writings and masters, and in this way, Greek medicine became widespread in Persia.

In the following century, the Indian pharmacopoeia also had its influence on the Persian pharmacopoeia. Khosro I (Khosroes I, 531-579), nicknamed Anocharuvan (of the immortal soul), the most brilliant king of the dynasty, sent the doctor Berzouilh (or Barsaya) on a mission to India, whence he returned with numerous specimens of medicinal plants unknown in Persia. Many Hindu works were translated and in the "Geography of Aboulfeda," we read that at this time, "the school of medicine founded by the Sassanid kings in Susian (Elam) in the 5th century, while very open to Greek doctrines, since some of those responsible for teaching the young were Nestorian Christians from the Eastern Empire, also accepted Hindu doctrines and treated with great importance the influence of the stars and the occult sciences, two subjects which enjoyed great credit in both the East and the West."

Finally, towards the middle of the 7th century, the Arab invasion took place and the conquerors quickly learned to use Persian therapeutics. As far back as the 4th century, the Arabs had come to study in Persia and had multiplied after the foundation of the Gundi-Sapur school. The Arab doctor Haress was born at Tayef a few years before Mohammed had conversed with King Khosro I, and regarding medicines, we may quote:

"As long as your health prevails, leave them alone, but once you fall sick, kill the sickness by all appropriate means before it takes root."

Persia, crossroads of civilizations, meeting place between East and West, was the cradle of a very old and brilliant civilization. If its pharmacopoeia remains obscure, at least we know that it was based on the knowledge of plants. The role of phytotherapy, still recognized today, and the borrowings of the Greeks and Arabs from ancient Persia, lead one to believe that the legend of the Gaokerena tree is not entirely unfounded.

God ordered all things to be tested, the good being retained, the true chosen and evil shunned; the doctor recommends abstinence as the first and last remedy for the body and soul in Manfred de Monte Imperiale's (14th century authour perhaps from Kayserberg) *Liber de herbis et plantis*. B.N. Latin MS, 6823, fol. 1 R°.

ISRAEL

It is commonplace to mention the exceptional destiny of the Jewish people, an insignificant oriental race among others with a comparable history, yet one that has played an immense role in the spiritual history of humanity. Longtime nomads before settling with difficulty in Palestine after the exodus from Egypt, this race, more than all the others, associated its religion with the most diverse aspects of public life and was original in that it rejected the divinities of other peoples passing from monolatria to monotheism, i.e., from the worship of one god alone to the belief in the existence of one god alone.

The constant presence of religion and the omnipotence of Yahweh resulted in ideas very different from ours or those of the Greeks of the Hellenistic period concerning illness and its remedies. Yahweh used sickness to punish or test man; he intervened should he so desire and banished the ill. Such an idea does not necessarily render all therapeutics useless, but makes medicine strictly dependent on the cult of the divinity.

The priest or "nabi" who was in contact with Yahweh was in possession of the widest powers. The healer used magic formulas and secret recipes at the same time. The medicines he knew how to use, endowed perhaps with therapeutic properties, were chosen mainly for their magic powers.

It has been said that the medicine of the Jews in biblical times was confined to a collection of sanitary prescriptions useful for a nomadic people. That is definitely a rather hasty judgment.

Today everyone knows that pork, in particular, contributes to the transmission of certain parasites to man and that eating it can be harmful in hot countries. Thus, it is difficult not to admire the wisdom of Moses in forbidding the Jewish people to eat it. Simply a pious pretext, we may say, hiding serious hygienic considerations. We can easily find in the Bible the marks of diseases such as gonorrhoea, leprosy, tuberculosis, bubonic plague, but very few epidemics caused by contaminated food. In this way, the attractive and now classical supposition that the Old Testament's prohibition of certain foods had a scientific value is confirmed.

Unfortunately for this apparent truth, the Bible's list of unclean species, apart from the pig, includes many animals whose prohibition is difficult to justify scientifically, while the prohibition of those said to be clean would be justified. That the meat of the hare (unclean) should be harmful is no more obvious than that the meat of a sheep (clean) should be regarded as harmless. Yet it is in mutton that the origin of certain parasites is to be found.

In the Bible, the physiology of nutrition remains a mystery. It is summed up as follows:
"Everything that goes into the mouth enters the stomach and is thrown out in secret places." Brief indeed.

Are we not tempted, therefore, to accept Doctor Georges Khayigaian's thesis that the prescriptions in the Holy Scriptures are not determined by physiological and hygienic considerations, but are inherited from a primitive mentality, or destined to combat the idolatrous practices of neighboring peoples? One is almost at the point of saying that the Jews ate no pork for reasons comparable to those forbidding New Guinea bachelors to eat lizards or those authorizing only the women and children of a region in the Congo to enjoy frogs. The meat of rat, cat or dog—much appreciated in the Far East—is despised by the European, and the English mock the "frog eaters" of the continent.

It could be the case that the microbe did not get the better of man for reasons that were not scientific, something that one should not find at all disconcerting.

If Yahweh supported his people in war, guaranteed their good fortune, gave them fertilizing rains, attended to the procreation of his faithful, and if he unleashed his anger—demonstrated by droughts, famines, plagues, defeat—whenever man was injust, the primary task of the priests would be, therefore, to preserve the physical and moral purity of the people by imposing a certain number of practices on them.

Thus, the Levites, who were the first to cure leprosy, isolated the patient, purified his body, and made expiatory sacrifices for which they chose lambs, birds and oil.

"If the leper is cured of the scourge of leprosy, the sacrificer will order two live and clean birds, cedar wood, cramoisi and hyssop to be taken for the man to be cleansed. The sacrificer will order the throat of one of the birds to be slit over an earthen vase and running water. He will take the live bird, the cedar wood, the cramoisi and the hyssop and will dip them together with the live bird in the blood of the dead bird over running water. Then he will use them to sprinkle seven times the man who is to be cleansed of leprosy. Then he will declare him clean and set free the living bird."

He who is cleansed washes his clothes, shaves his hair and bathes himself. He can then enter the camp, but he still has to stay outside his tent for seven more days; before entering it, he will again wash his clothes, shave and bathe himself. Finally, on the following day, he will offer a sacrifice to the Eternal One through the obligatory intermediary of the sacrificer.

To make a distinction between measures of hygiene and religious practices seems tempting but could give us the wrong idea about Hebrew therapeutics at the time of Moses. The use of water in cleansing is just as symbolic as slitting the throat of a bird, and the seven sprinklings are as necessary, practically, as the seven days of isolation.

From this mixture of traditions, superstitions and empiricism, Hebrew therapeutics evolved to make use of numerous plants and animal and mineral products. Various preparations are mentionned.

In the book of "Kings," the greatest admiration is shown for the therapeutic science of Solomon: "He spoke about trees from the Cedar of Lebanon to the hyssop which grows out of the wall; he also spoke about animals, birds, reptiles and fish."

In the Bible, it is also possible to find mention made of medicines such as myrrh, incense, aloe, colocynth, poppy (used with vinegar as a poison for those condemned to death), pomegranates, sandarac (prescribed by the "Arar" for plasters), caraway seeds, castor oil, garlic, onion, flax, laurel (against snake bites), lavender, mint, juniper, absinth, hyssop, etc. The Israelites used infusions and decoctions (of quince, dates, etc.), electuaries made from crushed and strained fruit with oil, honey, and powders macerated in wine or vinegar. They knew poultices (for example the prophet Isaiah healed Ezéchias who suffered frm an ulcer with the help of a fig poultice), creams, ointments, collyriums (one of which is made from a copper salt), and cosmetics. The constant presence of magic is particularly evident in the choice of vegetable remedies, like the berries and roots of the mandrake, *dudhaïm*, said to be endowed with a remarkable perfume. (One of Rachel's neighbors sacrificed a part of her herd and lent her husband one night to have a little mandrake, because she was sterile and wanted a child, was at the point of giving birth and feared the pain, or simply wanted to smell the unknown scent.) The supernatural qualities attributed to the liver of different animals, and the part it played in the practice of divination were also more important than its therapeutic qualities when the archangel Raphael advised the young Tobit to take fish liver against cataracts (grilling the heart on burning coals enabled evil spirits to be banned).

The art of pharmaceutics as practiced by the priests, kings and prophets, remained very rudimentary and, in a certain form, was quite comparable to the art of the perfumer. Similarly, it is possible to imagine that certain preparations were left to women slaves, the distant ancestors of female pharmacists.

In addition, in the Bible God alone is master of sickness and health, and man must always accept the will of the Almighty. The story of Job gives us the most striking example of this. Satan, with God's consent, ruins Job, destroys his children and strikes him with a malignant leprosy spreading from his head to the soles of his feet. Job, an upright and god-fearing man, is reduced to scratching himself with a piece of broken glass. He bears it all, then after a brief but violent revolt, he bows again to the will of Jehovah who, satisfied, restores all his possessions and doubles them. He also gives Job seven sons and three daughters, the most beautiful in all the world.

The exegetes supposed Job to have been struck by leprosy, a classic disease among the Egyptians and Phoenicians, but certain 16th century theologians attributed the terrifying scourge to syphilis; since then, scabies and pediculosis have been proposed. Doctor Joseph Rollet thought that Job could have been suffering from scurvy:

"This disease caused by moral and physical misery, these nervous prodromes, followed by a profound deterioration in the blood, Job's final cachexia, was scurvy. All the symptoms of the disease, whether in the mouth, the intestines or on the skin, are the symptoms of scurvy."

PRE-COLUMBIAN

The most recent research, devoted to the presence of man on American territory, leads us to the conclusion that the Protomongols arrived there, from Würm, approximately thirty-five thousand years ago, during a period between two ice-ages, Races came from Asia, through the Bering Strait and possibly via the Aleutian Islands, spreading across the continent during the next thoussands of years. According to certain theories, there were also small migrations across the Pacific Ocean. The on known fact is that the various populations of Pre-Columbian America differed from each other in their blood groups, the shape of their skull, their height and build, hair colour, skin colour...etc, the aforementioned having been established by antropological research. Since all contact with the worlds from whence they orgiginated had been broken after the ice melted, the groups that settled in America had to begin all over again to develop their agriculture, pottery-making and weaving, reaching, according to the group, a greater or lesser level of culture.

Apparently, in spite of the considerable differences between the least advanced cultures and the great Central American civilisations and those of the Andes regions, between the Eskimo "Shaman," the Guyane healer and the sometimes specialized one, who practiced in the Maya or Inca communities, the same basic conceptions of illness and its treatment continually cropped up. All over the American continent, men appear to have lived in a "magic universe" but, as the word "magic" has a pejorative connotation for the "scientifically minded" twentieth century man, it must immediately be added that, in principle, the term is directly linked with the idea that one has of the position of the human being in his universe. For the ancient Earth-dwellers, man was not the centre of the world and the master of nature, but an occupant thereof, in the same way as animals and plants. Forces existed, on earth as in heaven, as well as in the underworld, which controlled and protected all living things, and all of these living things had bonds with one another. Everything was, therefore, more or less sacred and the powers that ruled the world intervened in order to punish those who transgressed these interdicts. The spirit could temporally leave the body to travel through visible and invisible worlds; it could also be stolen away.

Thus, in as far as pharmaceutical history is concerned, a double phenomenon characterises these cultures, despite the geographical and temporal distance that separated them; the fact that the role of the healer and that of the priest or sorcerer was not separated and the intensive usage of hallucinogenic drugs.

The ancient Mexican ideas and practices concerning illness and medicine can be seen as an inextricable mixture of religion, magic and science. Of religion, as certain dieties were supposed either to send illnesses or to cure them; of magic, since illnesses were usually attributed to the black magic of some sorcerer and people thus tried to find a magic cure for them; and finally of science as the knowledge of plants and minerals, the practice of blood-letting and the presciption of baths gave Aztec medicine, in certain cases, a curiously modern appearance. There is, however, no doubt that, of of the three aspects, it was the first two which dominated and especially that of magic.

The doctor, "Ticitl" either mal of female, was in fact nothing more or less than a witchdoctor, but a good witchdoctor, admitted to, and approved by, society and who struggled against the powers of an evil Fate. (Soustelle.)

By the Maya, the treatment of sickness was an important part of a priest's duties, the first task being to divine the cause of the sickness, often found to have been "sent" by an enemy or to have been caused by "evil winds" or failure to make the required sacrifice and prayers to the gods or to carry out some ritual correctly. (Michae Coe)

Stemming from vastly distant cultures, geographically, such as the Nazca culture in South Peru and that to the Mayas in Central Mexico, and temporally, since two thousand years passed from the beginning of the Olmeca culture on the Atlantic coast of Mexico up until the Spanish conquest and the end of the Aztec and

Christ as pharmacist. "Chants royaux sur la conception," 16th century, B.N. M.S. FR. 1537, pl. 82.

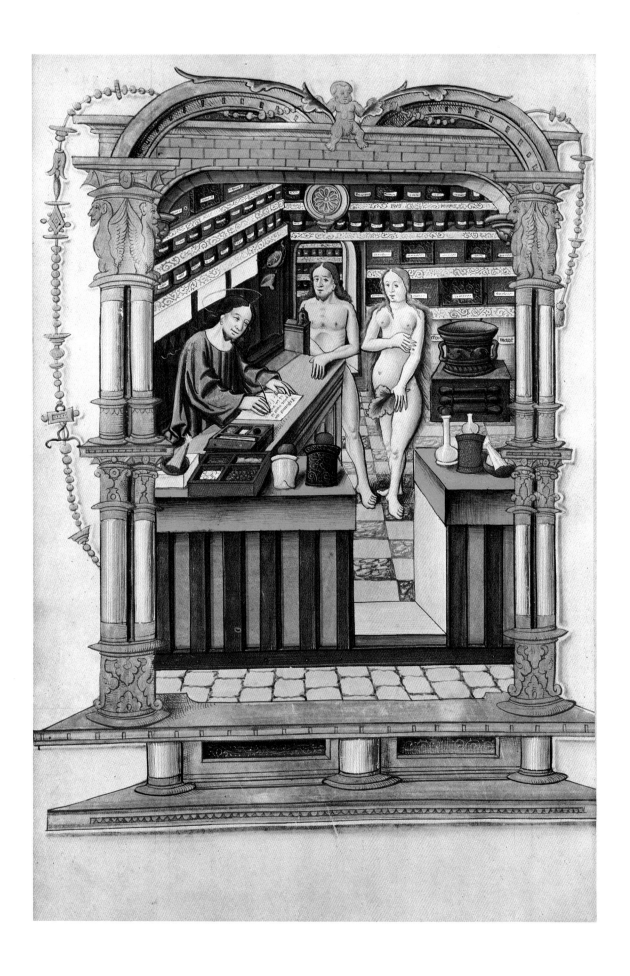

Inca empires, these various examples allow us to conclude that it was indeed the shaman who personified Pre-Columbian medicine and who united, in one person, the magic elements of rituals given to him by the gods and the knowledge of drugs and their preparation which he kept a secret.

It is worthwhile studyng the shaman. A good description is given by Marlene Dobkins in her study of the Nazca culture. With a few modifications to detail, her portrait is applicable to all Pre-Columbian cultures. Our study will be limited to the role of the shaman in the field of health and medicine, without delving in any depth into the no-less important role that the played in war and in predicting the future.

A number of motifs linked to plant hallucinogenic use based on the 1973 report can be examined among the ancient Nazca and derive from the influence of shamanism, the religion of the early hunters and gatherers of antiquity* (see Dobkin de Rios (1976b) for a documentation of these themes). The motifs include a consuming focus on the need for power over man and nature, exercised by leaders whose style was opposed to supplication and submission to forces deemed more powerful than themselves; this latter ethos is commonly found in so-called great world religions of the last 10 000 years or so. As part of his dominion over others, a combative motif fourished, generally featuring shaman against shaman, as opposed to groups of soldiers pitted against other groups of soldiers. Rather, forces of good and evil are seen to the constantly at issue. Further, and important to this discussion, is the relationship between the shaman and his animal familiars, or spirit forces which he is believed able to control and dominate, or at times transform which he is believed able to control and dominate, or at times transform into, in order to incorporate some quality of power, speed, vision, predation, fecundity or the like, which the shaman is able to use for his own ends (Dobkin the Rios, 1976b, p. 60).

The shaman's function is multifaceted and includes that of the psychopomp or spiritual leader of the community; he must be able to ensure the fertility of the land and water, and the animals upon which the

---

Mayan "mushroom stone" from El Savador, late formative period (300 B.C. – A.D. 200); height 13 1/4 in. (33,5 cm.) (Rietberg Museum, Zurich.)

Hippocrates, enthroned, holding the text of an aphorism in his hands: "Life is short and the Art long, the occasion urgent, experience deceptive..." 14th century work. B.N. Greek ms. 2144, fol. 10 V°.

This early sixteenth-century Aztec statue of Xochipilli, the ecstatic Prince of Flowers was unearthed in Tlamanalco on the slopes of the volcano Popocatepetl. The stylized glyphs depict various hallucinogenic plants. From left to right, the glyphs represent: mushroom cap; tendril of the Morning Glory; flower of Tobacco; flower of the sacred Morning Glory; bud of Sinicuiche; and, on the pedestal, stylized caps of Psilocybe aztecorum.(Foreman Archiv. London).

group feeds. He must also protect the group against the machinations of the enemy, sorcerers and political rivals. In non-state-level societies, the most powerful figure is often the shaman, or shamans. Their use of plant hallucinogens bestows upon them magical powers wich enable them to transform into those powerful familiars which they send to do their bidding, to kill their enemy by means of witchcraft, to voyage in the air to distant places to foresee the future, or else to take on the protective coloration of the microorganisms in the earth or sea to ensure fertility.

Shamanism leads us naturally to the problem of the extensive use of hallucinogenic plants or mushrooms in Pre-Columbian cultures. They were abundantly depicted. The Mochicas and Zacatecas had figures showing terra-cotta with hallucinogenic mushrooms over their heads. The water-lily recurs frequently in Nazca pictures and a collection of stones were found in Guatamala representing people crowned with hallucinogenic mushrooms. Three thousand years before our time, the Chavin tribe, who lived in the Peruvian mountains, used a hallucinogenic cactus, the Trichocereus.

The Nazca people already knew cocaine (Erythroxylon coca) still widely used by the tribes of the Andes. The use of "Trichocereus pachassoi" was also wide-spread in South America. The hallucinogenic plants were doubtless known by numerous cultures other than the Pre-Columbian ones: the Indian, Egyptian and Greek ones, to name but a few. Characteristics peculiar to Central and South American medicine, however, indicate that it was beyond doubt in this region of the world that their use was most wide-spread and regular.

Our knowledge of Preo-Columbian medicine in the lands now occupied by Mexico and its neighbouring countries has been culled, in the absense of a Pro-Columbian medical treatise, in the full sence of the word, with the aid of certain medical depictions evoking deities linked with various cures, childbirth and breast-feeding scenes, illnesses, sacrifices and death; but above all, thanks to chronicles written either by natives educated by the Spanish or by Spanish monks.

Pregnant women, protected by the small feminine deity of childbirth, "Ayopechcatl;" were put under the supervision of a midwife. The latter checked the position of the child, prepared the steam bath—temazcalli—, watched over the diet of the woman and supervised the birth. To speed delivery, she would prepare an infusion of "montanoa tomentosa"—ciuapatli—and, should this prove inadequate, she resorted to a drink, called "ciuapatlu," made of water in which a fragment of oppossum tail had been mixed, which induced a violent delivery. Women who died in childbirth were compared to warriors killed in combat or in sacrifice.

According to the "Codex of Florence" the curative agents were named: tetlacuicuilique, "those which removed stones from the body," tetlanocuilanque, "those wich removed worms from the teeth" and teixocuilanque "those which removed worms from the eyes," the illness usually being provoked by the so-called magic introduction of a foreigns body into the patient.

A gruel made of corn, mixed with the stalk of passion flowers—quanenepilli—was given to patients suffering from chest complaints. (2) "Pooralea pentaphylla"—iztacpatli—combatted fiits of fever, "Garrya laurifolia Hartut"—chichiquauitl—worked effectively against dysentry, "Commelina pallida" was used against haemorrhages, sarsaparilla, employed for its diuretic properties in the treatment of afflictions of the urinary system, was used, in a boiled form, against dermititis, and, as a gargle, for throat infections. Tobacco, pulverised and taken as snuff, was used to combat migraines, fainting-fits, numbness and afflictions of the nasal passages. Francisco Hernandez, Philip II's personal doctor, mentions sarsaparilla among the important Mexican medical plants. He had been sent, by the king, to study the flora in its habitat and he enumerated more than one thousand two hundred varieties; unfortunately a part of his "Natural History of the New World" has been lost. Would it be correct to include, among the medicinal plants of the Aztecs, "colorines," the pips of a type of red bean, which acted on the muscles which controlled the erection and constituted a powerful aphrodisiac?

The mineral world was not absent from the pharmacopoeia, the treatise on the art of preparing medicaments. Father Bernardino de Sahagun, who belonged to the Mexican college of Tlatelolco, founded in 1540, and who wrote a "Historia de las cosas de Nueva Espana,"—a history of the things of the New Spain—mentions that obsidian, (volcanic glass) "ground like flour and spread over recent wounds or injuries

35

cures them rapidly (1). He writes of stones, "called eztetl, blood-stones, which have the power to stop nose-bleeds," and adds "I have personally experienced the virtue of this stone, as I have a piece the size of a fist or slightly smaller and in this year, 1576, during the epidemic, I revived many people who were losing their life-blood from their nostrils. They had only to take the stone in their hand and hold it for a few moments and the haemorraging would stop immediately and the patients were thus cured of the disease which has been, and still is, the cause of death of so many people in New Spain. There are many who can bear witness to these facts in the village of Santiago Tlatelolco (2)." In fact, it was probably a plague epidemic which claimed such a large number of victims that year. Father Sahungun reports that a stone called quiauhteocuitlatl, "golden rain"—"is good for those shocked by thunder and also for those with an inner heat (fever.) The stone is found in Jalapa, Itstepec and Tlatlauhquitepec, and the inhabitants of these regions say that, when it begins to thunder and rain in the mountains, these stones fall from the clouds, penetrating the earth, where they grow larger each year and the Indians look for them...digging the earth and extracting the stones from it (3)."

The Aztecs also had sleeping potions and analgesics: teonaanacatl or divine mushroom brought about a pleasant euphoria and a stronger dose induced a deep sleep for several hours; camotl provoked apathy and deadened the patient to pain and outside influences. (The active agent was a small rhizome containing saponin.)

Another, collective, way of fighting disease had been instituted by the imperial Incan government. This was the "Citua" one of the four great ceremonious occasions of the year. This celebration was held every September to purify the people and publicly drive out disease. Foreigners, those with torn earlobes, hunchbacks, the physically disabled and all dogs were put out of the toWN. The healthy members of the population, who were left, respected a severe fast for three days—taking one meal only of uncooked corn and water—and abstaining from all sexual relations. The night before the celebration, each family baked a special kind or bread which they divided into two parts. In one part, they put some blood from a five to ten year old child, obtained from a small blood-letting between the eye-brows. Before dawn, each member of the family washed himself meticulously then rubbed himself all over with a piece of the bread to chase out impurities. The eldest member of the family rubbed the doorstep with the bread. In the Incan palace, it was the sovereign's eldest uncle who carried out the ritual. At sunrise, after these rites had been carried out, the community broke its fast on the part of the bread which had been prepared without having had blood mixed in the dough. Then a member of the royal Incan family would run down from the heights of the Sacsahuamun fortress; as a messenger of the sun he was richly dressed and armed with a lance adorned with feathers and golden rings. Four other nobles, dressed and armed like him, would be waiting for him on the main square; they clashed their lances against one another's while the messenger ordered all illness and misery to be banished from the town and its surroundings. The four warriors, (other chroniclers say that it was four groups, each one composed of a hundred men,) left, each taking one of the four paths dividing the Empire into four provinces. A quarter of a league away, they met other warriors, who replaced them and this continued in relays until they were five or six leagues from Cuzco, where the lances were stuck into the Ground to show the evils that had been driven away that they could not return. Meanwhile, the town's inhabitants shook their clothes in the street, with cries and songs of hapiness.

The next night, little balls of straw, coated in oil and attached to an arm's-length of cord, were set alight and swung through the air like slings while they were carried through the streets in order to expel the evils of the night, then they were thrown into the currents which carried them out to sea where they were lost for ever.

Two days later, the invalids returned and the celebrations finished with festivities (1).

In his history of the new world, father Cobo compiled a long list of remedies, which were being used by the Incas at the time of the Spanish conquest. Among those taken from the mineral world, bitumen in a powdered form must be mentioned, the afore-said, pulverized with oil, being used to close up ulcers and, in a mild dosage, mixed with a drink, soothed coughs. Llama sores were treated with sulphur. Chacco, white mud, dotted with brown spots, was used to combat gout and, thinned with vinegar, dried out haemorrhoids. Collpa, a natural iron sulphate, cured scrofula and healed ulcers; another kind of earth, called "tacu" absorbed in an alcoholic drink, was effective against bleeding stools. A transparent turquoise stone, the copaquira, cleansed sores; pulverized jasper stopped haemorrhoids; white calcareous tufa—"haqque" taken in a powder from, regularized profusive periods or suppressed blood in urine; a pulverized green stone "coracavi" was used as an insecticide; macaya powder (ash or chalk) mixed with warm urine, constituted a depilatory; the bezoar "illa"

36

was an important ingredient in many remedies especially antidotes; copper sulphate "lipis" closed ulcers and old sores.

In the animal kingdom, father Cobo mentions an insect belonging to the Pseudomeloë species, called chuquichuqui, which, when squashed, produced a liquid that killed warts and which, grilled and used in a powder form, prevented ulcer wounds from spreading. The Yanta Yanta, another insect, when reduced to a powder, was said to have vesicatory and aphrodisiac properties. Caterpillar cocoons, called "Musullu" grilled and pulverized then mixed with a red earth known as "Armenian bowl," were beneficial to cancerous ulcers.

Diptera, called "chiches," eaten alive, were diuretic and aphrodisiac. The larvae "Ascantuy" increased wet-nurse's milk. Oil from the "suche" fish was used to combat visceral scleroses and calmed ear-ache. To reduce a high fever, a live frog, the "Kayara" was set to walk across the body of the sufferer; if the former was then set free in the place from which it had been taken, it would carry off the fever with it. The meat-stock and flesh of the small vulture, the "suyuntuy" restored sanity to the mentally deranged. The condor was a precious source of medicine: the skin of its gizzard, when placed on a sluggish stomach, aided digestion, its fat relaxed the nerves and calmed pain, its wing was put on the woman's stomach during childbirth to facilitate the delivery. Humming-bird flesh, in powder form, cured epilepsy. Father Cobo goes on to quote the medicinal uses of llama wool, of fresh meat from the vicuna, armadillo fat...As in Europe, secretionary and excretory products of living beings possessed great therapeutic virtues, in particular fresh urine and excrement. The umbilical cord, when given to the baby to suck, cured any type of indisposition. Fat from a dead body was used for massages. Powder from a crushed baby's skull, mixed with a drink, allayed malarial fever. Human hair, sweat, and ear-wax, women's milk and menstrual blood...all formed part of the Peruvian pharmacopoeia at the time of the Spanish conquest.

Nevertheless it was the vegetable kingdom which supplied the greatest number of medicaments: roots, leaves, flowers, bark, wood, gum or resin; each possessed its individual therapeutic quality. The sap of maize leaves accelerated the healing of wounds and corn-grains, pulverized, cooked and mixed with a fermented liqueur, were used in the compounding of calmative poultices. Potato-based poultices were beneficial to gout. Peanut milk was said to induce sleep. Bean-flour was used for dysenteric troubles, and, mixed with pulverized garlic, served as a plaster to be put on poisonous bites. The Indian red pepper soothed acute tooth-ache and the fruit of the false pepper made a fermented diuretic drink, its resin made up the base of a gentle laxative, a vermifuge and an emetic. Peruvian balsam was used for embalming and a drink made of rasped wood, taken before eating, cleared the liver and spleen and cleansed the bladder. "Ratanhia" roots whitened the teeth and strengthened the gums. Mint—leaves, chopped up with egg whites, constituted the base of a plaster, used to maintain fractured limbs in position. Tobacco root, reduced to a powder and taken on an empty stomach with a bit of warm water, was prescribed as a diuretic and for use against certain pains.

A special mention must be made of cocaine: the shap from its leaves stopped vomiting and nose-bleeds and dried up ulcers, to tea made from its leaves allayed diarrhea and colic, its leaves, when reduced to powder form, were mixed with plasters applied to fractures, but, above all, cocaine, raised to a status of deification, had become an essential form of food for workers, making them forget hunger and giving them strength and energy. The leaves were harvested three times a year on the warm, humid slopes of the second cordillera at an altitude of about two thousand metres, dried in the sun and then carried in a bag, designed specially for the purpose, the "chapsa." The leaf was first mixed with an alcaline substance, "llipta" which was carried in a small gourd and then eaten, rolled up in a ball. After having qualified cocaine as "a useless object only good for encouraging Indian superstitions and rites." The one hundred and twentieth canon of the second synod of Lima tried in vain, in the middle of the sixteenth century, to prevent the Peruvians, Chileans and Bolivians from taking it. At the same time, the governement prohibited forced labour and payment in cocaine leaves in the mines and on the plantations, because, "this plant is nothing but an object of idolatry, a work of the Devil. It only appears to fortify, through the desire of the Evil One. It possesses no beneficial qualities, indeed, on the contrary, costs a quantity of Indians their lives. These people, at the best, only escape from the plantations with their health ruined. This is why they should never, under any circumstances or in any way, be forced to do such work. They should, on the contrary, be looked after and their health and life preserved." The plant continues to be grown in South America to this day.

For how long have the Peruvians known the febrifugal force of the bark of the Chinchona tree? An anecdote, amusing although of doubtful authenticity, proposes a satisfactory explanation of the discovery thereof. The various Peruvian barks had been used, up until then, solely as dyes. An earthquake, in the Loxa region, uprooted most of the trees surrounding a little pond and many of the chinchona trees fell into the water, where they gradually disintegrated. A Peruvian, who was passing by soon afterwards and who was suffering from a high fever, wanted to quanch his thirst. He drank so much of the natural infusion that the was cured.

The pharmacopoeia of the Inca empire was rich in many more wild plants, the precise qualities of which had been elucidated, numerous hallucinogenics were used to give the healer a vision of the sickness, many kinds of poison; and the Spaniards' admiration for the Inca healers' pharmaceutical knowledge was perfectly justified. They could justly declare that the sending over of Spanish doctors seemed superfluous, the native doctors obtaining far better results, the "plantgrowers," officially appointed by the Inca empire, having a remarkable knowledge of all the local resources and even the travelling apothecaries, the "callahuayas" knowing how to prepare all the plant—, mineral—, or animal-based remedies. It could indeed be claimed that the work of the Pre-Columbian pharmacologists is not yet finished; among the hundreds of plants which they used, certain ones remain little-known and some of them, were they to be studied with the scientific methods of the late twentieth century, would surely enable new steps to be taken in pharmacological development.

GREEK PHARMACY

"Medicine," wrote Hippocrates in the 5th century B.C., "has for a long time been in the possession of many things and has a principle and method which it has found. Many excellent discoveries have been made in the course of the centuries." Medicine, therefore, and thus pharmacy, was relatively advanced in pre-Hippocratic times, by the admission of the man who is always considered to be the father of medical science in the western world.

Hippocrates, before being an initiator, was a continuor and the inheritor of a tradition which was certainly long, but whose beginnings remain obscure. Without any doubt, the Cretan and Mycenaean civilizations knew the art of pharmacy. The Phoenicians, intrepid navigators that they were, certainly played a great role in the traffic of drugs, and traded with regions as far apart as the Mediterranean and India. In the book of Ezékiel in the Bible, it is said that the people of Israel bought money, oil, balm, cassia, aromatic reed and the most exquisite drugs from them. However, they did not, in all probability, prepare these drugs themselves. "They borrowed everything from neighbouring peoples for their own personal needs," wrote Mr. Bouvet. At least they knew how to make extremely curious glass vases for ointments.

In order to detect some of the elements of pharmaceutical art in archaic Greek civilization, two kinds of documents can be analyzed: the Homeric poems and the mythological tales. It is clear that this pharmaceutical art goes back beyond Homeric times, and it is strange to find that certain characters in the "Iliad" and the "Odyssey," who are particularly gifted in the art of healing, are presented as simple mortals only to become heroes and gods at a later date.

"A doctor is worth several men," said the wounded Idomeneas, "because he knows how to extract arrows and spread soft balms on the wounds." Malgaigne denied the possibility of internal medicine in the Homeric period. Daremberg, after admitting that the "Iliad" makes no allusion to it, demonstrates that it exists in the "Odyssey." In an epic poem like the "Iliad," it must be above all a question of therapeutics for wounds from the weapons of war. After extracting the iron left in the wound and pressing out the blood, the doctor applied medicines to calm "the black pains" and put on a bandage to keep the medicine on the wound. What were these soothing remedies? We are not told. So, for example, Patroclus put on Euryples' wound a powder made from a bitter root that he had crushed in his hands, and that had the triple effect of soothing the pain, drying the wound and stopping the blood. But we are not given the name of this root. The study of the texts led Daremberg to suppose that, in general, the medicines applied to wounds "were neither plasters nor liquids but powdered substances destined to stop bleeding and soothe the pain at the same time." Achilles, who had taught Patroclus the secret of gentle and beneficent juices, himself healed Telephos' wounds with the verdigris of his lance, and is also supposed to have discovered the properties of mercury and yarrow.

The nine-year-old balm, which he put on the wounds of the dead Patroclus in order to prevent decomposition before the cremation ceremony, was perhaps also a medicine.

At the siege of Troy, wine seems to have played a role comparable to that which it played during the wars of the 20th century. But its being used to revive the exhausted warrior is not sufficient to have it classified as a medicine. On the other hand, the drink prepared by Hecamede, Arsinoos' daughter, for Machaon, the surgeon, who was wounded in the shoulder, can indeed be classified as a stimulant. It was made from a sweet oily wine in which she had rated, using a bronze instrument, the curdled milk food of a goat. She then powdered the surface with a white flour. Onion and honey could also be added to this drink.

The world we enter in the "Odyssey" is more complex than that of the "Iliad." Medicine takes on a certain magic aspect, with the mention of poisons and certain internal medicines as possessing magic powers.

Helen taught Polydamna the Egyptian the power of many plants and expecially that of *Pharmacon Nepenthis,* the magic drug which makes one forget all misfortunes. When Menelaus received Telemachus in his home, Helen threw nepenthe into the pitcher where they drew wine, "a magic juice for soothing all grief and anger making us forget all misfortunes. Once it is mixed in the crater, whoever drinks it will not shed a single tear, but will laugh all day long, even if his father and mother had just died and even if the throat of his brother or darling son had been cut with bronze before his very eyes." This substance was at first taken to be hashish, then hyoscyamine, deadly nightshade, stramonium, mandrake and opium. We would be tempted to think of opium when reading about Ulysses' companions, who after eating "the enchanting fruit of the lotus eaters" forgot about their message and their return, preferring instead to stay with the lotus eaters.

We know, however, what is meant by the "moly", the precious antidote given to Ulysses by the gods that nullified Circe's love potion, the potion which had changed Ulysses' companions into swine.

Fearing the gods, King Ilos refused to give Ulysses, during his stay in Thesprotide, the lethal poison of Epirus, which he used to poison his arrows, and which could also be mixed with drinks. The Pretendants insinuated that Telemachus had, like his father, made the voyage to Epirus in quest of deadly drugs, so as to mix them with drinks some time later and kill them all at once.

Finally, sulphur is mentioned as a disinfectant in the "Odyssey" when Ulysses wanted to purify his palace after the massacre of the Pretendants on his return to Ithaca.

There is practically no mention of internal illnesses in the Homeric poems. Daremberg only quotes the melancholy of Bellerophon, the accidental madness of Ulysses' companions, and the plague that ravaged the Greek army at the siege of Troy. But this plague, which raged for less than ten days and which struck horses and mules before reaching the men, "corresponds to no pathological or historical reality."

Asclepius (Aesculapius), before being deified, was king of Thessaly and was both doctor and warrior. His two sons, Machaon and Podalirius, also doctors and warriors, fought before Troy at the head of the Thessalians from Tricca. Of his daughters, Iaso, Panacea, Aeglea and Hygieia, the second became the goddess who healed every disease and the youngest, the goddess of health. It was probably only at the time of Pindar, i.e., at the beginning of the 5th century B.C., that Asclepius became god of medicine and "healed wounds, ulcers, fevers and pains by means of gentle spells, soothing potions, incisions and external applications." At that time, the first temples were built in his honor, and a branch of medicine that had become sacerdotal was practiced in the Asclepions (temples of Asclepius), served by the Asclepiades priests while schools were being formed outside the sanctuaries from which scientific medicine was to emerge.

Thus the role of magic in Greek pharmacopoeia takes on its full importance only in the classical period, and we may note that the first medicines to be administered to the gods and heroes are still very near to the oldest empirical treatments. It is to Paion, doctor to the gods, that the discovery of peony is attributed. Hercules

Aesculapius discovering Veronica; illustration from a 10th century herb book (Codex membranaceus...) B.N. Latin ms. 6862, fol. 18 V°.

Scolapius
ꝗuueꞇonicã
inuēn.

41

gave his name to some medicinal plants like *Hyoscyamus albus* or *Heraclion*. Melampe, legendary doctor of Argos, discovered the therapeutic properties of hellebore and healed the impotence of the tyrant Iphiclos by giving him iron oxide—rust scraped from an old sword. Orpheus studied the medicinal powers of minerals. The centaur Chiron, to whom we owe the name "centaury," organized the cultivation of plants in Thessaly. Finally, we can quote a remedy for hemorrhoids attributed to Asclepius while he was still considered Chiron's pupil: "Cow sweat, the ashes of a dog's head, the skin of a snake macerated in vinegar and rose honey." A remedy composed of the ashes of a white dog's dirt and oil of roses, also attributed to Asclepius by Pliny, was just as effective for warts.

In the middle of the last century in Greece, healers passed through towns and villages shouting: "Here's the good doctor!" The remedies they proposed must not have differed very much from those just quoted. No doubt they are still effective.

In the ancient and positive current that one notices in the art of Greek pharmaceutics, two characteristics emerge as the most striking, noted as they were by L. Bourgey: "The importance of precise knowledge correctly set down and the absence of any real concern with systemization." Homer refers to the properties of certain plants and the effects of certain drugs, but in his works it is impossible to find the shortest sketch of any pharmacological or even medical doctrine.

Hesiod, who was perhaps a doctor, exclaims at the beginning of his poem, "Works and Days": "Insane... ignorant of the use to which mallow and asphodel can be put!" and makes some allusions to dietetics or to the healing power of water, but he leaves to the gods or to fate the major role in the causes and cures of disease.

Later, at the beginning of the 6th century B.C., Solon, the reformer of Athens, writes with melancholy skepticism in a fragment kept by Stobée: "Doctors have the art of Paion steeped in the knowledge of medicines, but their efforts do not always meet with success; often, a grave illness comes from a slight pain and is not countered by soothing remedies. At other times, the touch of the hands promptly restores the health of an individual sunk in painful and dangerous disease."

Aeschylus, whose definition of a good doctor was one who could apply suitable remedies at the appropriate time, has Prometheus say: "My greatest achievement is this: before my time and before I had learned to make these mixtures of health-restoring substances to be used against all diseases, if somebody fell sick, he was neither helped by remedies nor by a healthy diet; there was nothing with which to anoint the body, no health-giving drink, and everything stagnated for want of medicines." While Sophocles condemns "the doctor who prescribes a remedy too strong for the particular ill," Euripides declares that "the doctor should first think of the illness and not prescribe remedies which do not treat it directly." Aristophanes rails at drug vendors, who in their medicine boxes conceal not only the raw materials that doctors will use in the preparation of their remedies, but also beauty products, love potions and amulets.

In his "plutus", he shows us how to prepare a poultice for certain ocular ailments: in a stone mortar, crush three cloves of garlic of Tenos with a mixture of gum (or sap of Silphium) and lentisk (lentiscus) sap; sprinkle it all with Sphetto vinegar, then oil the inside of the patient's eyelids with this mixture. He also shows us, with sacrilegious irony, how the doctor-priests or Asclepiades proceeded in the temples.

Asclepius, once deified, had temples et Titane near Sicyon, at Epidaurus, at Balagrae of Cyrene, Cos, Cnidos, Cyrene, Rhodes, Tarentum, Pergamum. His priests would interpret dreams, and many sick people, laden with presents, came to sleep in these holy places. After the sacrifice to the god, after placing the offerings on the sacred tables, the night was passed in silence. The next day, the offerings and sometimes the disease had disappeared and the priests gave their consultations.

"Asclepius' temples," wrote Doctor Gaston Baisette, "were situated in salubrious places and health resorts. They were surrounded by a sacred wood. Hypogenous springs were to be found there, rich in carbon dioxide, and mofette caves, where the gas emitted at the prevailing temperature was invisible and caused inexplicable madness. Gradually, these temples became clinics of a kind, where the sick could stay and surgical operations could be performed."

Great steles bearing inscriptions found in the vicinity of some of these temples, give the names of those

---

Orion. Snake-hunting in winter with a bamboo. 11th century painting, illustrating the work of Nicanders, "Theriaca et Alexipharmaca." B.N. Greek Suppl[E]., 247, fol. 2 V°.

treated and the wonderful cures brought about by the god. It has been said, a little rashly, that the cures were never pharmaceutical but were mere dreams or visions. Yet, the ointment mentioned by Aristophanes casts this assertion into doubt. Other texts point to the use accompanied of course by religious practices of certain plants or, stranger still, of animal saliva.

The temples must have possessed their sacred animals, especially dogs and snakes. The medical scene in "Plutus" shows us the priest, disguised as Asclepius, doing his nightly rounds of the sick sleeping in the temple. He stops near the blind Plutus, feels his head, wipes his eyes and covers his face with a red veil, whistling at the same time. At this signal, two enormous snakes slide gently under the veil to lick the eyes of the patient who recovers his sight. An inscription found at Epidaurus says that a man was healed of an ailing finger by a snake. This man was also suffering from a cruel cut in his toe. The servants of the temple carried him outside and placed him on a chair. Once he was asleep, a snake came out of the dormitory and healed his toe with its tongue, then went back to the dormitory. When the man awoke and found himself healed, he said that he had dreamed that a handsome young man seemed to have applied a remedy to his toe.

Dogs played exactly the same role. Thus a blind infant, Thyson of Hermione, was treated and healed by the dogs of the temple of Epidaurus, if we believe the steles.

Were other animals trained in the same practices? Artemidorus tells of a woman suffering from a pain in a breast, who "dreamed" that an ewe sucked the milk of her breasts, probably in one of Aesculapius' temples.

After this dream, the patient applied the plant named arnoglosse, i.e., lamb tongue, and recovered. The therapeutic use of the plant called cynoglosse must also have originated from the patient's dream of having been licked by sacred dogs in the night. The role that salive continued to play in popular therapeutics is important enough for us to accept that such practices were general in the temples of ancient Greece.

More perhaps than the development of scientific medicine and the preparation of effective remedies by good technicians, it was competition that gradually led to the decline of the medicine of Asclepius' priests. All the Olympian gods and then the simple heroes acquired therapeutic powers, and the faithful made them into healers. At Ephesus, Diane treated eye ailments; Venus treated chin tumours; Bacchus, Mercury, Vulcan and the sons and sisters of Asclepius—all of them had their specialities. Treatment based on the interpretation of dreams began to lose effect.

Pliny or Celsus and later certain historians of medical science in the last century saw only darkness between the Homeric period and the time of Hippocrates, who is supposed to have appeared miraculously. On the contrary, it is appropriate to recognize the existence, running parallel to sacerdotal therapeutics, which became important quite late, of a traditional knowledge of medicines, whose gradual enrichment enabled the Hippocratic school to be built on a solid experimental foundation.

In the name of Hippocrates, born around 460 B.C. in the Agean archipelago of the Sporades at Cos, more than forty medical treatises are conserved, which attest to the immense importance of medicine in Greek intellectual life towards the end of the 5th century. A contemporary of Socrates and Plato, of Sophocles and Euripedes, of Thucydides and Aristophanes, Hippocrates is traditionally considered to be the father of medicine. Nevertheless, the life of the "divine old man" is little known. Quite paradoxically, some have gone so far as to deny he ever existed, like J. Boulet in the year XII. Historians were obliged to reduce to insignificance fine legends like the one in which Hippocrates of Cos rejects the presents of Artaxerxes, then his voyage to Abdera to heal the madness of Democritus, his triumph over the plague of Athens, which he achieved by lighting fires in the squares and hanging sweet-smelling garlands in the streets. Yet, the accounts of his contemporaries remain. A doctor by the name of Hippocrates, contemporary of Socrates, did exist. He belonged to the family of the Asclepiads. His father, Heraclides, was a doctor like his sons, Dracon and Thessalus, and his son-in-law, Polybus. He had many disciples, to whom, in return for his salary, he taught his art. No doubt he travelled widely from town to town practicing his art, and he died very old.

Are the tracts in the Hippocratic Collection all written by Hippocrates or were they written by collaborators or disciples? Today it is still an open question, but as Louis Bourgey noted, "such an important collection of works as varied as this definitely presupposes an exceptional driving force and a doctor who personifies the genius of the art."

Legend has made of Hippocrates a universal man, the first and greatest of all doctors. It has aggrandized the individual and simplified him at the same time without really deforming him.

No tract in the Hippocratic Collection is purely pharmacological, which does not mean that medicines are never mentioned in the work of the doctor of Cos. They are, on the contrary, extremely varied and often complex.

No doubt Hippocrates started by using the simplest remedies, and among these he judged the diet to be the first and foremost. He certainly placed great importance on the diet of the sick. During acute illness, he recommends, for example, tisane. i.e., a broth of hulled barley. It was prepared by boiling twelve or fifteen portions of water for one portion of barley and when the barley swelled, adding a dash of vinegar with a little oil and salt and sometimes a little anethole or leek. The patients who were well enough to eat had to choose refreshing foods like beet, pumpkin, melon, or mountain spinach. They drank water with honey added or drinks of more delicate preparation, like that recommended by Hippocrates for tuberculosis in which there was rue, anethole, celery, coriander, pungent red wine, water, wheaten flour, barley flour and old goat cheese.

Purgatives, generally of a violent kind such as ricin, black hellebore and colocynth were used prudently by Hippocrates. Mild purgatives were *Euphorbia peplus* or *Peplion, Euphorbia retusa* or *meconis, Daphne Guidium,* cabbage and melon. White hellebore and hyssop were advised for their emetic properties.

All diseases, according to Hippocrates, are stopped or healed by evacuations from the mouth, the stomach or the bladder, but perspiration is common to all diseases or checks all of them as well. Among diuretic remedies, he recommended garlic, onion, leek, cucumber, melon, pumpkin, fennel. To make the patient perspire, he asked him to eat a lot of cooked flour, drink pure wine, wrap himself up in blankets and rest. If sleep had to be induced, black or white poppy, mandrake root or hyoscyamus seed were used.

Baths, fomentations and fumigations were among the remedies considered most effective by Hippocrates. In certain cases, the sick part of the body was dipped in a decoction of suitable simples; in others, a bladder full of hot water or a large sponge dipped in a hot liquid was applied; other fomentations were made by applying a sachet full of salt or roasted millet.

In the tract, "Women's Diseases," there are many formulas for fumigations meant to treat feminine organs. In one of them, small pieces of red-hot iron are thrown into urine several times; in another, a mixture composed of goat dung, the hair of a hare and seal oil was poured on damp straw covering lit coals.

To relieve inflammation of the tonsils, Hippocrates made one inhale, by means of a tube, the smoke from a hearth in which hyssop, sulphur and bitumen were burning. The treatment could be accompanied by gargles made from origan, savory, celery, mint and niter, the lot being cooked in water with a little vinegar.

To soothe pain, break an abscess, or make the body supple, Hippocrates used oils and ointments. The oil could be of pure olive or more or less made up (rose, myrtle leaves, fleur-de-lis, infused in olive oil). The preparation of certain Hippocratic ointments was very complex. Cerates were for him those made mainly from oil and wax. The one destined to soften tumours and clean wounds consisted of goose marrow or fat, the quantity being as large as a walnut, lentisk or terebinth resin, the volume of a broad bean and as much wax. All this was melted over slow heat with rose oil.

Poultices were medicines of the same kind, but of less consistency. One made from barley flour cooked in a mixture of oil and wine was recommended against tonsillitis. Certain poultices, made from the leaves of olive, fig or oak, cooked in water, were considered refreshing.

Numerous recipes for pessaries, which did the same work as their modern equivalents, are given in the tract, "Women's Diseases," e.g.: "A pessary which gives an ample and thorough purge: clove of garlic, niter, the oily interior of an oak-gall, and apply. Another one: caraway seeds crushed in wine and applied in wool. Another: white clay, which is worth a potion... Another: Knead silphium and figs together into the shape of an acorn... It's also good to crush a gourd in the same way. Another: the bile of a bull, red niter, netopon, cyclamen, all in measures the size of an oak-gall, except for cyclamen which is better mixed with honey. The woman to be treated will apply that..."

Formulas for injections, enemas and suppositories can also be found.

Hippocratic pharmacy is therefore very rich. Taking on very varied forms, it uses, for the most part, vegetable products without neglecting certain animal and mineral ones. Among the animal products are: donkey droppings, donkey meat, butter, stag, goat and its milk, fat, hide and horns, dog, frogs, cow-, ewe-, and mare-milk, honey, snakes, worms, etc. Among mineral medicines, one finds: bronze, alum, silver, magnetite, magnesite (pierre magnésienne), soil of Egypt, the black soil of Samos, etc.

With Hippocratic empiricism, this polypharmacy offers sufficient proof of the contribution of numerous generations. As an epigraph to his thesis, Laennec took a quote from Hippocrates: "Medicine is not a new science." We can rest assured that at the time Hippocrates was writing, pharmacy was no new science either.

* * *

The principles of the school of Cos became "articles of faith" for those who are traditionally considered to be Hippocrates' immediate successors, i.e., Thessalus and Dracon, his sons, or Polybus, his son-in-law. Equally faithful were Plato, Philiston of Locri, Ctesias of Cuidos, Diocles of Carystus, who formed the first dogmatic school, still called the Hippocratic School. They do not appear to have enriched the pharmaceutic arsenal very much.

Like Hippocrates, Plato thought that the duration of diseases was fixed for a certain time and, consequently, it was preferable to hinder or check their course by keeping a careful watch on food, drink and exercise rather than to interrupt them with medicines. He feared purgatives and, in particular, those that he said were capable of making a minor ill worse and engendering several ills from the original. He tolerated them in the most urgent cases only. Despite such mistrust, some medicines bear the name of Plato, and Galen attributes their invention to him. This appears to be without the slightest foundation for Daniel Le Clerc, Plato's name being chosen simply to give greater value to such remedies.

Aristotle, author of a "History of Animals," was described by Milne-Edwards, as the "father of natural science." Judging from a letter attributed to Epicurus, certain authors have claimed that this philosopher, before becoming Plato's disciple, practiced the profession of pharmacist in Athens. It is easier to acknowledge the fact that at this time he was practicing medicine and that, like his colleagues, he also sold medicines. Was his father, Nicomachus, not a doctor himself and a descendant of Machaon, son of Asclepius?

The doctor, Diocles, son of Archidamos, who was born at Carystus in Euboea, was the greatest doctor after Hippocrates, according to Pliny. His herbalist's manual, the "Rhizotomokon," remains the most ancient Greek treatise on botany. It gave the most precise prescriptions not only for the sick, but also for those in good health, and authors who came after quoted from it constantly. For example, on vomitory medicines, he wrote: "Medicines named vomitory will not be chosen among the very active drugs, but for treatment, we can be inspired by the patient's habitual diet: let us take, among other things, the infusion of green cucumbers cut in slices, the infusion being effected by maceration in water. This infusion is mixed with lukewarm water to be taken after meals..." Fenugreek was used by Diocles in gynecology. He ground it in cooked wine. As a great remedy for women who gave birth with difficulty, he ordered them to take a hot bath after drinking a third of this mixture, then drink the second third when the heat of the bath caused perspiration and the rest after getting out of the bath. He also made pessaries to relieve womb pains with fenugreek flower mixed with barley and grains of flax, all of which was cooked in honey water, this also being applied to the lower stomach. The same remedy healed galls, sores and spots on the face, once an equal portion of sulphur was added and the skin prepared by frequent lotions of niter, but he forbade rubbing the patient with it.

In his "History of Plants," Theophrastus quoted Thrasias, the drug-seller, who boasted that he had found a drug that killed painlessly. This doctor, incidentally, was intelligent in stating that all men do not react in the same way to medicines and that which was a purgative for one could have no effect on another. For example, he saw a shepherd eating a handful of hellebore without feeling a thing. Neither did this purgative have an effect on his disciple Alexias, the doctor, nor on Eudemus, the seller of medicines, nor on another Eudemus of Chios.

The geographer and botanist, Eudoxos of Cuidos, a contemporary of Plato, was also a dogmatist and had a certain influence on physicians such as Philistion of Locri or Chrysippus, also of Cuidos. The former recommended cabbage and cabbage stock to treat heart troubles, stomach upsets and epilepsy. The latter, who

Portrait of Hippocrates as the 17th century imagined him. B.N. Engravings.

Hippocrate Medecin'
né dans l'Isle de Cos, les Ecrits qu'il a
laissés servent de base à l'étude de la
medecine il vivoit ——— l'an du monde 3560

de   Desrochers

also extolled the powers of the cabbage, condemned basil, judging its effect hostile to the liver and the stomach, and deeming it capable of stopping urination and weakening sight. Celsus quotes one of Chrysippus' formulas concerning an ointment to be used against pains in the joints, and which was made from pepper, wax and the liquid resin of sandarac. Against kidney complaints, he advised, according to Rufus, a poultice made from galbanum, turpentine and ers flour. He was the first to forbid those with fever to drink.

La Bruyère, who translated the "Characters" of Teophrastus, Aristotle's successor and historian of plants, observed "that he was remarkably prudent, worked for the welfare of the public and was industrious, obliging, affable and philanthropic." Regarding his works, La Bruyère wrote: "they are infinite and we know no ancient writer who wrote more than Theophrastus. Diogenes Laertins enumerates more than two hundred different treatises written by him on all kinds of subjects. Most of them have been lost with the misfortunes of time, and the rest amounts to twenty treatises collected in the volume of his works. This consists of nine books on the history of plants and six books on their growth. He wrote on wind, fire, stones, honey, signs of good weather, rain and storms, odours, perspiration, giddiness, fatigue, relaxing the nerves, fainting, fish that live out of water, animals which change colour, animals subject to desire, characters and customs. That is what is left of his writings." In the ninth book of the "History of Plants," Theophrastus writes on poisons and the healing power of herbs, counting the soil of Lemnos among medicinal soils and describing an opium-based preparation known as "mekonion."

Among the dogmatists, direct disciples of Hippocrates, Doctor Gilbert Medioni still counts Dienchidas and Mnesitheus. The former, an anatomist, recommended this diet to those who had to risk going to sea: "It is neither easy nor useful, at least when one embarks on a boat for the first time, to counter the vomiting caused by voyages on the sea. Such vomiting is advantageous from all points of view. After vomiting one eats neither copiously nor indifferently. Instead, one takes well-cooked and soured and adds a little pennyroyal or bread dipped in aqueous and sweet-smelling wine... Against umpleasant emanations, one inhales a perfume of quince, thyme or pennyroyal. As far as possible, one avoids looking at the sea until one is used to being on board." Mnesitheus feared hellebore taken as a drink. "Either it heals immediately or it causes serious ill and prolongs the sickness."

Two illustrious figures can be mentioned among the Hippocratic School and on whom legend bestows pharmaceutical knowledge. Queen Artemisia, daughter of the king of Caria, gave her name to *Artemisia vulgaris* or mugwort, and Alexander the Great is supposedly responsible for the diffusion of aloes since, after his Indian conquest, he sent a division of his troops to discover the island of Socrota, which produced them. According to Symphorien Champier, in his "Myronel des Apothicaires," quoted by Mr. Bouvet, "Alexander the Great, king of Macedonia... was also a great apothecary and healed Ptolemy, who was mortally wounded, by means of a herb he had found himself and which healed all those wounded in battle."

Founded by Alexander the Great, the city of Alexandria became, under the influence of Ptolemy I Soter, Alexander's satrap successor, then king of Egypt in 305 B.C., the capital of Hellenistic civilization. The Museum, a sort of academic research institute, soon assembled famous philosophers, brilliant philologists, mathematicians, astronomers and doctors. These scholars benefited from good material conditions and had a rapidly stocked library. According to Aulus Gellius and Ammien Marcellin, it counted seven hundred thousand volumes housed in two centers, one in a district of Alexandria known as the Brucheion and the other in the Serapion (temple of Serapis).

The Hippocratic writings were collected and codified, permitting methodical and, no doubt, almost religious study. That did not prevent the physicians living in the Museum to pursue the analysis of the human body and make great progress in anatomy, physiology and experimental pathology. Alexandrine pharmacy developed along parallel lines, the precise knowledge of the body and the functioning of the organs being sought first so that therapeutics could be adapted to every pathological case.

Among the first physicians to practice in Alexandria, the most famous were Herophilus and Erasistratus. Both were interested in the science of medicines and proposed new formulas.

Herophilus, known especially for his anatomical work and for the numerous dissections which he carried out in public, can also be considered as one of the founders of *materia medica*. We know that he wrote

Preparing the theriac after the illustration of Nicander's treatise, *Theriaca et Alexipharmaca*. B.N. Greek suppl[t]. 247, fol. 5.

ς δ οι ξηριτας ομιγαοτη ιλαιμαος κα ιτοη·
λι ος αγρι α δ ο μολοχη ο τὴ κι μοριι κα ρ δ ε
γι α το θριζ μ τω σασ ε λααοα ο μ ι κα κ το ο κ ε ρι δ υ οιο
τη χιὸ ο δ ιὸ τη α ξ μ ε. τω ρ ο μ α ξ ο μ κη μι ὸ τη τι θυ χη ο
ὸ η ιων τι απ ρο το π ο ο ι ο δ ιν ο ο κο μ ε ο ω μ τα ι ο ὸ ρα μ κ ο ι ο·
κα ρ ο λα μ ο υ α γ ε μ ι χ ο λ ι η ὸ δ χ ο ι ὸ δ ε χ ο ι ο α ο ο ο ο θ λ ω
ὸ η δ ε χ ρ β ο τ ο μ η σ η ι ε α ρ τ ω ο η ὸ τη μ ιο τα λα χ μ ο ι
μ ο α ι η ε μ τ ρ ι σ α τη ρ ι γ α θ ε τω ρ ο χ ε θ ι ὸ δ ο η τ ο λ α ο ω ν
τω ρ ο σ α ε η τ ο ο σ κ ι ο ὸ η π ι κ η γ ε ὸ η ο η τη σ α δ ε ι χ ω ρ α.
α η α λ δ η ο ὸ ρω π ο μ δ ρ υ π τ ο ς α ο η ι κα ρ ι α μ μ τω α η ο ι ο:

ΓΕΩΡ ΓΟΣ
ΤΡΙΒΩΝ
ΒΟΤΑΝΑΣ·

ΜΟΛΟ
ΧΗ

ΡΟ ΔΟ Ι

ΚΑ ϹϹ
ΠΗ·

ϹΙΛ
ΦΙΟΝ

Nascitur hęcherba ostriago. quąpunici saramuris uoc
eis ea monumenta aut in monumtis aut in parietlib; qfcirca
Radices eius facit ad eas rés quas in homine   I montib;
nascuntur. herba ostriago tunsa &inposita ab om
nibus rebus quae in corpore nascuntur sanat. hanc herbā
suolueris euellere mundus &ante solis ortū legis eā m seruit.

HERB·ARGIMNIA ʃxxx

Omoeos unone. alu umunula. Romani argemo. alii libur
nia. alii uerbalis ma. alii ēcordialis ior. tusci rucilia
aluriminalis ālii domētrix callica. alii sarcocolla
Nascitur in campis uel circa sepibus.

Deurruub;
Argimonię

several works (lost today) on the properties of medicines, but he deserves to be remembered for expressing this thought alone: "Above all the doctor should know the limits of his power; only he who can distinguish the possible from the impossible is a perfect doctor." He was perhaps the first to realize that no disease can be treated without medicines and that these, well employed, were comparable to the "hands of the gods." He often used appropriate images and, for example, compared, according to Pliny, white Hellebore to "a brave captain who takes the first men out of a town after stirring into action all those who will follow him in a sortie."

More physiologist than anatomist, Erasistratus had a point of view that differed significantly from that of Herophilus concerning *materia medica*. He feared medicines that were too complex, mistrusting antidotes of which his colleagues boasted and preferred to recommend to his patients "a diet for living," i.e., a hygiene. Gymnastics and steam baths encouraging sweating counted among his medicines. He extolled the virtues of chicory for liver or intestinal disorders and carefully described its preparation: "Boil it in water until it is cooked, place in a second pot of boiling water to remove its bitterness, then take it out and put in a pot with oil. Before using, add a dash of vinegar which is not too strong." Apart from simple remedies such as honey, with which he purified polluted water, moneywort, discovered by King Lysimachos, (golden) ivy twenty grains crushed in a *setier* of wine which he considered sufficient to eliminate in the urine, water infiltrated between the flesh and the skin, Eraristratus preferred external medicines. He gave the recipes for a great number of fomentations, poultices, ointments, liniments, etc. Ptolemy Philadelphus was cured of an attack of gout by an Erasistratian plaster. Compresses made from colocynth, melon and apple crushed together in wine helped against dropsy. Erasistratus prepared a mixture of burnt copper, burnt iron sulphate (Misy), saffron and myrrh in order to combat by means of friction illness of the eyes, ears, nose and ulcers of the testicles. He used woman's milk against the bites of poisonous animals and cow's milk mixed with honey and salt against paralysis. He also recommended bird's brain macerated in wine against the venom of snakes. A mixture of ivy berries and pomegranate bark crushed together with oil of roses assumed, perhaps, a magical character since it had to be placed in the right ear of those suffering from the left side of the jaw, but, as Doctor Medioni remarks, "every great scholar of antiquity had his own personal book of magic recipies and nobody can explain why."

For a long time after the death of Herophilus and Erasistratus, the schools, natural rivals that they were, founded by these two physicians continued to flourish, something that did not prevent a third school, that of the empiricists, from being founded soon after they had disappeared. "What is the use of theoretical discussions?" asked these newcomers. Why look for obscure causes? Diseases are not healed by eloquence but by remedies. Experience alone enables us to know what will succeed. Philinus of Cos and Serapion of Alexandria, both disciples of Herophilus, were the first leaders of the empiricists. Philinus annotated Hippocrates and dealt with poisonous animals. Serapion, whom Galen described as "extremely vain", dared to counter certain Hippocratic theories and left behind numerous prescriptions, certain of which appear bizarre, to say the least. Galen mentions his yellow plaster for healing wounds. This wade made from lead monoxide, wax, galbanum and oil; Celsus quotes his preparation against impetigo made from niter, sulphur and resin. He ordered epileptics to paint the neck with vinegar and the body with oil of roses or also to use the brain of a camel, the heart of a hare, the testicles of a wild boar, the blood of a tortoise. It is said that he used crocodile excrement so much that a fraudulent market of imitations sprang up in Alexandria.

After the founders of the sect, the most illustrious empiricist is undoubtebly Heraclides of Tarento, disciple of Mantias the Herophilian, who had written a "Treatise of Medicines" and a book called the "Apothecary in the Iatreion." Heraclides also devoted most of his efforts to pharmacology and toxicology. Galen thought him "more credible than the others" and said "that he never told lies to defend the interests of the sect, as other doctors did either in this sect or in others. He was sincere and only reported what he had experienced himself." He tried out several poisons and antidotes on himself and was one of the first to understand the salutary properties of opium. Galen describes one of the remedies he made up to soothe pain and induce sleep. This consisted of pills made from four portions of hemlock juice, as many of henbane and one portion of castor, one of white pepper, one of costmary, one of myrrh and one of opium. All this was mixed in cooked wine and exposed to the sun so as to obtain the desired density. To calm coughing and induce

The plant which cures lencoma from a 10th century herbarium. B.N. Latin MS, 6862, fol. 46 V°.

49

sleep, Heraclides of Tarento, according to Celsus, prepared pills made from saffron, canella, castor and "poppy tears." Pliny quotes a formula based on anise, castor and honeyed wine against "swelling of the stomach and the intestines." The treatment he recommended for inflammation of the brain and delirium is also worth mentioning. The patient was kept in a dark place. He was given an enema and then bled; another enema followed and this was repeated daily during the illness. The head was shaved and washed with a decoction of laurel leaves before being anointed with oil of roses. Then a poultice was applied (to the head) made from flour, mead, iris powder, oil of mastic and sweet sedge (*Calamus aromaticus*). Finally a make-up was applied in which Heraclides mixed *Poucedan,* opium, castor, the oil of bitter almonds, vinegar and oil of Iris. The question, ironically asked by Galen, is how nature or chance, which according to the empiricists had found all the other remedies had been able to teach man to mix together drugs which had so little relationship with one another ?

FROM ROME
TO BYZANTIUM

With his conquests Alexander was responsible for the birth of Greek civilization; in the last two centuries before Christ the Roman conquest was to give the civilization of the High Empire its unity. The flourishing of the Egyptian, Mesopotamian or Aegean civilizations cannot, of course, be compared to the Etruscan, Carthaginian or Gallic civilizations at their peak nor to Rome in the first centuries of its existence. Yet, if the countries of western Europe merely represented lands to be colonized for the inhabitants of the Middle East, the sight of Rome extending its sway over the Mediterranean obliges us to take the civilizations that preceded this conquest into consideration.

Only a few hypotheses on the pharmaceutical art of the Etruscans or the Carthaginians have been voiced. These peoples must have had in their possession a small number of simple and complex remedies that were traditionally handed down by word of mouth. They were not ignorant of the virtues of thermal springs and believed in the possibility of divine intervention in the course of diseases: numerous ex-voto representing sick or healed parts of the body bear witness to this.

The Romans also asked multiple gods to watch over their health and fight against their ills. The offering of fat and broad bean mash pleased Carna, goddess of "visceral functions." Those with fever prayed to the goddess of miasmas and smoke. The goddess Carmenta presided over childbirth, etc. Like the Etruscans, the Romans possessed a small number of remedies that tradition had judged effective. The father of the family, rich both in his own experience and in that of his ancestors, treated the diseases of his family and consulted his neighbors when his own knowledge was insufficient. As late as the first century A.D., Tiberius declared that once a man reached thirty, he should be his own doctor. The municipal statistics of this period, extremely incomplete as they are, do not permit us to test the truth of this declaration.

In Rome's five hundred and twentieth year, 234 B.C., the champion of what is termed routine therapeutics, M. Porcius Cato, Cato the Censor, was born at Tusculum (Frascati today). Farmer, lawyer, soldier, quaestor to the great Scipio Africanus, consul and censor, Cato remains famous for his patriotism, his hatred of Carthage, his distrust of the Greeks, the austerity of his morals and also for the treatise on rural economy, the only work he wrote that has survived.

It is a collection of recipes and advice for those about to take possession of a country domain. We are told how to choose this domain and how to get the best out of livestock, olive groves and vineyards. He also explains how to treat the wounded, heal the sick and keep personnel in good health. Whether or not the simple methods, poor remedies and the naïveté of the author have been ridiculed, all historians agree that Cato lived to the age of eighty-five. While that might serve as an argument in favour of his therapeutics, it is no doubt preferable to put it down to chance, a strong constitution or a healthy, frugal life.

For old Cato, the most precious of medicines would seem to be cabbage. It maintains health and cures most diseases, its use being both internal and external. Applied as a poultice, cabbage leaves crushed and dipped in hot water are remedy for wounds, tumors and ulcers. It also cures dislocations and bruises, killing the pain at the same time. To get rid of a polyp in the nose, crushed wild cabbage is placed in the palm of the hand and inhaled energetically. The polyp will disappear after three days. The juice of cabbage leaves crushed in wine and instilled warm into the ear will improve hearing.

"If you cut, wash and dry cabbage leaves which you digest with salt and vinegar, you will obtain one of the healthiest of foods. To make it more palatable, sprinkle with honeyed vinegar, flavour with dry mint, rue and curshed coriander and add salt. This excellent food destroys the source of all illnesses it has laxative properties and cures all the diseases already in the body. Headaches, eye troubles, whatever, it gets rid of everything and heals everything. It should be taken on an empty stomach in the morning. It cures melancholy, spleen, palpitation, diseases of the liver and lungs, stomach cramps and all internal pains." Mixed with rue and coriander, raw cabbage is a remedy for gout. Grilled, rubbed with oil and slightly salted, it cures insomnia.

Cato gives the following laxative preparation: "Put six *setiers* of water and a boney end of ham into a cooking-pot. Should the latter not be available take half a pound of ham. When this is almost cooked, add two small heads of cabbage, two beets with roots, a little polypody, mercury, two pounds of mussels, a tadpole, a scorpion, six snails and a handful of lentils. Reduce all these substances to three setiers without adding oil. When lukewarm, take a setier of this beverage, add a ladle of wine from Cos, drink and rest. Take the second and third portions which will act as a purgative. If you want to drink more wine of Cos, feel free to do so. Of all the substances I have just mentioned, one would suffice to loosen the bowels but putting them all together gives an effective and pleasant beverage."

Cabbage possesses other, more bizarre virtues. If the urine of a person who has eaten cabbage is mixed with a hot bath, it will cure the sick and applied as a rub will strengthen sickly infants, clear the sight and get rid of headaches. The vapor from this urine boiled below a chair with a hole in it will stop the fetid discharges of a woman who should be seated on the chair and wrapped in her clothes.

A final piece of advice from Cato concerning cabbage deserves to be mentioned. It is intended for those who as quests want to eat and drink to their heart's content. All they have to do is to take cabbage macerated in vinegar before the meal. If, after leaving the table, they want to continue eating, taking five macerated cabbage leaves will give them back en empty stomach.

The therapeutic arsenal of "De re rustica" does not restrict itself to cabbage; an important place is given to wine, and certain recipes magical in character are not neglected. Thus, for abrasious suffered while travelling, Cato proposes that a small branch of tall wormwood should be placed under the anus. He mentions a charm for the treatment of dislocations: "Take a green reed four or five feet in length, split it down the middle and let two men hold it on your dislocated thigh. You begin to chant: "Daries, dardaries, ascataries, Dissunapiter," and continue in this fashion until the parts of the split rod join together again. Brandish a sword above it. Once the two parts touch and join together, cut them up and use them to make a ligature on the fractured or dislocated limb. It will get better. But repeat the same invocation every day or the following one: "haut haut haut ista sis tar sis ardannabon dunnaustra."

A little magic would also have seemed to slip into Cato's prescriptions for sick cattle. Make them eat a raw hen's egg, then the next day the bulb of an onion crushed in wine is perhaps useful, but why should the ox and the man treating it be standing and have an empty stomach during the operation? Why should the figure three appear in this recipe against diseases of cattle? "Three grains of salt, three laurel leaves, three leaves of leek, three cloves of rocambole, three cloves of garlic, three grains of incense, three stems of savine, three rue leaves, three stems of bryony, three white broad beans, three burning coals and three setiers of wine." This potion is to be administered to each ox three times a day for three days and there should be nothing left when the last dose is swallowed.

It is certainly more difficult to consider as superstition the fact that Cato violently rejects Greek doctors because they practiced their profession "for a salary." Here it must simply be a question of an extremely keen sense of economy. Cato's contemporaries were beginning to lose this sense since Archagathos, a Spartan and the first Greek doctor to practice in Rome in 219 B.C., rapidly attracted many clients. The Censor vainly claimed that the Greeks had sworn to exterminate the Romans "by means of medicine." The Senate granted the Greek Archagathos Roman citizen ship and slet a shop near the Forum for healing the sick and giving them new remedies. The first western European pharmacy was born.

*   *   *

The shop founded in Rome just before 200 B.C. by Archagathos the Greek housed a surgery, a pharmacy and a hospital like the houses of assistance found in the most important Greek cities of this period. There the doctor received the sick (humble folk for the most part), dressed wounds, sold remedies he had prepared or had prepared under his supervision and, if necessary, kept patients who were seriously ill and needed constant attention and care.

Thanks to the different specimens kept in museums and the witness of Latin authors such as Pliny, it is possible to get a clear idea of the pharmaceutical material used in these dispensaries. To make powders, mortars usually made of agate but also of stone, lead or copper were used. Superimposed plates also served to crush substances. The practitioner had at his disposal spatulas, spoons, bronze or bone droppers, sieves and of course different furnaces. Gypsum vases and bowls of different sizes were used for maceration sut, calcination and infusions. Medicines were kept in boxes made of wood or horn, in pewter vases, earthen pots and glass flasks. Near at hand were forceps, scalpels, cauteries, lancets, bistouries and also bandages, compesses, sponges and lint, indispensable for surgery.

Archagathos the empiricist was nicknamed the "healer of wounds" after his successful operations and then "the executioner," no doubt because of his brutality, and he is said to have invented a painkilling plaster made from burnt bronze, white lead and turpentine.

Doctors, in fact, often became torturers by rigorously applying a brutal treatments. A century later another Greek doctor also established in Rome criticized this practice. Asclepiades, born in Prusa in Bithynia, had studied medicine in Alexandria.

He banned emetics, much used by the Romans, and purgatives such as black hellebore, flakes of copper, the juice of *Euphorbia Cyparissias,* the milk of a she-ass with salt, and wrote a treatise on the beneficial effects of enemas. His favorite remedies were taking walks and baths, massage and wine either taken as a medicine or not at all. He recommended wine for those with fever (they needed an uplift), for the restless (who have to be calmed and tranquillized), for the lethargic (who have to be roused) and for those with heart conditions (who, since they perspire profusely, must get their strength back and be warmed up again).

If he generally refrained from giving medicines for acute illness, he acted differently with chronic diseases and wrote that "it is a poor doctor who has not two or three remedies already made up and tested for all kins of diseases." Showing his preference for external medicines, he gave his patients frictions oils, ointments and poultices; he also used perfumes, sternutators and gargles, not to mention lavements. He is considered the inventor of the "white plaster" made from white lead monoxide, oil and water to treat burns and scratches.

In the course of the 1st century B.C., Rome was invaded by numerous Greek doctors, among whom were Themison of Laodicea, a disciple of Asclepius and founder of methodism, or Thessalos of Tralles who, after putting the patient on a diet and bleeding him, "reincorporated" him with the help of honey mixed with poppy infusions, grains of mustard macerated in vinegar, baths and poultices. Antonius Musa, an emancipated Greek and doctor to Augustus, composed several formulas for the treatment of ulcers, catarrh, nephritic pains, etc. Two of Antonius Musa's formulas met with a long history of success. One included the flesh of a viper to treat ulcers thought to be incurable and the other was prepared by using the white excrement of a dog mixed with honey as a cure for tonsillitis. Galen was to write of this second preparation: "We know no better remedy for tonsillitis, inflammation of the tonsils and choking caused by the glands."

During the years 25-35 A.D., probably in the reign of Tiberius, a popular work was written in Latin that was of capital importance for the history of medicine and pharmacy, the "De re medica" attributed to Aulus Cornelius Celsus, the patrician. Though perhaps no doctor, Celsius managed in his treatise to trace the vital progress made in medicine and surgery from Hippocrates to the time of Augustus. The work includes an important preface and eight books divided into three groups. The second group (Books V and VI) is dedicated to pharmaceutical medicine. Book V begins with a classification of medicines that could be considered a veritable pharmacopoeia. Celsus distinguished among substances which stop the flow of blood (vitriol, incense, alum, vinegar), those which close and heal wounds (myrrh, snails crushed with their shells, spider webs), maturative remedies (spikenard, costmary, bitumen, fat), appetizers (cinnamon, pennyroyal, bdellium), detergent (verdigris, orpiment, pigeon blood, horseradish, stag horn, leek), corrosives (alum, gall-nuts, sea foam, bilue), substances that consume the flesh (salt, orpiment, different stones), those that burn (vitriol, borax, ewe droppings, cantharides), and that determine the scab on cuts as if there had been cauterization. Scabs are gotten rid of by using flour mixed with. The inventory continues with medicines for resolving humors (southern wood, elecampane, iris, bitumen, origanum), those that attract the humors and drive them out (verjuice, pumice, niter), those that remove lumps (gum, the white of an egg, milk), those that help wounds to heal (ochre, wax, butter), the emollients (burnt bronze, antimony, boiled snails, "refuse from the gymnasium", etc.) and those that cleanse the skin (honey mixed with gall-nuts, lentils, iris).

Having drawn up this list, Celsus goes on to deal with the mixing of medicines and the resulting remedies: "This mixture is made in different ways without being subject to any limit, since we may add or take away such and such a substance and even when they axe putt together them show differences relative to weight. Thus it follows that, without having infinite, medicines lend themselves nevertheless to numerous combinations in which it would be pointless to interest oneself even if all of them could be encompassed, given that the same effects are to be found in a small number of compositions easily modified to one's taste when their properties are well-known." Celsus describes at length ointments, plasters and lozenges or pastilles, then pessaries and powders. The antidotes "should cure the gravest of accidents" and are indicated especially against poisons. He gives three formulas, one of which is the antidote of Mithridates. Certain medicines are tonics like the acopes (one of them being made from wax, oil and turpentine, the lot being boiled together and then mixed with honey, oil of iris and oil of roses). Finally Celsus indicates how some liquids used for making ointments should be prepared. In Book VI Celsus devotes a chapter to the study of eye lotions. "The greater the inflammation," he wrote, "the more urgent the need to make eye lotions soothing by adding the white of an egg or certain quantity of womans milk. One of these agents alone would often suffice to calm the violence of the pain and should a doctor or another remedy not be available, it is applied to the eye by means of a brush designed for that very purpose." The eye lotion of the Nile was made from Indian spikenard, opium, gum and saffron. Book VI ends with a study of the ailments of the "shameful parts" and Celsus has great difficulty to find in Latin the right words to explain the different cases and the means to treat them.

* * *

Gaius Plinius Secundus, Pliny the Elder, born at Coman in 23 A.D. and killed in the eruption of Vesuvius in 79 A.D., wrote much, read more and worked ceaselessly. Of his many works, only one has come down to us, his vast "Natural History" which, with the Bible, was one of the first works to be printed (in Venice, 1469), appeared in numerous editions and for centuries was used as a book of medicine and today is either neglected or severely criticized. Pliny was a philosopher, astronomer, geographer, botanist, doctor, a great soldier and a lucky speculator, but of all these he preferred to remain a "compiler of encyclopedias," and if at times he expressed his personal ideas, it was only by accident, without claiming to bestow any new wisdom on the world. Such absence of pretention coupled with an extraordinary capacity for work could not fail to worry many of his readers.

In his "Natural History" alone he acknowledges having collected about twenty thousand observations taken from two thousand volumes. He retained the essential ideas of one hundred authors and, in addition, quoted 146 Roman authors and 327 foreign authors. For a writer whose intention it was only to popularize

Fracture split. (Gallo-Roman Museum of Dijon.)

and write for humble folk a sort of big book of recipes, he showed extreme professional conscientiousness. From his collection (in which there is no disparaging criticism) of an enormous mass of diffuse information and strange and marvelous tales of people without head, feet or eyes, we have deduced, perhaps too quickly, that he lacked discernment and that he was naïve. In that case many folklore enthusiasts could be judged likewise.

If he was too credulous, Pliny nevertheless left behind a work interesting to read and which remains a document of capital importance for the history of human beliefs and, in particular, for the history of pharmacy under the Roman Empire.

The last 18 books of the "Natural History" (containing 37 if we count the first which provides the contents and bibliography) relate to medicines: vegetable remedies (20-27), animal therapeutics (28-32), mineralogy and mineral remedies (33-37).

Wondering at the diversity of plants and at the therapeutic qualities of each one, Pliny thanks nature for producing the plants and making them known to us and sings the praises of the Roman Empire that made it possible to ask Spain, Asia, the British Isles, Central Europe, Africa and the whole world for plants necessary "in aid of man." "These are the fruits of peace which the earth enjoys under the vast and majestic Roman Empire which shows us men from such diverse lands and nations and mountains whose summits touch the sky, their respective products and the plants which cover them. Long live this gift of the gods who seem to have given the Romans to the world, like a second light to illuminate the affairs of men."

In no way, however, does this prevent Pliny from showing the greatest mistrust of foreign medicines, since the remedies that individuals from different countries try to sell to the Romans have not been prepared for the Romans, and must have already proved useless in their own countries, otherwise the inhabitants would not get rid of them abroad. Defender of traditional therapeutics and reviver of Cato's ideas, he judges Greek theoreticians who have brought their quarrels to Rome to be extremely dangerous. « We are carried away by the wind of Greek charlatanism and it is notorious that their most able speaker immediately becomes the master of our life and death as if thousands of nations lived without doctors or any medicine at all. Such was the case of the roman people prompt enough, however, to welcome the arts and even avid for medicine until, once put to the test, they rejected it."

He tries, in vain, to oppose the passion of his contemporaries for the "theriac," this "preparation conceived for luxury," this "imitation of art," "this monstrous, pseudo-scientific display." He opposes, with as little success, "the silly pretensions of those who imagine that the only good remedies are expensive ones."

To join the ranks of the Greek doctors practicing in Italy came the Persian "magi," charlatans proposing mysterious remedies and amulets and taking advantage of the credulity of the sick with "revolting lies." Yet Pliny does not allow himself to forget these foreign medicines and writes them all down without bothering to refute them but simply adds: "it is said," "they say," "it is claimed." Thus popular, traditional remedies, local superstitions, still-valid observations, and odd, repulsive or absurd recipes are to be found closely linked together in his work, which in the centuries to follow was to bring readers first to accept it all and then to reject almost everything. We read, for example, in the "Natural History" that the blood from a dog acts against poisoned arrows, that fresh sheep droppings cooked in wine and applied locally are good for snake bites, that bugs help fight the effects of all venoms and that "some people crush them with salt and woman's milk in eye ointments mixed with honey and oil of roses for the ears." The ashes of the head and tail of a rat cure baldness, and should one desire to dye the hair black, first the head is shaved, then the scalp is smeared with a crow's egg beaten in a copper vase making sure that the teeth are not blackened at the same time by keeping the oil in the mouth until the scalp is dry. Moreover, this should be done in the shade and the scalp should not be washed until four days have passed.

Pliny also spoke of the virtues of mineral waters and described their diversity. Did he not give us 156 recipes and observations concerning them? He draws our attention to numerous mineral, vegetable and even animal recipes that common sense still accepts. He mentions, for example, the use of ephedra crushed in black wine for coughs and asthma and prescribes the juice of the scarlet pimpernel before a cataract operation, which led C. Himly in 1800 to discover the dilative action of deadly nightshade and henbane on the pupils.

Doctor Paul Seidmann has written that, for Pliny, "what caused wonder was as attractive as the truth." That disconcerted his readers, especially those for whom the truth could never be a source of wonder and they reluctantly refer to the "Natural History" in which the supernatural occupies too important a place.

*   *   *

Despite the "universal" empire of Rome in the first century A.D., the Latin West and the Heltenic East continued to exist side by side, if not actually to confront each other. The Latin authors who deal with pharmacy remain less numerous than the doctors who spoke Greek and it is no coincidence or prince's fantasy that Nero granted the title of *Archiatros* to Andromachus, the Cretan. Andromachus, usually called Andromachus the Elder to distinguish him from his son, owed his reputation not to his scholarly arguments or any original doctrine, but to his art of composing and administering medicines.

The emperor's doctor had already discribed several original remedies relating to specific diseases when he undertook the preparation of the panacea which was to bring him glory. This was the *galena* (silent), socalled because as Bauderon said, "those who had been struck by the plague or bitten by some poisonous animal were healed and quietened by its use." It was only at a later date that Crito, doctor and contemporary of Trajan, gave the remedy the name of *theriac*. To avoid possible alterations, Andromachus described in a Greek poem written in elegiac verse the electuary whose power would surpass even the asatidorie of Mithridates, much used in the Roman Empire since Pompey discovered its formula in the library of Pontus.

Nicander, Greek poet of the second century B.C., had, under the title "Theriaca", described serpents and poisonous animals, precautions to be taken to avoid their bites and appropriate remedies to heal them. These are a long way from the theriac of Andromachus. The same cannot be said for Mithridates' antidote, at least if its most complex formula is retained, containing as it does 46 substances including opium and numerous aromatic herbs. The other formula brought back by Quintus Serenus Sammonicus is really too simple: 20 rue leaves, half a drachma of sodium chloride, two nuts of almonds and two fatty figs.

Forty-six substances were still not enough for Andromachus. Not only did Nero's doctor increase the proportion of opium in the new electuary, he also added squill, aristolochia root, dry bitumen from Judea, centaury, castor and above all viper lozenges to be prepared as follows: "At the end of spring or at the beginning of autumn select long, heavy vipers with a sharp eye and jaws turned back which have fed on the seeds of green fennel. Cut off the head and tail, remove the skin and entrails and boil their trunk thus skinned in water with a little salt and dill. Then press lightly the cooked flesh until it detaches itself from the bone and mix it with powder of dry bread so as to make small lozenges which dry at after turning them over frequently." These lozenges were the original base of Andromachus' galena and certainly contributed to the success of the preparation, an exceptional success since the theriac was to be considered by the majority as the most precious antidote for eighteen centuries. T. Bordeu wrote as late as 1764: "Andromachus would be a subject of ridicule among us if he tried to answer all the theoretical objections which could be raised to his composition; he would not pass his baccalaureat but his remedy is the fashion everywhere. For years I have seen a bowl of theriac being given to all the sick every night in Montpellier hospital while the schools of ths metropolis of medicine resounded with invectives against this composition. I have seen old people of great experience administer the theriac and that in strong doses for all kinds of illnesses in all kinds of households. I have also seen this ploy succeed on many an occasion when I didn't know what side to take while following the indications prescribed by the principles of theory. Today in the center of Paris formulas are in great vogue which were merely pet names for the theriac! What great efforts have been made by those who decry these formulas to imitate them!".

Today this "amorphous chaos," this "monstrous invention of a monstrous age," is neither prepared in public nor in pharmacies, but since it has definitely gone out of use, a certain indulgence towards the electuary seems to have emerged. The composition is no longer dismissed as absurd. "In the theriac," wrote Doctor Cabanès in 1911, "antiseptics dominate and are combined with stimulants tempered by the moderating action of opium; to help eliminate them, a substance was added which was predominantly diuretic, i.e. scilla. Old as it certainly is, the formula for panacea is one of the most rational and conforms on all points with orthodox science." This is also the conclusion reached by Doctor Jean Hacard, author of a study called "The Theriac and the Society of the Theriac of Parisian Apothecaries."

Mithradites' antidote had given Andromachus the idea for his galena. The work of Cratevas (who was the king of Pontus' doctor), was certainly the main source of the Greek doctor Dioscorides, a contemporary of

Andromachus, who lived in Rome, then followed the armies as military doctor in order to broaden his observations. In Italy, Gaul and Spain he took an interest in the pathology of the region, medicinal plants, hygiene, the eating habits of different populations and the farming methods, etc. His reading, but above all his personal notes, enabled him to write a great treatise on medicines in five books from which Greeks, Romans and Arabs borrowed freely until the Renaissance.

Each chapter is dedicated to a therapeutic agent taken from one of the three kingdoms, mostly from the vegetable kingdom, and gives the name and synonyms, the origin and the most useful variety, a brief description, how each is grown and prepared, occasional directions for recognizing adulteration and, finally, healing powers and medical applications. Certain authors have criticized his classification for being confused and his descriptions for incompleteness. The latter, at least, had the merit of being written, in general, with the model before him rather than merely being taken from the writings of his predecessors. Dioscorides, who had made known 519 species of plants, claims in his preface "to have travelled throughout different countries to find substances which could be useful for medicine." As for his classification, based in most cases on analogy, it has enabled us to make helpful associations.

The first book deals with aromatic drugs, oils, ointments, trees, resins and seeds; the second with animals, honey, milk, fats, wheat, kitchen herbs and herbs which are "acrid and pointed." The third book concerns roots, juices, seeds and herbs while the fourth ends with the description of herbs and roots and the fifth deals with wines and metals. The chapters dedicated to animals are relatively few, but one finds interesting observations like the one concerning the variation in milk caused by the plants on which they feed. He tasted himself the milk of cows, goats, she-asses and ewes, and was aware that summer milk is no match for that of the spring, that the milk of northern Italy is much superior to that of the center and that, should one find in the pastures scammony, hellebore, mercury or clematis, the milk of cows grazing there is liable to cause disorders. "You can believe me," he wrote, "for I have tried it out. This milk upsets the entrails and troubles the stomach."

In the course of his voyages he drank milk on farms and tasted the local wines, appraising them as a hygienist; he was one of the first to have provided recipes for aromatic wines. We may smile at the thought of Dioscorides giving advice on the use of athlete's dirt which was supposed to be a particularly emollient substance, but he also gave precise indications for the preparation of oxymel of squill and ironated water (by immersing a red-hot rod of iron in water). He gave good advice on the picking of plants (when the weather is good and preferably "in high, cold and dry places exposed and wind-beaten") and on their preservation (flowers being kept in boxes of lime wood). In addition he founded geographic botany by describing with great care the habitat of the rarest plants.

His chapter on hot baths in sea water is important for the history of hydrotherapy while the one on ammonium chloride (sal ammoniac) is important for the history of chemistry. He left indications for the preparation of writer's ink, cobbler's pitch, colors for both artists and dyers and perfumes and make-up for women.

Maurice Albert wrote that his "Materia medica" was not only medical but universal in its subjects. It could still be said today that in Dioscorides' pharmacy we could expect to find everything an American pharmacy would have and much more besides.

Littré's dictionary tells us that the term "galenical remedies" is given to vegetable remedies "as opposed to spagyrical or chemical remedies." Now it is obvious that the medicines prescribed by Hippocrates more than five centuries before were also of vegetable origin, yet this was a matter for the historians of Hippocratic pharmacy alone. Galen, in fact, is of particular importance both for the history of pharmacy and for that of medicine.

Philosopher, grammarian, physician and astrologer as well, doctor and pharmacologist of course, grand voyager and violent polemicist, Galen wrote on everything because interested him, but his work makes up a complete whole because it is still with us.

Born at Pergamum in 130 A.D., Galen studied philosophy, then medicine, first at Pergamum, then at Smyrna, Corinth and Alexandria. After his studies he practiced the medical profession in his native city and at

An amusing portrait of Galen inhaling the odor of a plant, from the frontispiece of Otto Brunfels' work *Spiegel der Artznen*. Library of the Paris Faculty of Medicine, 22860.

58

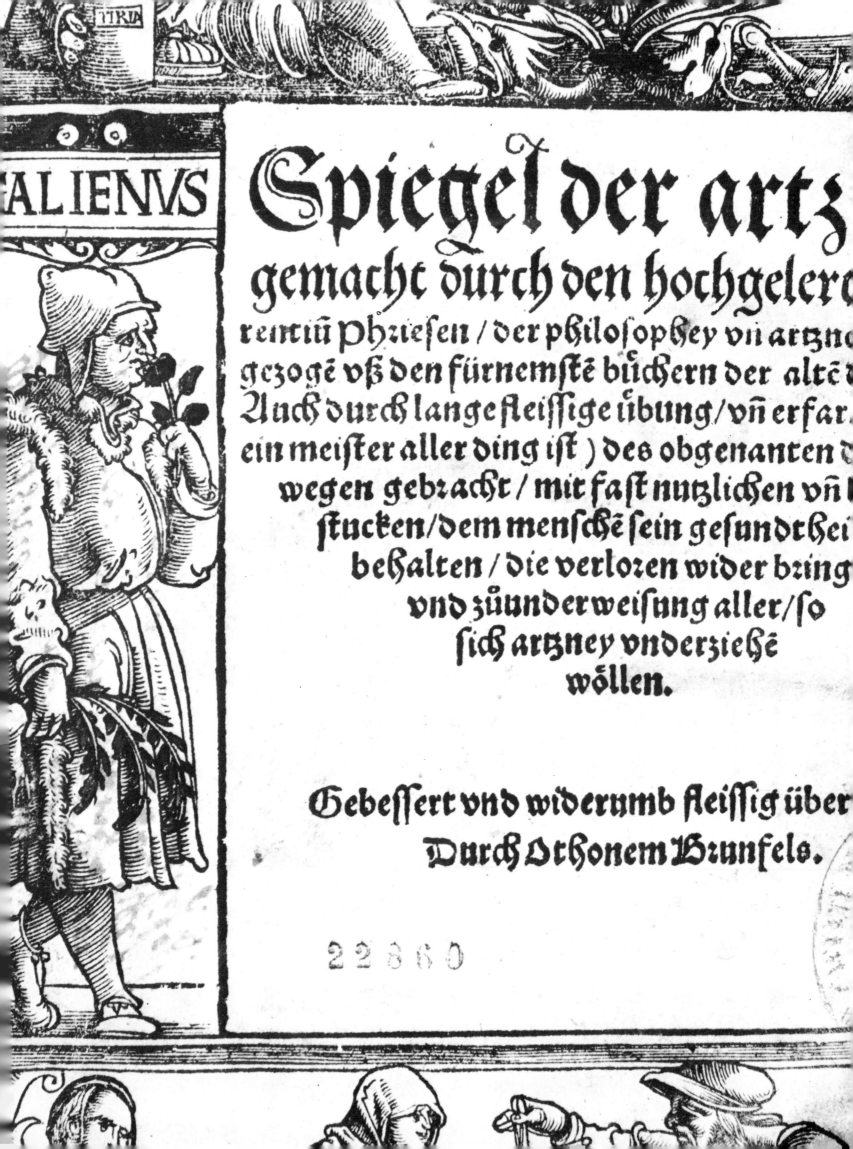

ALIENVS

Spiegel der artz[

gemacht durch den hochgeler[
...rentiū phziesen / der philosophey vñ artzn[
gezogē vß den fürnemstē büchern der altē [
Auch durch lange fleissige übung/ vñ erfar[
ein meister aller ding ist) des obgenanten d[
wegen gebzacht / mit fast nutzlichen vñ [
stucken/dem menschē sein gesundthei[
behalten / die verlozen wider bzing[
vnd zuunderweisung aller/ so
sich artzney vnderziehē
wöllen.

Gebessert vnd widerumb fleissig über[
Durch Othonem Bzunfels.

22860

Rome where he treated Marcus Aurelius and Commodus. Historians and bibliographers still disagree on the number of works written by Galen. Some attribute 500 treatises to him, others, 640, and it is not unlikely that several of his works translated into Arab or Hebrew in manuscript form lie sleeping still in the libraries of the Middle East.

Galen was in Rome in 192 at the time when the Temple of Peace on the Via Sacra and with it all the palace's great libraries were destroyed by fire. Some of his manuscripts disappeared in this disaster, in particular his treatise on the "Composition of Medicines." Fortunately he found time to rewrite it.

"The beginning of this book," he wrote, "is intended for those who deride the powers of simple medicines and mock those who have written that they could be of benefit to different parts of the human body, such as the liver, the lungs, the kidneys and the bladder.

"The food which enters the stomach is sent to the liver, then to all the different parts of the body and each part retains the action of the simple proper to it. The sea hare, for example, only ulcerates the lung and the cantharides ulcerate the bladder without harming the other parts of the body.

"In the composition of simple medicines, if the action of one of the components varies, the rest should not be thrown away. Some are active in their natural state while others act according to an acquired quality. For example, you will see a simple, by nature cold, becoming warm if heated."

We know, in fact, that according to the Galenic doctrine of the four humors—blood, phlegm, yellow bile and black bile—they are themselves the product of four fundamental qualities: heat and cold, dryness and wetness. Illness results from a disturbance in the system of the humors and, consequently, it is appropriate to use medicines that are hot or cold, dry or wet. After fourteen centuries of admiration, the rigidity of this system provoked violent and often unjust criticism, but a reading of the treatise "The Composition of Medicines" proves that Galen the practitioner did show the necessary flexibility himself:

"In composing medicines one should not use those which have the same medicinal action, but often those whose actions are in opposition. Take, for example, the medicine composed of verdigris and cerate. Verdigris ulcerates the skin and is warm and acrid. Cerate is milder but instead of making the skin grow again, it dirties it. Yet the two together are good for ulcers. There are four kinds of warm simples and according to their degree of heat, their action is more or less intense. The same applies to cold, drying or moistening simples. There are many whose effect is due to occult and unknown properties. It is not sufficient, therefore, if the action of a medicine is to warm up or cool down again, but to what extent. The common factor in the resins is that they warm up again, though to a greater or lesser degree and this also applies to rue, dile, onions and all warm medicines. Medicines are made from plants, metals or animals. Not only is it necessary to know the actions by which they heal the diseases of a sick body, but also the diseases themselves with their causes and different symptoms."

With sound, good sense Galen *considered* that a medicine can only be judiciously employed if the doctor knows perfectly the patient's constitution, age and what the weather, season, place and air, etc, where he lives are like. The success of a treatment depends on the particular moment one administers it and on the quantity. A doctor is better able to judge the gravity of a disease if he has known the patient in his normal state of health.

With the same good sense Galen offers advice on dietetics, gastronomy or pharmacology, for example: "the best cheese may be recognized by the eructations it causes; the one which causes eructations that gradually disappear is the best. The cheese which causes persistant eructations is bad since it is clear that it is transformed and assimilated with difficulty." In the same way he finds quid pro quos absurd and is of the opinion that it is as much a waste of time to substitute real cinnamon in the theriac with double the amount of cassia as it is to drink double the amount of adulterated wine when one has no wine of Salerno, or to eat twice as much bran bread when good bread is in short supply.

In his treatise on simple medicines, Galen mentions no less than 473 medicines of vegetable origin without neglecting, however, those of animal origin. He holds in particular esteem, for example, the remedy of Aeschrion the empiricist against the bites of rabid dogs. It was composed mainly of the ashes of river crayfish burnt alive in a bronze pan until they can easily be made into a powder. The treatment lasted forty days. If one began the cure immediately after the patient was bitten, a large spoonful of these ashes in water would suffice.

"Venus Saponaria." Protectress of drugs manufacturers.(Epinal Museum.)

This dose was doubled if the treatment was late in starting. Occasionally, Aeschrion added for every ten parts of crayfish ashes one part of incense and five of opoponax. For one pound of the first product he counted three ounces of the second and dissolved the lot in a sufficient quantity of vinegar.

If Galen considered this crayfish powder effective against rabies, he would not devise a doubtful argument in its defense after the fashion of Pelops: "Wanting of justify the effect of crayfish on rabies, my master Pelops, claimed that crayfish prove useful against this disease because it is an animal that lives in water and rabies needs extreme dryness thus causing those suffering from it to fear water. "He added that freshwater crayfish are cleaner for this purpose than the saltwater variety because the latter partake of the salt in the sea which is extremely dry in nature. But when the objection was raised: "If what you say is true, how is it that all aquatic animals are not equally effective against this disease?", he replied that not all of them could be prepared in the same way as crayfish, whose shell can be reduced to a dry ash which consumes and absorbs the venom of rabies. Pelops contradicted himself in this way since he was vain enough to want to explain everthing. "As far as I am concerned, if I am not sure of knowing something perfectly, I do not attempt to convince others."

The doctor of Pergamo paid for the excesses of the cult of which he was the object until the 16th century. His work has been torn to shreds bit by bit. His self-importance, errors and naiveté have been ridiculed. He was called an arriviste and a coward and his medical system judged superficial. His detractors, proud of the wealth of their new science, wanted to cast him into oblivion forever. With them in mind we are tempted to make a last appeal to Galen when he compared wealth to a fountain: "We come to draw water as long as it is there, but once it has run dry, we relieve ourselves there after removing our tunic."

* * *

Because of the complex history of Rome's Eastern Empire—which lasted over a thousand year—it does not generally overburden our memory to admit that the Greco-Roman civilization lives on. Nor should we exempt ourselves from getting to know the Byzantine civilization, and it is appropriate to call to mind the fire in the library of Alexandria in 641 or the taking of Constantinople by the Turks in 1453. After Galenism, with which one associates the end of Greco-Roman medicine," wrote Doctor F. Brunet, "we jump to the African school, the Arab or the School of Salerno, sparing only two or three lines on the names which do not belong to the eras of conventional history." Byzantium, however, remains the essential intermediary and the medical and pharmaceutical traditions of the Muslims or the Byzantine Christians would not be understood without the presence of a link far too little known.

Many were Galen's disciples, both in Rome and in Greece, who confined themselves to repeating the teachings of the master, clouding them or expanding them with popular remedies or long and useless theoretical discussions. Oribasus, born in 325 in Pergamum, like Galen, and coming from a patrician family, studied medicine in Alexandria under the direction of Zenon of Cyprus. As a young man he made himself a great reputation and on the recommendation of his master became the doctor and friend of Flavius Claudius Julianus, called the Apostate when he was neither emperor nor restorer of paganism. Julian the Apostate, named Caesar by Constantius in 355 and sent to Gaul, had Oribasus follow him. He was to ask him to edit and abridge Galen's writings. This pleased him and Oribasus was to do the same work on other writers on medicine. In 361, Julian succeeded Constantius and appointed his doctor quaestor of Constantinople.

In 363 the emperor Julian was killed during an expedition against Sapor, the Persian king. Oribasus was at his side. Deprived of his protector, the doctor was to lose his position, be stripped of all his possessions and sent into exile, no doubt among the Goths. He had kept his knowledge and he won the confidence and respect of his hosts. His banishment came to an end before 369, his possessions were restored to him and he married well, had four children and continued writing. The date of his death is unknown.

More than two thirds of his works have not come down to us. The synopsis of Galen, his first work written for Julian, has not been preserved. The emperor had ordered him "to research and collect the essentials of the best doctors and all things that helped to attain the aim of medicine." This became the great "Medical Collection" in 70 books, only 25 of which survive. At the end of his life he was to write a "Synopsis" of his great collection for the benefit of his son Eustathios, also a doctor: "I have done this work willingly for I thought it would be very useful, not only for you during your voyages but also to others thoroughly versed in medicine." This synopsis, translated into Latin in the 7th century with its nine original books, was a great success. Oribasus had also written a work destined for prudent travellers and giving indications of medicines easy to find. It was called the "Euporistes." This little manual of practical medicine for general use is divided into four books and describes the symptoms of each disease, enumerating the main simple medicines useful for each case and gives, at the same time, the substances most used in medicine and their effects. The work, which includes extracts both from the great collection and the "Synopsis," seems of the greatest importance for the "History of Pharmacy" due to its variety, the richness of its documentation and the precision of its information.

The prudence of Oribasus in his prescriptions also deserves our attention. In the case of poisoning, for example, he recommends first the drinking "all at once of oil beaten in water in as great a quantity as possible." Then one stuffs the patient with all kinds of food and "causes vomiting; in this way the poison will be rejected with the food or its malignancy will be tempered by the mixture. If, after vomiting, the stomach is taken by a burning heat, one prescribes a mixture of water and oil of roses and again makes the patient vomit." The prescription of the theriac in wine is only given afterwards and Oribasus immediately adds: "Should the theriac not be available, crush and administer either juniper berries and twenty rue leaves or wall germander with wine. The patient should be completely deprived of sleep and to keep him awake, one tickles his feet. Once the poison seems to have abated, given that it causes colic in the lower stomach, one administers acrid enemas containing plenty of honey and foam of soda or other medicines whose action is more relaxing on the stomach."

Oribasus prescribes instillations of hot oil against earache. On the subject of jaundice he remarks: "When the sick become yellow after an attack, they can easily be cured by taking baths in fresh water and with rubs of some resolvant oil such as camomile, dill, fleur-de-lis or *Origanum maru*. If jaundice is caused by blockage of the liver, it can be healed rapidly and easily first by getting rid of this blockage and then by using a medicine which evacuates the bile. All remedies effective against inflammations are suitable for jaundice when it results from inflammation of the liver. Arrach seeds, calamint and cyclamen root also heal jaundice by purging the intestines and evacuating in perspiration the bile which is spread all over the body; three drachmas of this are given as a drink with sweetened wine or mead. Sweating is to be recommended."

Of course, using rat or billy-goat dung against thinning eyelashes has died out and the recipe against enuresis seems difficult to prescribe today: "Burn the bladder of a goat or ewe. Drink the ashes with vinegar and water and at night go to bed thristy. Equally effective is the brain of an eagle as big as a chickpea with one part of goosefat and one of gum to be taken as a drink or grilled with alphiton and eaten. Boil a hare's testicle in wine that smells good, let the patient drink this and the disease will disappear. Before the meal give calamint and myrrh to be drunk in wine. Rub the penis with cutler's clay mixed with lickwort juice."

It is Oribasus who describes for the first time the delirium of melancholy called lycanthropy (Synopsis, VIII, 10): "People suffering from lycanthropy go out at night and perfectly imitate wolves straying around sepulchres. This disease may be diagnosed thus: paleness, a languishing look and dry eyes with no tears. You will also notice that the eyes are hollow, the tongue extremely dry and that no saliva at all comes from the mouth. The sick are thirsty and have incurable ulcers on the legs because they fight among themselves. Such are the signs of lycanthropy. But you should be aware that this disease is a kind of melancholy which, once these signs become evident, is treated by bleeding until the patient faints and by putting him on a diet of food full of good juices. Freshwater baths are prescribed, then whey for three days after which he is purged two or three times with the holy colocynth. After the purgatives, the viper medicine used for treating the poisonous bites of animals is administered. One also uses the different treatments for melancholy already enumerated. When the patient feels the symptoms of the disease coming on, apply the embrocations normally used for inducing sleep. Once asleep, apply opium ointments to the nose and ears."

Certain historians have regarded Oribasus as a mere copyist. Others, hardly more indulgent, have made a encyclopedist of him. If this prudent and well-informed therapeutist was a compiler who had an admirable knowledge of the bibliography of his subject with a flair for choosing the most typical and important passages, that would perhaps suffice to make him one of the essential authors of ancient pharmaceutical literature.

*   *   *

HISTORY OF PHARMACY

Alexander of Tralles who, according to the most recent medical historians, was "undoubtedly the greatest of all Byzantine doctors," owes much of his fame to a methodical and scholarly study of the medical resources of the Mediterranean world. His work, which Doctor F. Brunet described as "a unique and complete monument to the medicine of the 6th century A.D.," was to inspire every western European therapeutic school of the Middle Ages.

The son of a reputed doctor, Alexander was born at the beginning of the 6th century in Tralles (known as Sultan-Hissar today), a small town in Asia Minor not far from Ephesus. His father, whose formula for a gargle against tonsillitis is still mentioned today, first entrusted him to local masters and then sent him abroad to master the art of medicine. He went to Ephesus, perhaps to Pergamum and Athens, certainly to Alexandria where he studied medicine in particular. Once an erudite doctor, he went to Constantinople to join his elder brother Anthemius, already a famous engineer and mathematician, for the emperor Justinian had entrusted him with the building of the church of Saint Sophia in collaboration with Isidore of Miletus. The young doctor was probably at the service of Justinian's generals-in-chief, certainly of Belisarius, the greatest of all. Surely he went to Armenia, Thrace, Dalmatia (Corcyra), Africa (Cyrene), Italy (Tuscany and Rome), Gaul and Spain, precisely those countries conquered by Justinian's armies throughout the principal wars of his reign.

The date of his death (like that of his birth), supposedly at Constantinople, remains unknown. According to his biographers, he lived long. When he no longer had the strength to practise his profession, he found the time to write the works which have come down to us through the centuries.

Alexander of Tralles was a sensible man who wanted to pass on the fruit of his observations and not do the work of a mere compiler. He thought that the first priority of a doctor was to heal the patient or relieve his suffering by all possible means, whatever they might be. To do this he borrowed from his predecessors, mainly Hippocrates and Galen, but he was eclectic enough to avoid being classified in a sect. Independent in outlook, he was more attached to the medicines at his disposal than to theories themselves, his first priority being to relieve suffering; he did not even hesitate to mention certain superstitious practices that might help the sick. He wrote, for example, about epilepsy: "Since some people like talismans and amulets and want to use them to attain their ends, I thought it appropriate to point out a few of them to those who wanted to learn. In this way the doctor will be well provided with all sorts of means to heal the sick." He goes on in the same vein concerning gout: "Since those who cannot keep to a long diet nor accept the remedies of pharmacy oblige us to heal their gout by remedies said to be natural or with amulets, and since the perfect doctor should be equipped with all kinds of resources to heal his sick, I resort to these means. But since there are many of equal value, I shall restrict myself to those which have long experience behind them."

Some writers have, a little rashly, reproached him for considering the desires of his clients once the classic remedies had failed, without understanding the role played by such practices on the credulous minds of the sick and, therefore, their possible power to do good.

Nor was he unaware of the dangerous effects of some remedies widely used in Byzantium. Against cerebral disorders, for example, he was wary of using white hellebore, which could cause fanting. He advised against administering a medicine containing opium to those suffering from tuberculosis: "It might kill extremely weak subjects or those whose chest holds an excessive quantity of matter to be rejected. Should its action appear to calm the cough and induce sleep, in reality it aggravates thoracic difficulties so that many of the sick are choked as if strangled by a rope."

If James the Psychreste was definitely the first Byzantine doctor to use colchicum against gout pains, Alexander of Tralles, while acknowledging the learning of this "great man so utterly blessed by God in his art," managed to perfect this medicine, which, originally given once and in strong doses, had its drawbacks. No doubt it immediately relieved the patient's pain and enabled him to walk, "but it has the disadvantage of

Harvesting of medicinal herbs in latin manuscript of Albucasis (1013-1106).

Next top: One declares that any man who wants to keep both his friends and his reputation while practicing medicine has little chance of doing so and the other states that medicine consists of a theoretical and practical part and that the former has three sections, etc.
Bottom: Hippocrates and Galen discussing food. One must eat to live and not live to eat and the diet is a salutary remedy, after Manfred de Monte Imperiale (14th century author, perhaps from Kaysersberg), *Liber de herbis et plantis*, B.N. Latin ms. 6823, fol. 1 V°.

Femenin...

Natur. c. et f. in .i. melior ex eo domestic. Juuamenti.
... ... nocumenti. ... ... remotio
... ...

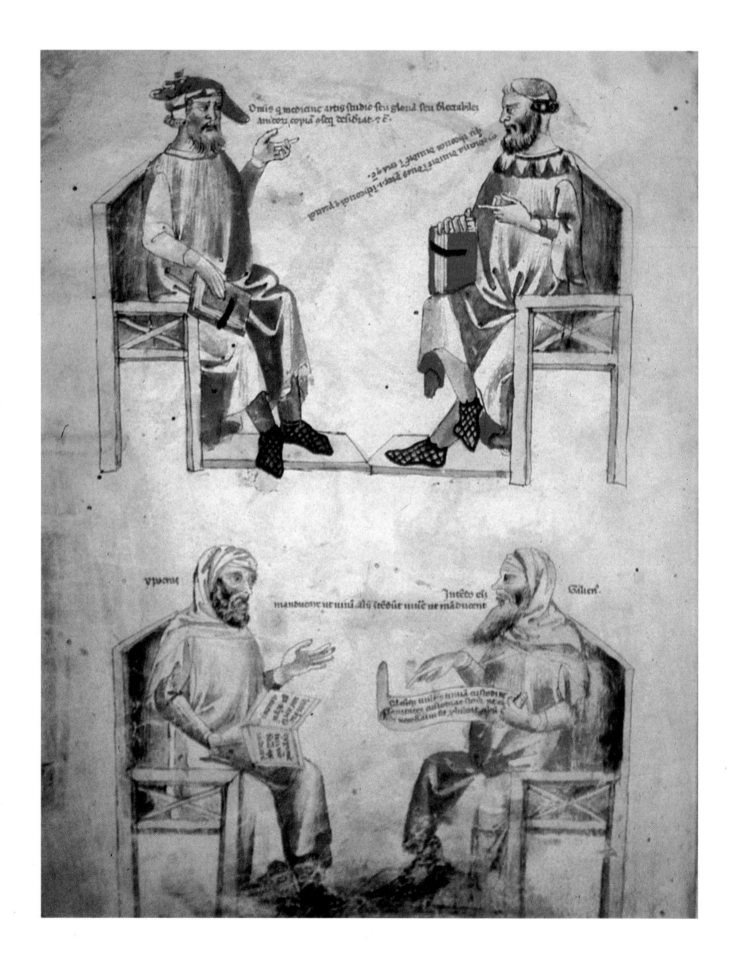

Christ curring the sick. Cathedrale of Monreale. 12th A.D.

making those who use it fall victim to inflammations more frequently. All those who have taken this remedy are aware that their stomach was out of sorts when they wanted to eat the same day. It is therefore advisable to mix it with caraway seeds, ginger and pepper, substances which relieve the bad effect this drug has on the stomach. Yet nothing can improve it more than the addition of aloes." This is followed by several formulas.

The simplest consists of:

Hermodactyl (*Colchicum autumnale*, L.)	1 drachma (4 gr. 363)
Ginger (*Zingiber officinale*, Rosc.)	9 siliquas (2 gr. 170)
Pepper (*Piper*, L.)	2 siliquas (0 gr. 484)
Anise (*Pimpinella anisum*, L.)	2 siliquas (0 gr. 484)

"All this together makes a strong dose. If you want to relax the stomach, add four siliquas of scammony (0 gr. 968). In this way the sick may be purged without troublesome side-effects or pain."

For the sick unable to go on a diet or take medicine there is the possibility of using talismans. For example, the tendons of wild donkey, wild boar or stork are attached to gout-stricken feet, the tendons from the right being used for right feet and those from the left for left feet. Otherwise, rubs made from torpedo oil (*Torpedo Galvanii*) and Narcissus (*Narcissus*, L.) or "a compress stained by the first menstruations of a young virgin." Alexander of Tralles also mentions the claws of vulture, the paws of a hare, the skin of a seal, the claws of a chameleon, etc.

In his "Letter on Intestinal Worms" he distinguishes between flat, round or thin worms and proposes special treatment and food to be used against each one. Against flat worms he recommends castor oil and tea made from watercress, costmary, myrtle, pomegranate, mulberry, heliotrope, hyssop, wild cucumber, etc. "Flat worms may also be killed," he writes, "by taking the root of a female fern crushed in honey." This famous and forgotten recipe was to be bought for the sum of 1800 francs from Mme Nouffer by Louis XVI. "Round worms can be poisoned and got rid of by taking the seed of farm cabbage, especially Egyptian cabbage, in a drink. Similarly, the oil, ordinary as it is, boiled with rue and taken hot in a dose of 6 drachmas (26 gr. 178) kills round worms by evacuation... Cedar oil as an emetic kills worms and ascarids and so does a poultice made from wine and flower in which fennel flower is cooked. Better still is to make up a decoction of camomile. All worms and ascarids are exterminated by taking ivory chippings... Eating raw garlic is good..."

Alexander of Tralles mentions in his work a considerable number of drugs, mainly of vegetable origin, and he managed to combine them in very different ways but always with prudence so as to correct, as far as possible, their respective ill-effects. He did his best to act gently, not out of weakness, but with "compassion for the hardships of life," considering that "the art of healing should not neglect the well-being of the patient." He believed in the value of hygiene, in the good done by physical treatment and thought that the diet was "the first and most important element in the treatment of all diseases." The fact remains that with his eclecticism and curiosity, the wealth of his knowledge and the breadth of his experience, and his respect for truth and generosity, he was "the doctor par excellence" and one of the greatest pharmacologists of classical antiquity.

If, in the first centuries after Christ, Greek scientific thought evolved after its own fashion in the midst of the new world being built around it, it did not escape the influence of Christian thought. Furthermore, in Christianity itself, we can distinguish between the East and the West, between what is mainly the product of the Greek mind and that which is particularly Latin. The barbarian invasions in the West accentuated the particular character of each of these worlds and the Greek spirit disappeared in the West around the sixth century while it lived on in the East under the new form of the Byzantine civilisation.

Byzantium, the mediator, enabled Europe to learn the science of the Persians, the Arabs and the Chinese and preserved classical Greek science transmitting it to the West before its decline. But Byzantium hand also its own particular physiognomy and brought together a wealth of knowledge which still escapes us, too many texts remaining unpublished. It gave to the Renaissance more than it had received from Antiquity and we might add that Byzantium did not die after the Turkish conquest. She continued to influence both the conquerors and in the West this influence could still be felt only a few decades ago.

Byzantine pharmacy follows on, without interruption from Graeco-Roman pharmacy since the barbarian invasions of the fifth century only succeeded in penetrating oriental society in the 15th century. For more than two centuries, therefore, the science of medicine and the art of its preparation was able to be continued and perfected in Byzantium. Nicolas, the preparer of drugs, for example, wrote in the 13th century the most complete treatise on medicine which had ever been seen. It is also appropriate, however, to take the new spirit, which Christianity introduced in the early centuries, into consideration. Doctor Alexis Carrel wrote in the fourth chapter of *Man unknown*: "In every country and at all times people believed in miracles and the more or less rapid healing of the sick in the sacred places of pilgrims or in certain shrines. But after the great blossoming of science in the 19th century, this belief completely disappeared. Not only were miracles not believed in, it was simply impossible for them to exist. Just as the laxs of thermodynamics make perpetual movement impossible, so do physiological laws contradict the miracle. Today this attitude is still shared by the majority of physiologists and doctors. Yet it does not stand up to the observations we have at our disposal today . . ." Doctor Carrel believed in "the objective importance of spiritual activities" and in the reality of "faith healing".

This was already believed possible in Babylon, Assyria, Egypt and Ancient greece. The early Christian church was to lend weight to the conviction that man could be healed by faith. In the 4th century Saint Basil of Caesarea declared that the origin of disease was divine: it was fitting, therefore, to adopt a patient attitude towards physical suffering and seek recovery only in God and his saints.

In the second half of the 3rd century, two (supposedly twin-) brothers in Asia Minor had similar ideas even though they were doctors. At least we may imagine so since their life remains obscure. No doubt they studied in Pergamum and then became itinerant doctors, travelling to distant countries to treat their patients. Being devout Christians, they gave their services freely which earned them the nickname of *Anargyres* (without money). Unfortunately, however, no account of a medical cure brought about by the Brothers Comus and Damien has come down to us. Legend has it that they simply received from the Holy Spirit the favour of healing all the diseases of men and horses. They are supposed to have restored a sick camel to health. In the year 287 they were arrested for being Christians and died martyrs. After their death, miracles began to take place: serpents and devils were cast out, a dead Moor's leg was transplanted to replace a leg eaten by cancer, etc.

Saint Comus and saint Damien were to become the patron saints of doctors, surgeons and of certain guilds of apothecaries as well. In the 3rd and 4th centuries, in Asia Minor, there were numerous doctors who were priests, monks or bishops at the same time and this Christian tradition was to continue for a long time without eclipsing the Greek tradition.

Paul of Aegina, the great Byzantine surgeon of the 7th century, devoted the seventh and final part of his *Synopsis of Medicine* to simple and composed compound medicines. In the 10th century, the doctor to the emperor Constantine VII Porphyrogenite, Theophannes Nonnos, wrote by order of his master a collection of 727 chapters on *Easily obtainable Medicines*. In the following century, Michael Psellos drew attention to the marvellous virtues of precious stones in his *Treatise on the Properties of Stones*: agate is good for inflammation of the eyes, onyx helps against melancholy and nighmares, jasper is useful for headaches, beryl for spasms, etc.

Simeon Seth, perhaps one-time secretary to Michael Psellos, compiled a *Collection in alphabetical order of the value of foods*, a veritable dictionary of medicine in which he describes not only the qualities—hot, cold, wet and dry—of each one, but also the details of their therapeutic value. He said that camphor, for example, had a sedative effect on the kidneys and sperm canals.

The last doctor to make his mark on the history of Byzantium is also the one who seems most closely linked with the pharmaceutical art, i.e. Nicholas the drug-preparer who was born in Alexandria and lived in Nicea and then in Byzantium where, between 1270 and 1290, he wrote the forty-eight chapters of his treatise *On Medicines*. He gave no less than 2.656 formulas for compound medicines and a great number of different preparations. He mentioned more drugs than any of his predecessors and indicated in great detail how to prepare them: ointments, syrups, plasters, suppositories, electuaries, clysters, decoctions, perfumes, collyriums, poultices, cerates, pills, aromatics, powders, pastilles, juleps, etc. The work of Nicholas the drug-preparer was to become the apothecary's guide throughout the Western World, not only in the Middle Ages but up until the 17th century and few scientific books have received such a wide audience. Of course, he has been criticized for mentioning everything, religious or superstitious invocations included, and also for the confusion caused, for example, by is recommending arsenic as a spice suitable for curing the harmful effects of poisons.

THE BEGINNINGS OF WESTERN PHARMACEUTICAL ART

Since we must leave to imaginative prehistorians and novelists the task of describing the ills and remedies of manking in the Neanderthal or Cro-Magnon periods and since the different theories advanced concerning magic medicine and the famous *dancing witch-doctor* whose portrait is to be found in a cave in the Ariège go too far towards satisfying would-be sociologists to be taken seriously by methodical sceptics, it would seem rash indeed to accept certain hypotheses concerning Celtic pharmacy despite arguments taken from contemporary folklore.

According to Doctor Jules Guiart, the picking of herbs on Midsummer's Day, the celebration of the summer solstice, is a very ancient therapeutic tradition which comes from the Celtic sun-cult. Among the different herbs, wormwood, burdock, chamomile, couch grass, ground ivy, lycopodium, St. John's Wort, orchid, brookweed and vervain genrally taken as an infusion had the best reputation for dispensing with numerous ailments. The herb called *Sedum Telephium* or *Orpine* held in the flames of the Midsummer's Day bonfires, then rubbed against the eyes was still said to cure burns and fever a short time ago in the northern Finistère. It is relatively easy to accept that the sun, fire, water, and herbal teas were considered therapeutic in ancient times since they are still considered such by the most diverse peoples.

St. John, the supposed successor of the sun god, has become a saint of healing. In Brittany, for instance, the fountain in the grounds of the church of St. Jean-du-Doigt relieves eye-troubles and every year the precious relic representing the Precursor is plunged into this fountain so that this miracle water keeps its therapeutic power.

Popular medicine made as much use of stones with mysterious powers. For example, dust scraped on a menhir to favour pregnancy, passing under a dolmen to heal rheumatism, gout, madness...passing through a hole cut in a stone. Here we have rites which still survive, so why should these not go back to the Celtic period and beyond?

Leaving the worship of texts to historians themselves, the real history of French pharmacy begins with Gallic medicine still known as Druidic. Of course, texts are extremely rare, but there are texts all the same.

We know only vaguely who the druids were, where they came from and what they taught, but several Latin writers mention them and describe the role they played in medicine and pharmaceutics in independent Gaul. Of the three druidic classes—bards, ovates or seers and the druids themselves—the second had to do with medicine and pharmacy in that treated the sick with herbs and by exorcism. The ovates gathered the plants prescribed by certain rites at certain hours of the day, especially in the morning before dawn using a bronze or gold bill-hook.

Pliny describes at length the Gallic ceremony of cutting mistletoe from an oak, this heavenly gift used as an antidote for poisons and making barren animals fruitful.

Among the medicinal plants of the druids, historians mention Sélage whith its purgative properties; henbane, a tranquillizer and antineuralgic; brookweed, good for the stomach and an antiscorbutic; Vervain, called oak of the earth by the druids, which was supposed to heal stone and headaches; the primrose was antineuralgic; clover, sage, etc. Pliny relates that the Gauls also used vervain to draw lots and tell the future.

The druids were not content with gathering simples from their lands. Thanks to the trading they practised, they also used imported drugs, exporting at the same time their own medical wares, such as larch turpentine. The knowledge they possessed for preparing composed medicines was recognized by the Greeks and the Romans and Pliny goes as far as to credit the Gallic doctor Crinès with the invention of the theriac. They knew how to make different aromatic wines obtaining, for example, mastic wine by boiling the berries or the new wood of the mastic tree with must. They also mastered the art of making numerous poisons which they used in war, hunting and for committing suicide.

Like the Greeks, the Romans and nearly all ancient peoples (and many people today), the Gauls thought that amber had therapeutic qualities. Thus the wearing of an amber necklace prevented disease. There is an abundance of amber necklaces in Gallic tombs.

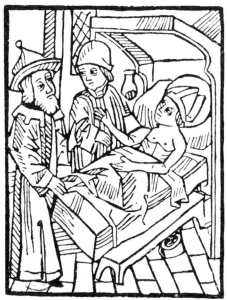

Saint Côme et Saint-Damien. Gravure sur bois de la *Vie des Saints* imprimée à Augsbourg en 1488

Cosme and Damien (Strasbourg 1488).

In Roman Gaul the development and use of the waters was essential for medicine, but the majority of springs, particularly hot springs, were already known when Gaul was independent and archeologists have found at Bourbon-Lancy, Plombières, Luxeuil, Bourbonne, Mont-Dore...at levels lower than in the Roman period Gallic coins, piles, wooden pipes, stonework, swimming pools made from great beams which bear witness to the therapeutic use of water before the Roman invasion. There were different gods and goddesses of springs whose names changed in the Roman era just as the architecture became more significant, yet the worship of water was practised in the same way with both Romans and Gauls invoking together the healing power of the spring, giver of thealth and fertility.

* * *

The Gauls were proud of being the "friends" of the Romans and the former had much regard for the latter. While writing his famous *Gallic Wars* with political ambitions in mind, Julius Caesar had to pass over this aspect of Gallo-Roman relations which had remained constant for many years in order to highlight his armed intervention. The rareness of contemporary texts on the subject, the fact that the most important traits of Roman civilisation were to be found in Gaul after Caesar's campaigns together with a certain liking for ease have led us to accept this logical impossibility; an entire race living in a region the size of modern France was subjugated by the legions of Rome to the extent of adopting the beliefs, customs and language of the victor and thereby abandoning for ever its own language, customs and beliefs. Yet the Romanization of Gaul, it appears, could only be explained by the strong will of a people to make a neighbouring civilisation its own.

It is certain that in Roman Gaul medicine and pharmacy were more and more frequently practised, as was the case in Rome, by Greek doctors and if one insists, in this particular case, on speaking of a conquest, then it is the conquest of Greek therapeutics very soon to be practised by men born, incidentally, on Gallic soil. There were doctors living in Marseilles and Lyon whose fame had spread throughout the Empire and Galen, for example, quotes some of the formulas of Abascantus, the Lyon doctor, and recommends those used for diarrhoea, consumption and the poisonous stings of animals.

Serenus Sammonicus, whose name might indicate Gallic origins, gave numerous recipes often meant for the poor and sick in his poems written in the 3rd century. At the end of the following century, Marcellus of Bordeaux methodically classified the flora of Gaul in his *Medicines,* adding a certain amount of magic formulas at the same time. Among the medicinal plants mentioned by Marcellus, whose therapeutic use could be pre-Roman, are: *Baditis* (waterlily), *Blutthagio* (marsh plant), *Bricumum* (mugwort), *Galliomarcus* (coltsfoot), *Calocatanos* (red poppy), *Gigarus* (arum arrowroot), *Gilarum* (thyme), *Halus* (comfrey), *Odocos* (dwarf elder), *Ratis* (fern), *Vernetus* (marsh plant), *Visumarus* (clover).

From the 2nd to the 4th century, one particular branch of medicine seems to have developed greatly in Gaul, that of the ophthalmologist. Archeologists have discovered instrument cases containing all the necessary material: the little bronze mortar for crushing medicines, bronze bowls which contained the powders, small iron jugs for eye lotions, little Roman scales for weighing, spatulas which were placed under the eyelids, the stylets, the tenacula, the forceps and scalpels of the experienced surgeon. The eye specialist also had a seal or initalled stone with which he marked the medicines issued and gave the name of the disease for which it should be used. Thus the formula: "*L. Pomp. Nigrini arpaston ad recent(es)* odent(es) die(m) ex ovo" meant "Eye lotion of Lucius Pompeius Nigrinus, made from amber, for recent inflammation of the eye irritated by daylight, to be mixed with the white of an egg". Another example: *Q. Albi(i) Vitalionis mixtum ad omnia prater lippitudinem",* i.e. "(Eye lotion) of Quintus Albius Vitalio, compounded for all ailments except eye inflammation" or: "*L. J. Dociliae penicillum authemer(um) ex ovo*", i.e. "Eye lotion of Lucius Julius Docil to be applied to the brush (or to the penicillus, sponge?), made the same day, to be mixed with the white of an egg."

The dry eye-lotions discovered take the form of small elongated rolls of about five centimetres thinning at the ends. The analysis done by Baudrimont and Duquenelle in 1863 on those found in Reims ten years earlier showed: silica 4 %, black copper oxide 4,32 %, iron peroxide 16 %, calcium carbonate 17,66 %, organic matter 33,33 %, loss 1 %. Others were richer in iron and lead. According to Mr. Bouvet, the oculists' marks mention, in particular, the following substances: amber, saffron, galbanum, haematite, balsam juice, yarrow, vervain, gale, ivy, clay of Samos, celandine, incense, balm of Judea, myrrh...Occasionally the collyriums bear the names of colours: green, yellow, swan coloured (white). The seals also gave the directions for use: the

HISTORY OF PHARMACY

liquid (white of an egg, water, sweet wine, woman's milk) in which the little stick would be ground or mixed and how it should be applied: with a little sponge or brush.

Much frequented as they were in independent Gaul, the spas were much more so in Gaul under Rome. As Albert Grenier, the archeologist, wrote: "All the springs known today and even many others where ancient remains have been found, neglected as they are by modern times, were all used by the Romans." Unfortunately for researchers, "Their luxury at first invited devastation and pillage; and then after being abandoned for centuries, their ruins were used as quarries and during the Middle Ages some portions were put to poor and indescriminate use only to be followed by the great modern establishments whose buildings covered the remaining ruins without, in the majority of cases, the ancient remains even being reconized and, more importantly, a plan of the whole site being made." However, a few exceptions give us an idea of what these spas were like. Hundreds of ex-voto found nearby, i.e. the sick parts of the body cut in stone or engraved on bronze plaques witness to the patients' faith in the miraculous powers of water.

One Gallo-Roman sculptor perhaps wanted to represent a protecting goddess of pharmacy in bas-relief in soft stone. This was discovered in 1842 and is now in the Epinal museum. A young woman is sitting in the centre; on her right a furnace whose grate is full of logs; at the top a cauldron and a vat bound in wood in which there is a spoon whose end forms a caduceus. On the young woman's left another woman is standing holding a testing-glass above another vat. Esperandieu, the archeologist, called the central figure *Meditrina,* "the woman pharmacist;" Camille Jullian thinks that this is simply a representation of soap-making. Salomon Reinach advances both theories and Paul-Marie Duval, the most recent, reckons that it is the patron saint of pharmacists. The two large spheres to be seen on the right are not balls of soap but glasses being drained. Thus the Epinal stele shows one of France's oldest dispensaries.

The period between the fall of the Roman Empire (395) and the taking of Constantinople by Mahomet II (1453), generally known as the Middle Ages, is undoubtedly better known today than was the case a hundred years ago. The famous "night of the Middle Ages," like shagreen, never stops dwindling. The Carolingian Renaissance, the European awakening in the 11th and 12th centuries and the civilisation of the 13th and 14th centuries, without diminishing the glory of the great Renaissance, led historians to doubt the originality of certain aspects of the latter and to regard as an evolution what their predecessors considered a revolution. The fact that the sciences do not necessarily progress in the same way as the arts complicates the problem further. A rapid look at the evolution of Western pharmacy since the 5th century will lead us to admit that curious contradictions exist.

The invasion of the Roman Empire by the Teutons, who were vanquished by the Slavs themselves assailed by the Huns, ruined Roman civilisation without leaving anything comparable in its place. With the triumph of Christianity there emerged a contempt for the world of the flesh and the idea that disease was a sign of the wrath of God or the hatred of the devil. Were the Jews and then the Arabs not considered the Christian's worst enemy in the following centuries? The former were to live apart, deprived of many rights while the defeat of the latter at Poitiers in 732 was to be regarded as one of the most significant events in W. European history. Now historians also agree that first of all the monasteries—in which the most devout Christians were to be found—saved the Latin tradition as far as possible and further that Greek learning was passed on to the Europeans who had become Barbarians by the Jews and Arabs. Even if we are not astonished to see the Jews who were well furnished with the basic pharmaceutical ideas scattered about the Talmudic treatises and the fanatical Arabs, whose pre-Islamic tribes hardly knew more than a few recipes tainted with magic, capable of assimilating, enriching and communicating what was essential in Graeco-Latin medicine and pharmaceutics, the way in which the western Barbarians tasted the fruits of the "Greek miracle" still has to be explained.

It is true that the Barbarian invasions had raged continuously since the 3rd century and that, if the battle of the *Catalonian Fields* put an end to them in 451, economic recession, political disorder, intellectual and moral degeneration were to the order of the day for a long time to come.

The sanitary conditions of the populations were terrible. An examination of bones dating from Merovingian times indicates both rickets and a high rate of infant mortality. A reading of the chroniclers reveals the existence of numerous ailments despite their imprecision in terms: crippling rhumatism, diverse fevers and psychological disorders...not to mention frequent epidemics of the plaque, dysentery and smallpox. Leprosy was permanently rife.

The glory of famous Carolingian Renaissance was to be short-lived and of only limited scientific

72

importance. It asserted itself for the most part in creating a new and minuscule handwriting and in reviving elegant Latin.

In order to explain the great revival of the 11th century, the welcome given to Jewish and Arab scholars and the position they held in W. European teaching, it has to be admitted that an interest in this kind of study had constantly been shown and that a certain erudite tradition had been preserved throughout the many vicissitudes of time.

Cassiodorus may be considered as the continuator of translators, compilers and commentators who had been writing in the 3rd and 4th centuries. Born in the second half of the 5th century, he was secretary to Theodoric, king of the Goths, and then he became quaestor and master of offices. Later he became a praetorian prefect under Athalaric before retiring to the monastery of *Viviers* which he had founded and richly endowed. No doubt it was Cassiodorus who pushed Theodoric to reintroduce the Latin medical legislation. In his Calabrian monastery, he wrote his *Institutiones divinarum et Humanarum litterarum,* an encyclopaedic compilation, and occupied his monks with the task of copying the manuscripts in his library and others he could acquire; the most learned monks translated Greek works into Latin. He advised them to study medicine and in particular the works of Hippocrates, Galen and Caelius Aurelianus and to practise pharmaceutics: "Learn to distinguish between all sorts of plants and to mix prudently all kinds of drugs . . . Should you be unfamiliar with the Greek tongue, study first of all the book in which Dioscorides writes so well on medical plants, describing them with such marvellous precision."

Cassiodorus' example was followed not only by the Benedictines, but also by the most important monastic orders. In this way precious fragments of ancient heritage were saved and passed down. As Mr. Bouvet has observed, we must also acknowledge our debt to the monks "for having collected the popular Celtic and Germanic traditions and increasing in this fashion the knowledge passed on by antiquity." Medical works—and, as a result, those concerning pharmacy—were always present in monastic libraries for the use of monks whose duty it was to care for the sick. The catalogues occasionally mention one or several books "of medicine;" one or two give details about them mentioning Galen, Hippocrates, Quintus Serenus, Alexander of Tralles or note that the work is a collection of practical pharmaceutical recipes: "*de olei confectione,*" "*de confectione malagmarum,*" etc.

The taste for compiling persisted and among the most important works we may mention the 7th century *Origines* of Isidore, Bishop of Seville, whose 4th book deals with medicines. In the 8th century, the Venerable Bede, Prior of Warmouth in England, treats medicine and medicinal plants in his *Ecclesiastical History* and his *Elementa philosophiae.*

Outside the monasteries there were many doctors in the towns of the Merovingian period, judging from the accounts of the chroniclers—in particular Gregory of Tours—, the lives of the saints and official acts. In the service of sovereigns, they received enormous salaries but had to be prepared to run certain risks. For example, Queen Austrechilde supposedly said: "I should still have had the will to live had I not fallen into the hands of bad doctors. The potions I took have deprived me of life and killed the light too soon. Let me not die without being avenged." And the king "acting in accordance with the oath he had taken, had killed by the sword the two doctors who had treated her." Generally the texts are not very explicit as regards the nature of the medicines used. We read of "beverages made from juices artfully chosen," of "remedies previously gathered from ancient books," "herbs which fight poison and relieve those suffering from dysentery..." Charles Lelong quotes oil of roses, a reputed antipyretic, scammony which "cleans the stomach," hyssop which cleans the lungs, feverfew "which purges the head" and aloe which speeds digestion. Poultices and cantharides are applied to pustules by plague victims.

* * *

The elementary therapeutic practices of the Merovingians survived the centuries by the very fact that they were elementary and represented a heritage which was more essential than the rest. The Gallo-Romans had preserved many medical practices from free Gaul and enriched them. The Merovingians succeeded in preserving an important part of this whole on to which the art of the barbarian invaders had been grafted. The Carolingians did the same thing...and we could mention even today certain practices which go back to prehistory.

Charlemagne wanted to improve his churches and, for that reason, he opened schools and had the liberal arts taught and books corrected where certain negligent scribes had corrupted the text. Though medicine and pharmacy were not taught as liberal arts, it was good for a clerk to know the remedies appropriate for different diseases. To quote Emile Lesne, medicine actually "inhabits both the cloisters of the canons and the monks. The sick and infirm should find here all the care required by their state fo health." In addition, it was customary for a monk to do a weekly medical round in the town or village near his monastery so as to comply with this rule. Thus, every monastery must probably have possessed a collection of medical texts resembling the Carolingian manuscript kept in the National Library and originally found in the abbey of Echternach (in the Grand-Duchy of Luxemburg). There are numerous recipes some of which seem to be direct borrowings from Celsus' *De re medica* while others, judging from the writing, are from the Merovingian period. The most recent, being Carolingian, were copied by the monk responsible for medical care and were based on formulas no doubt brought by the pilgrims or travelling monks.

The abbot Jean Lestocquoy has illustrated the important role played by spices in these recipes and by pepper, in particular. Cinnamon and fiftysix grains of pepper are added to certain herbs to cure the insomnia caused by inflammation, headaches and ulcers. Migraine is relieved by earthworms crushed with eleven grains of pepper. "A gargle *ad caput purgandum*" consists of ginger and origanum while another one requires one hundred grains of pepper. Cloves, myrrh, pimento and pepper make up a soap for the humours of the head. To treat kidney pains, ninety grains of pepper among others ingredients are macerated in wine. If you want an electuary, take cloves, sesame, galangal, rhubarb, ginger and pepper in equal measure. For all head and body pains: *"Gariofile* (cloves), *Spica indica, Cinamo, Nitro, Alo."* For headaches and eye troubles: sal ammoniac, ordinary pepper, white pepper, long pepper, ginger, origanum, hyssop arc mixed with some other herbs." Abbot Lestocquoy found quite similar recipes in Anglo-Saxon manuscripts of the same period. Against gout, for example, *Hermodactylus* heads must be dried and added to cinnamon, cummin, laurel berries and six grains of pepper, then pound into a powder and wine added. For liver diseases a daily spoonful of honey, vinegar, mustard and ten grains of pepper. For swollen stomach take the juice of boiled sweet apples, pure honey and twenty grains of pepper, etc.

Thus the great abbeys of the Carolingian period used diverse spices in large quantities not for cooking but for the treatment of the sick. Once the sea traffic was interrupted in the Mediterranean, where did the spices come form? In a letter to Louis the German about 876, Salomon of Constance enumerates certain products from the East which had just arrived in Germany: cloth, cinnamon, galangal, cloves, packets of mastic and pepper, parrots and a long "thorn" of a fish (narwhal or sawfish). E. Sabbe writes that pepper, ginger, cloves, spickenard...were to be found in Mainz in 973. In the Baltic island of Gotland, 22902 Arab coins have been discovered and were mostly from the 9th or early 10th century. Thus trade with the Arabs and Byzantines through the intermediary of Russian Scandinavia has to be accepted and we are led to suppose that the land route enabled W. Europe to provide itself with spices.

The great revival of the 12th century was made possible by the survival of a certain routine therapeutics, the passing on of empirical knowledge and continuing trade with the East. The monasteries preserved the elements of ancient medical literature and as dispensors of Christian charity, had all their infirmary as dispensors and little botanical garden. In the monastery of St. Gallen in the early years of the 9th century, the *armarium pigmentorium*—, i.e. the spice cupboard, the "pharmacy" directed by a pharmacist-monk with a doctor-monk keeping the key—the garden of medicinal herbs and a place reserved for bleedings and purgations, were part of a *domus medicarum,* the medical centre of the monastery. At the end of the 10th century, Notker of St. Gallen, called the Physician and nicknamed the "grain of pepper", had an amazing knowledge of plants and medical precepts and was to effect wondrous cures.

On the island of Reichenau in the middle of Lake Constance, the monk Walahfrid Strabus—Walahfrid the Squinter—described his little garden *Hortulus* in a 9th century didactic poem of 444 lines. He sings the praises of his cherished pumpkin and boasts of the smooth shape, fresh juice and scented fruit of his melons

---

The master teaches the characteristics, properties and drawbacks (with the means to neutralize them) of the theriac, after Albucasis' *Observations* on the nature of different alimentary and hygienic products (Italy, first half of 15th century). B.N. Nouv. Acq. Lat., 1673, fol. 87 V°.

and enthusiastically presents the most modest plants and the plainest herbs. He mentions their therapeutic powers at the same time, thus giving a lesson in medical botany which is often too vague for our taste. Sage "mildly scented, full of qualities, good as a beverage has proved useful for several diseases of men;" rue "a remedy with many powers is best for fighting occult venoms and for banning from the tissues the troublesome poisons which invade it;" southernwood "fights fevers, cures stings and is useful for limbs tormented by the capricious affront of stealthy gout;" common wormwood stills a dry thirst and gets rid of fevers: "Should it happen that your head suddenly begins to suffer violently from a sharp pain or should dizziness tire you, use this remedy: cook the bitter leaves of a bushy wormwood, pour its juice into a large bowl and spread it over the top of the head; after sprinkling the ends of the hair with this liquid, don't forget to tie the leaves together and apply them to the head; then a head bandage should be tied gently around the scalp after applying this fomentation and after a few hours, you will admire this remedy, also for its other qualities." Horehound "fights terrible pains which torment the chest" and fights victoriously against poison. Fennel is good for the eyes, iris gets rid of pains in the bladder, pennyroyal relieves a malfunctioning stomach while radish heals a cough, etc.

J.-K. Huysmans devoted several passages of *A rebours* and *L'Oblat* to the charming *Hortulus* and its author. Huysmans contempories "welcomed these revelations with less enthusiasm than they showed at the news of new handlebars for velocipedes or an oil for greasing cars running on petrol," but curiosity was awakened. Meanwhile Doctor Henri Leclerc has written a French translation of the work had anybody reading *Hortulus* today gets the impression of an absolute tranquillity, a relaxing serenity and the sensation one has after visiting an old presbytery in the country on the edge of a wood where no noise troubles the peace and silence."

Sedulius Scottus, who attended the court of Charles the Bald (823-877), describes the pharmacy of a monastery, the "house of medicine" in a short poem in Latin translated by R. Gorlin (*Revue de la Pharmacie*, June 1940). Descending from Paradise, medicine brings remedies: "on this shelf there are ointments giving out sacred odours which surpass the offering of incense and precious balms. On this other row shine scented antidotes by which all the ills harmful to health are banished. I think that in coming down from the stars she brought them from the garden of Hesperides. The gifts plucked from the top of a hill covered with olive trees and mixed with the juice of plants shine with a beauty as wild as nectar. Hail demure saint, supreme source of Medicine, the hope of multitudes, full of odoriferous treasures."

As early as the 9th century, the monk responsible for the monastery's dispensary "full of odoriferous treasures" had become an important figure.

BEGINNINGS
AND RENAISSANCE
THE ARABS

A certain tradition sees Arab pharmacy before Islam as a mere mixture of empiric remedies and magic. Even for Arab writers the Arabian peninsula was covered until then in a barbarian darkness, but this time of "ignorance" simply marks the absence of the divine revelation still to come and, as Gaston Wiet wrote, "the success of Koranic preaching would prove to it alone the brilliance of pre-Islamic civilisation." It is appropriate to consider pre-Islamic civilisations for the way of life of those who lived in the south of the peninsula—farmers, artisans and traders—was very different from that of the nomads of central Arabia or of Arab tribes living around Petra, in Syria or on the borders of Mesopotamia.

The Mediterranean world was greedy for perfumes and spices—incense and myrrh—produced by Southern Arabia which also gave them pearls found in the Persian Gulf, rice, silk, cotton, Indian ivory and pepper, gold, ivory, ostrich-feathers, slaves from East Africa...Caravans transported precious merchandise along the west coast to Gaza to the shores of the Mediterranean; others went to Gerrha on the Persian Gulf. The Egyptians and Greeks had already equipped ships for trade with the Far-East without using the Arabs as middlemen. Then Byzantium and Sassanid Persia launched expeditions against Southern Arabia. The latter was to fall to Persia at the end of the 6th century. Its economic importance had diminished while the nomads began to take an active part in the trade on the land of the west coast. The shrine of Mecca, first a stop at a watering place, then a trading centre in the 5th century, came to the forefront in the 6th century. "An Arab State guided by an Arab ideology and adapted to the new conditions yet still near the Bedouin milieu" was born. Mohammed was to give the peninsula a religious, national and linguistic unity.

Once it is realized that the Arabs played a major role in the history of therapeutics, the birth of the Prophet on the "incense route," in the tribes of the Koraichites who monopolized trade in drugs and perfumes, assumes a particular importance. If we add that Mohammed had Al-Harith as friend and advisor—from the

Thaqifi family of Tayf on the caravan route — the first "among the Arabs to deserve the name of doctor, the first to apply to the practice of medicine the doctrines by which it is governed" (L. Leclerc), what is commonly called the "medicine of the Prophet" is of great therapeutic interest, quite apart from its religious value.

Al-Harith had studied, then taught his art in the medical school founded by the Sassanid kings at Jundishapur (or Djondisabour, or Goundi-Sappour, or even Djondy-Shapour) in the ancient state of Elam. Now, this school had welcomed in the 5th century the Nestorian monks banned from their school in Edessa after the condamnation of Nestorius, patriarch of Constantinople by the council of Ephesus (Nestorius had adopted the idea of Athanasius, the Christian priest, which made a formal distinction between the human and divine nature of Christ.) In 525, the philosophers who had been teaching in Athens and whose school Justinian had just closed came to join the ranks of the erudite Nestorians. Jundishapur, therefore, was in the second half of the 6th century an intellectual centre where Greek scientific traditions were both maintained and enriched by Syrian, Persian and Indian elements. The first translations of Greek works into Syriac were done in this school whose influence continued to grow until it was supplanted by Bagdad.

After being admitted to the court of King Chosroes, Al-Harith had a long conversation with the king in which he expressed his ideas on the elements and the humours, the rules of alimentary and sexual hygiene and his attitude to medicines: "As long as your health prevails, don't touch them, but should the disease appear, stop it by all appropriate means before it takes root." He recommended enemas and advised the use of cupping glasses when the moon was on the wane, in good weather and when the body was disposed. Back in Arabia his knowledge of medicines enabled him to cure the sick who seemed to be an embarrassment for Mohammed. The latter, in fact, practised medicine but, according to Renan, refused to work miracles. He wanted to be a prophet and a prophet without miracles.

God created disease, said Mohammed, and also the remedy. The *Medicine of the Prophet* is the "complete work comprising maxims, beliefs, advice. Observations, practice and examples left behind by the founder of the Musulman religion and preserved by tradition." Several of these collections exist. One written by the Sheik Djelal Ed-din Abou Soleiman Daoud has been translated by Doctor Perron. The second of the three parts of this work deals with medicines and foods. It begins with some general remarks:

"When treating the sick, age, habits, the seasons and the profession must be taken into account."

"Therefore a purgative is not given (if it is not absolutely necessary) to a very old man, a patient suffering from abdominal flow, a young child, a person who is very tired, who is taking a bath, or who is weak, whose constitution is weak, who is replete, bilious or suffering from an ulcer. Nor should it be given during great heat or cold and not to those unused to medicines."

"No medicine should be used if it is not in the desired condition or maturity."

"A bath before taking a medicine stimulates its action. Sleep immediately after taking a mild medicine nullifies or weakens its action while it intensifies the effect of a strong medicine."

"After taking a medicine, wait until it has begun to act before eating." "Should the patient be nauseated by a medicine, let him chew *Dracunculus hortensis* (Tarkhoûn) or jujube leaf or sniff an onion. If he is afraid to vomit, let him hold tight the tips of his toes and chew a slightly acid pomegranate, *Rybas* (Rhubarb of Syria) or apple. If there is stomach pain, let him drink hot water and walk a little. Vomiting can be caused without medicine by drinking hot water. After vomiting *Plantago psyllium* is taken with apple preserve and later ordinary soups are given." "Two purgatives are never given the same day..."

"Whenever treatment may be limited to mild and simple medicines, no others should be used. In addition they are administered gradually, starting with the mild and progressing to the most active should the mild prove ineffective. No single medicine is administered exclusively since the patient becomes used to and familiar with it so that there is practically no result."

"Should you find the disease to have no distinct and positive character, don't rush to give medicines but wait for some pathological certainty."

"Once the patient can be treated by alimentary means (i.e. a special diet), medicines are no longer required."

At the beginning of the third part, the author writes on compound medicines: "We prefer the simple medicine to the compound when the former is sufficient. However, we resort to the compound medicine either to aid and complete the action of the simple medicine, or because it is too nauseating to produce the desired effect. Other reasons for choosing the compound medicine may be to increase the potency of the medicine as, for example, when one mixes ginger with turpeth root; to weaken this potency by adding, for example, wax to verdigris ointment. It could also prevent medicine from having a harmful effect as is the case when tragacanth gum (Kathirah) is mixed with scammony. Another reason for preferring a compound medicine may be to conserve the power of one substance by adding another which acts as a catalyst or to use it to fight a complex disease, the medicine itself being complex or compound. Sometimes the disease may be malignant and no simple medicine with the power to counter and defeat it may be available. Again, when the sick organ is far from the stomach and the medicine to be used would only reach it in a weakened state, a composition is used which will reach the sick part quickly, for example: saffron is added to camphor, cinnamon to cannabis or hemp. The indispensability of a sick organ might also require compounds, so one adds to the healing substance another which preserves the medicinal action of the former an astringent or odoriferous one. And finally, since the medicine might have a harmful effect on a given organ, one adds whatever corrects its action or deprives it of such harmful effects."

After reading this, it is difficult to share the very critical opinion of Ibn Haldun, who about the year 1400 wrote *Prolegomena to the Study of History* on the *Medicine of the Prophet*. For him it is merely an "indigenous Arab medicine" and he dismisses it, adding that we should not follow its rules since "the Prophet's mission was to give us the prescriptions of divine law and not to teach us either medicine or the common practices of everyday life." He goes on: "Thus, we are not obliged to believe that the medical prescriptions handed down by authentic traditions are to be treated as rules to follow. Nowhere do these traditions tell us to do so. However, it is a fact that we may benefit greatly by using these remedies to win divine blessing with a faith that is sincere even though they do not belong to the realm of real medicine."

Basil is odoriferous, astringent and a laxative with the drawback of diminishing the vision which can be remedied by adding euphorbia leaves, after the work of Albucasis, *Observations on the nature of different alimentary and hygenic products* (Italy, first half of the 15th century). B.N. Nouv. Acqu. lat., 1673, fol. 22

Common sense, as everyone knows, being by no means so common, the majority of people would class the burning of the library in Alexandria by the Arabs during the great 7th century expansion as a historical commonplace, as they would the fact that, after destroying this rich depository of Ancient Greek learning, they passionately translated Hippocrates, Galen and all the other ancient writers with the sole purpose of handing over this heritage to the West once it had emerged from its barbarianism. By the same token, they are ready to admit that among the Arabs were the greatest doctors, the first chemists, the best pharmacists...and that virtually all these scholars were really Persians, Syrians, Greeks, Jews or Christians. Yet they take for granted the transition of the pharmacy of the Prophet to scholarly pharmacy as early as the 9th century. No doubt they also share the thoughts of the sceptical Arab poet who wrote these lines on the death of Yuhanna ibn Masawayhi, better known as Mesue in 857:

The doctor with his drugs and medicine
Certainly cannot stop death when the time comes.
How is it then that he himself dies of a disease
He used to heal quite normally!
All are dead; he who prescribed the drug
He who took it, he who took it with him,
He who bought and he who sold it.

The poet's patient, doctor and pharmacist are dead. The 700'000 volumes kept in Alexandria's libraries disappeared, but is it so important to know on what date? Making Omar, Mohammed's successor, responsible for the destruction in 641, the traditional version is spiced with a fine reflexion on the part of the chief of the faithful: "If the contents of these books conform to the Book of God, the Book of God will suffice. If on the other hand they do not conform, they must be destroyed." It is said that the precious works were distributed to the public baths of Alexandria, enabling fires to be lit for six months.

It is unfortunate, in the first place, that this anecdote is found in a story told six centuries after the caliph Omar's time and, in the second, that the narrator, Aboulfaradgus, was a Jacobite bishop and not a Musulman while, in the third place, in 641 there had been no real library in Alexandria for almost three centuries.

Founded by the Ptolemies, the library had two stores of books. The first was burnt in the disaster which destroyed the fleet in the harbour in Caesar's time. The second, which was housed in one of the buildings of the Serapeum and enriched by the 200'000 volumes taken from Pergamum and offered by Antony to Cleopatra, was sacked and destroyed in 391 by the populace when the emperor Theodosus ordered the destruction of pagan temples. If there was any effort to restore the library between the 5th and 7th centuries, the result was insignificant.

Though the extraordinary intellectual haven of Alexandria was smothered by fanaticism and if the caliph Omar showed his intolerance, the Arabs cannot be charged with Christian sins. The caliphs who were to follow from 750 to 850 generally showed, on the contrary, an astonishing broadmindedness and displayed such a love of learning that one of them was given the title of "commander of the unbelievers" by the mere orthodox. Soon the royal library or "the house of wisdom" in their capital of Bagdad was filled with learned manuscripts—especially Greek ones—which they had obtained by force, purchase or exchange. They lured learned scholars to their court who could translate them into Arabic directly from the Greek or by the intermediary of Syriac.

Medicine and Alchemy seem to have been the first objects of their curiosity. Alchemy in the words of Doctor Lucien Leclerc "is a legacy coming directly from the school of Alexandria. Its last scholars brought it to

---

Harvesting of medicinal herbs in latin manuscript of Albucasis (1013-1106).

Next page : The healing snakes in the *Book of Theriac* (12th century). B.N. Arab ms, 2964, fol. 5.

Page 81 : Fragment of the *Treatise on Plants* by Dioscorides; an apocryphal title attributes it to the learned traveller Ibn Abi Zohr. Manuscript written in Spain in the year 125 of the Egire. B.N. Arab ms, 2850, fol. 114.

Salina.

Nature c. a. h. i. z. melior erca domestica. Juuamentum
paralesi. et neruis. nocumentum. denigrat capilos. remotio
nocumeti. cum lesiuis inquo sit mirt. t ciui orientalis.

ما بحا من قبل الملك على انتباه وكانت كثيرة اما تخرج اليها في الاوقات الرذينة الصف والشتاء وتخرج ذلك وعلم الى بعض القرى على شيخ فرائخ
من المشرع في اصل شجرة وكان خرخا شديد الحاجة نفسه

فاتا به فخرج فضربة في يده

وقد القها على الارض شديدة تعب ٭ كانتبه بفرح وعلم ان هذه الاية قد رحمة ٭ ولكن بطن على القيام انقل الاغنى ٭ واخذه الموت الغنى والكرب ذنب
رحمة ٭ وعلما اسه في تلك الشجرة وعلمها ما في تلك الشجرة ٭ ثم ما فضله سيرة في الجرة في اصل تلك الشجرة ٭ وكان قد غلبه العطر فقرب منه شرب اكل
ثم ما ثل الآني جوه حتى ماكان بها ٭ من قرنة الامن ٭ وابل لذلك منجا ٭ ولم يعد ان ماكان بها نزل الماء شديد حتى انقطع من تلك الشجرة حتى ماء الاية ذكره
ان نفسه يذكره ٭ فاذا ابوه اني ٭ هذا فلاح ماء يا ٭ واقبل اخي هذا ٭ وموجح طرها جايه ٭ وترك العمل الذي كان فيه ٭ واخرج على الذي كان يخاتني

الأوجاع اروطس

ومن الناس من يسميه ارقطل
من نبات قد تم انطاشيه وفي
قلوب مع الا انه اكثر ذكا منه
واشر الشرارة واقل لين منه
وساق خو كورا تم شبيه بالكمون الصغير الحب واطراف النبات ومنه اذا
لحظ الشراب وانبط كيف ضياع الم سكر وجع الأذن اذا اصب على حمو
الظهر على من الظهر لاخر من الظهر اذا دفع منفط وفرشه مع الشراب ابل النسا
وعسر البول اردطس

٢٩

ومن الناس من يسميه مرو سوس
ومنهم من يسميه مرو سمور هو
بات له وقد شبيه بورق الفرع الا انه
اكثر منه واصلب وافرت الى السواد
وعليه حب ولين له ساق بول ضل كين ابيغ اذاش هم ارد رجى مع
الصور جري العلى الكل المقرر الاخنوا ولا انا نصر شكر بح تم مع
من الحكم الملفه وفرشه بقوة هذا النبات شلق بجح الم

١٦٠

الا اسطس هونبات له
نضيب نحو من ذراع واكثر يعلوله

the Arabs where it quickly bore wonderful fruit. Hermetic studies mark the first awakening of Arab thought and it was from its weakest side that they affronted ancient science." The hope of discovering a panacea or the transmutation of metals was not as vain as we might imagine since it enabled them to enrich their medicine and begin chemical research.

In the 8th century, Gabir ibh Hayyan—Geber in medieval Europe—tried to find the philosopher's stone and the elixir of longevity, but as Hoefer says, he represents "in the history of chemistry what Hippocrates is to the history of medicine." His direct successors knew how to make alcohol, aqua fortis, oil of vitriol, corrosive sublimate, silver nitrate...Geber assumed that all things had their opposites or antagonists: hot being the opposite of cold and dry of wet. Similarly the elements of a remedy are contrary to those of the disease, so to counter biliary troubles he recommends gourds, whey, psyllium mucilage. For blood diseases he advises cold or dry substances like bamboo concretions, vinegar and pomegranates while onion, wild cress and honey water are good for atrabilious ailments. For pituitary troubles he recommends castor, opopanax, assafoetida, etc. He uses the cadmium and crude zinc oxide of collyriums.

The Arab doctors of the 9th century had at their disposal translations in the current language of the main works of Hippocrates, Galen, Dioscorides, Rufus, Oribasus, Alexander of Tralles, Paul of Aegina...It has, of course, become a commonplace to say that the treatises of Arab medicine were for the most part written by Persians, Syrians and Christians, but did an Arab nation exist? Invaders were few in the vast Islamic world of the time. As Doctor Sanjurjo d'Arellano remarks: "The customs and culture was of a specific character and were only the result and reflection of the Greek and Persian civilisations which had presided over their creation."

Thus the Persian Abou Bekr Mohammed ben Zakarya, called Ar Razi or Rhazès, may be regarded as one of the first masters of Arab medicine. This sage, who died poor and blind in the first half of the 10th century, was director of the hospitals of Ray, his home town, and Bagdad. He wrote more than 200 works on the most diverse subjects. His major work, the *Continent*, is a survey of the medical knowledge of the time, a treatise of practical medicine and an original work.

Rhazès listed the medicinal plants used in his time and taught the art of preparing vegetable extracts in order to get thickened fruit juice from them, the art of obtaining psyllium mucilage and of making up ophthalmological lotions. He prepared the oil of eggs by squeezing their yolk and *Oleum Scorpionibus* by treating scorpions with almond oil and *Unguentum Aegyptiae* by mixing *Flores d'Aeris* with vinegar, honey and a fatty excipient.

It is also appropriate to mention the work of Ali Ibn al-Abbas who deals with the subject of pharmaceutical practice in his treatise entitled *Kitab Al Malaki*, "The Royal Book", and the treatise of Abu Mansour Muwaffaq Harawi who mentions no less than 585 different remedies, several of which are borrowed from Hindou pharmacology, but the figure of Rhazès adequately indicates that in the 10th century those we call the Arabs "not only emancipate themselves from their initiators who have become incapable of following the new directions they have taken, but already take the unknown paths of the Greeks by enriching the ideas they received or by systematizing the totality of the knowledge in their possession." (L. Leclerc).

* * *

In the 10th and 11th centuries A. D., a surgeon, a doctor and a philosopher of the Arab school effectively contributed to found the art of modern pharmaceutics. Surgery was hardly practised in 10th century Spain, nevertheless it made famous Abul-Quasim az-Zahrawi, or Albucasis in the West—a fame that was largely posthumous. Albucasis, who was born in Cordua around 926 and who, according to Leon the African, died in 1013, taught how to cauterize cuts and ligature arteries, how haemostatic substances should be used and gave precise details concerning certain operating techniques. His authority was constantly invoked by the surgeons of the Middle Ages, but today historians of surgery judge his contribution to science rather weak. In his capacity as a doctor, he had the grace and kindness to keep his home open day and night with his yard always full of the poor waiting for his help. As a writer his thirty volume medical encyclopaedia, *Kitab al-Tasrif*, has one part devoted to surgical practice (the former being translated by Gérard de Crémone in the 12th century), but it seems to have concentrated on compound medicines (Books 23 to 30), simple medicines and foods, synonyms, substitutes, weights and measures. The twenty-eighth book deals with

Harvesting of medicinal herbs in latin manuscript of Albucasis (1013-1106).

simple medicines and divides them into three classes according to their animal, vegetable or mineral origin. Not only does it give precise indications for their preparation, but it also shows how remedies should be stored and the material of the recipients best suited to hold them.

About the same time—the second half of the 10th century—the doctor Mohammed ben Ahmed ben Saïd Ettemiry, or simply Teminy, became known in Irak due to his knowledge of simple medicines. He wrote several treatises on the theriac and a great work on foods and simple medicines, the *Merched*. In chapter 11 he deals with dew and how it varies according to the air, the place, the land and the plants on which it falls, and on bitumens he pays special attention to the mummies and bitumen of Judea. Chapter 12 treats salts and clays, chapter 13 metals and chapter 14 stones.

Persia produced Rhazès and was still to produce Avicenna, perhaps the most famous of Arab scholars in the West. Abu Ali al-Hussein ibn-Abdallah ibn-Sina, called Avicenna (980-1037), was gifted with a high intelligence an astonishing capacity for work and a prodigious memory. Bertrand Russel sums up the opinion of Avicenna's biographers when he says "that his behaviour was hardly exemplary; he had a great liking for wine and women. For the orthodox he was suspect but enjoyed the friendship of princes thanks to his medical skill. He had occasional problems caused by the hostility of Turkish mercenaries. At times he had to go into hiding, at others he was in prison." His itinerant life and the constant possibility of continuing his works shows to what extent the sciences were diffused in the Persia of that time. In a life cut short by overwork and excess, Avicenna found time to write 156 non medical works and 16 books on medicine, if traditional figures are accepted. His most famous works are the *Qanun* and the *Poem of Medicine,* equally known as *Canticum* or *Cantica.*

The second part of the *Quanun* (which has five parts: general science, medicines, particular diseases, diseases common to different organs or parts, pharmacopoeias) was the most complete treatise on simple medicines then known and comprises about 800 paragraphs mentioning numerous new medicines. Avicenna also wrote treatises on medical tonics, on oxymel and alchemy, not to mention his astronomical and philosophical works. Eight of his sixteen medical works are written in verse which is exceptional for scientific writers, even in the Middle Ages.

On drugs, he distinguishes between those "which drive out harmful humours with motions, those which master a temperament, get rid of humour, free blockage or weaken it, those which burn, contaminate, bring the disease to a head, harden, occlude, attract, fluidize, agitate, granulate the flesh and those which scar." Scammony radically evacuates yellow bile and it is improved by mixing it with quince to neutralize its harmful effect on the stomach and the liver. Other purgatives which evacuate yellow bile are aloes combined with bdellium as required or tragacanth, yellow Myrobolan, cassia and Indian Tamarind. For driving out phlegm, he recommends colocynth pulp improved with bdellium; to evacuate black bile, senna, fennel, dodder, black Myrobolan bark, fumitory and borage.

Avicenna explains: "Simple medicines should be administered as long as they are effective and compound medicines should only be used for the following reasons: when the disease itself is compound (for example, a disease resulting from phlegm or yellow bile), the medicine should then be improved (with honey) by giving sweetened food and adding something to heighten its effect should it not be able to reach the sick organ. One should make it easier to swallow and even help it to pass through the intestines." He adds: "If you use a composed medicine plan carefully its composition. Take a dose of each purgative, counting the doses and neglecting nothing, pound with each simple medicine that which improves it and mix them altogether. Then divide it into doses and repeat this for all compound medicines. Administer several times in beverages and keep the rest for later."

Among the drugs which cool down and are astringent, he counts myrtle, sumach, myrobolan, iron slag, coral, Armenian clay, bramble, dragon's blood, nutmeg galls, pomegranate flower mixed with the ashes of burnt ivory, cinnamon with plantain...Among those simple drugs which warm but are not purgatives are soapwort, incense, pepper, cardamoms, pimento, mint, cinnamon, mugwort, nettle, stavesacre, origanum,

---

Characteristics, properties and disadvantages of honey, with means of remedyina the latter, from the work of Albucasis, *Observations on the nature of different alimentary and hygienic products.* (Italy, first half of 15th century). B.N. Nouv. Acq. lat., 1673, fol. 82

Mel.

b. naturc. c. 7. l. i. z. meli' ex eo q̃ est i ꝼauo. Iuuamentŭ.
mondificat larɡ̃t 7 ꝓbulet corruꝓtione carniū. 7 aliorum
hunnectat. nocumenti. sitim effiat et gŭnŭt. remotio nc̃i.

lichen, amber, melilot wich dodder, ginger, gentian, peony, lac, dill, corn poppy, common star thistle, etc. Medicines which bring diseases to a point are warm and viscous like fat, pitch, pine resin, oil and wax mixed, oil beaten in hot water or wheat cooked in oil. Emollient medicines warmer than the organ to be treated are galbanum, bdellium, ammoniacum, storax and the marrow of an antilope's tibia. Black nightshade or foam, cold and wet, are medicines which harden. Roots of lily and narcissus, natron, caper and lupin open the pores and vessels. Broad bean, honey and sweet almonds are cleansing medicines. Castor oil, chamomile, rue and fennel distend. Garlic and onion open the orifices of the vessels, etc.

In this golden age of medicine and pharmacy in the Islamic countries, it would be appropriate to mention the names of other doctors who worked on pharmacology. In Persia, El Birouny (of Biroun, a town in India), a friend of Avicenna, wrote a treatise on natural medical history in which he studies the medical use of stones in particular. Miskaouih wrote a treatise on simple medicines, beverages and the preparation of foods. In Irak, the Jacobite Christian *Mesue the Younger* studied in the works which have come down to us corrective medicines, simple medical purgatives (54 in number), compound medicines and the appropriate medicine for each particular disease. In Spain, Abul Motharref Abderrahman ben Mohammed ben Abd el Kebir ben Iahya ben Ouafed Ellakhmy, or simply Aben Guefith, gave recipes for gargles, confections, potions, fumigations, poultices, collyria, robs, pastilles, pills...Strange as it may seem, he prescribed rice boiled with rose water, roast pigeon, quince preserves, beverages of pomegranate water with sugar, etc. to treat kings gone astray. He draws our attention to a preparation recommended by Frankish doctors against stomach and liver problems made from cloves, galangal, cinnamon, spikenard, mastic, ginger, saffron, rhubarb, agaric, aloes...given in pill form. The geographer El Békry described many medicinal plants in his texts.

Finally Constantine the African deserves special mention. He was a scholar and a great traveller who finished his life in Mont-Cassin where he was the first to translate into Latin not only the Arab authors but Greek writers as well and played, therefore, a major role in the renaissance of medieval pharmacy in the West.

While in the East in the 12th century one crusade succeeded another, heralding trouble, Islamic science continued to flourish both at home and also at Cordoba, in almost the whole Iberian peninsula and in N. Africa.

The botanist Er'r'afequy, probably born at Rafeq north of Cordoba in the second half of the 11th century, brought together what Dioscorides, Galen and their successors had written on simples and completed the whole with his own observations made both in Spain and N. Africa where he studied cardamom seeds, euphorbia and Star Thistle...in particular. He methodically made notes on synonyms and brought to light certain things that had been confused, for example Alypum or Dyers' Woad of Dioscorides, Turpeth Root or Indigo, water parsnip and water cress, etc. He did not accept without reserve the stupefying properties attributed to coriander by some of his contempories. He gave curious information on deposits of yellow amber in Spain and on the preparation of sal ammoniac.

Avenzoar is the name of an important family of Arab doctors. The most illustrious of them lived at the court of abd al Mumin, the first of the Almohades Caliphs and died in 1162. Certain authors dwell on his aristocratic manner of practising medicine, on his disdain of practical surgery and on the preparation of medicines. Yet he was chosen to prepare the great theriac for the Caliph. It is also to him that we owe the original idea of treating the constipation of abd al Mumin by making him eat the grapes of a vine he had sprinkled some months before with a purgative solution.

Among his pupils, Avenzoar probably counted the illustrious Averroes (Ibn Roschd, 1126-1198), certainly the greatest name of Moorish Spain, and the standard bearer of the unbelieving in the eyes of the Christians of the Middle Ages. This philosopher was also a great doctor well versed in the art of medical preparations. Book 5 of his treatise on General Medicine—the *Koullyat* or *Colliget*—is dedicated to medicines and foods. He is also the author of small works on simples, purgatives and the theriac.

In his *History of Arab Medicine*, Doctor Lucien Leclerc classes Moses Maïmonides (in Hebrew Mosheh ben Maymon and in Arab Abu Imran Musa ibn Maymum 'Abd Allah) among Egyptian doctors because, though born in Cordoba in 1135, he spent the second part of his life in Egypt where he died in 1204. This

---

The preparation of remedies after Joannes of Cuba, *Ortus sanitatis*. Argentinae, J. Grüninger, post 1550.

Des Animaux.   2. Figure.

doctor, theologian and Jewish philosopher, remains nonetheless one of the greatest figures produced by Moorish Spain. He left his home country to flee persecution and began to practise the medical profession in Egypt, simply to save his family who had been ruined by the unhappy dealings of his brother David. After a difficult start, he was appointed court doctor to Saladin the Sultan and was soon overwhelmed by his many clients. The Arab Historian Al Kitti tells us that he refused Richard the Lionheart's offer to become his personal doctor. Maïmonides, spiritual leader of the Jewish community in Egypt could not give up his post. The medical works he wrote suggest that recovery has to be attempted by dieting before administering drugs and that preventive measures are the most important. He thought that "medicines only serve to help the work of nature but can never replace it." In some cases the doctor should abstain from all treatment and should always think before acting: "Only charlatans think themselves infallible, no serious or difficult cases existing for them. They even claim that thinking about a disease is a waste of time." In his *Aphorisms and treatises on The Convention of Health, on Asthma, Piles, The Life of the Couple, Poisons,* Maïmonides mentions a certain number of remedies and even wrote a *Treatise on Drugs* whose title has alone survived.

In the 13th century the destiny of the Islamic world born of conquest was set. However, from the perspective of the history of pharmacy, this century may by considered one of the greatest since Serapion the Younger, Ibn el-Beïthar and especially Cohen el Atthar all lived at this time.

Serapion the Younger's *Treatise on simple medicines,* a simple compilation based on Dioscorides and Galen which mentions, nevertheless, sixty authors, was translated—badly—in Latin at the end of the 13th century by Abraham the Jew and Pope Nicholas IV's doctor, Simon of Genoa. The work contains 462 medicines in animal, vegetable and mineral classifications. Lack of critical judgements, confusion and numerous contradictions make it much inferior to the methodical and critical compilation composed by the botanist Ibn el-Beïthar under the title of *Collection of Simples.* Doctor Lucien Leclerc, who translated this work into French, wrote: "It is the most serious, complete and by far the most extensive that the Arabs have left us on medicine...(it) is far superior to all the works of this kind handed down to us by the Arabs. It leaves far behind the 2nd book of Avicenna's *Qanun* and Serapion's *Treatise on Simples...*"

Ibn el-Beïthar's *Collection* comprises 2330 paragraphs in alphabetical order. Some have claimed that more than two thousand plants unknown to Dioscorides are mentioned. But this was to ignore the synonyms, plant products and animal or mineral substances... Doctor Leclerc estimates at around two hundred the number of new medical plants mentioned by Ibn el-Beïthar and "much reduced as it is, this number is for all that no less remarkable." Each article has a general description, indications concerning its properties and finally a critical passage from the author pointing out contradictions or errors. More than 150 authors are drawn upon: a score of Greeks and, apart from the Arabs, Persian, Syriac, Indian and Chaldean doctors.

This work by Ibn el-Beïthar on simple medicines in which he describes not only their exterior characteristics, but "their properties, application, their disadvantages and the means to correct them, dosage, etc, directions for use as a substance, extract or decoction, and finally their substitutes when they fail," this work remains vital for those wishing to assess the breadth of Arab pharmacopoeia just as the *Manual of the Dispensary* written in Cairo in the course of the 13th century by Cohen el Atthar—the pharmacist-priest—remains the principal source of information on the professional life of Arab apothecaries.

* * *

In his *History of Pharmacy in France,* Maurice Bouvet points to the mention made for the first time of the pharmaceutical profession as such by the philosopher Olympiodorus in the 6th century A. D.: "The doctor prescribes and the *pigmentarius* carries out the prescription." Antiquity had only known doctor-preparers, often very knowledgable and the sellers of drugs, pigments...dye-stuff, amulets and poisons and who were in general ignorant and unscrupulous. Since he was responsible for preparing the medicine prescribed by the doctor, *the pigmentarius* was a new appearance, the ancestor of the apothecaries and modern pharmacists. In the Christian West, the first *pigmentarii* were only to appear at the end of the 11th century and a distinct separation between medicine and pharmacy, was not to be felt before the 13th century.

Among the Arabs, the Graeco-Latin scientific tradition seemed to be pursued, the pharmaceutical knowledge of the ancient writers was preserved, professional practice is maintained and, very quickly, remedies, pharmaceutical forms and material as well as the organisation of work were to be perfected. As far

Galen examining ink sketch decorating a Greek manuscript by Paul of Aegina (15th century). B.N.

back as the 7th century A. D., apothecaries were reported to be preparing the prescriptions of doctors in the dispensaries of Bagdad.

The name of one of these drug preparers has been preserved in a historical anecdote which shows him doing something which was more or less usual and generally restricted to the world of medicine. Khirouzan, the favourite of Mahdi the Abbasid Caliph (775-785), told one of her retinue to take her urine to a doctor. This attendant preferred to entrust it to a nearby apothecary, Abou Quoreich, saying that it was the urine of a poor woman. The latter being gifted for analysis knew that it was a sultana's urine and that she was going to give birth to a prince. Khirouzan was amazed and when the prediction came true, she overwhelmed the apothecary with presents. Some time later, Abou Quoreich again predicted the birth of a son to the favourite against the opinion of a court doctor, and once again the apothecary prevailed. The caliph raised him to the rank of his private doctors.

While the science of pharmacology was evolving in the vast Arab empire, the dispensaries were perfected and the apothecaries became more aware of the significance of their task. "Pharmacy, *Sanaat Essildla*, also called the art of drugs and beverages, is, after medicine, the most noble of sciences" wrote the pharmacist priest Aboul Mean ben Abi Nasr ben Haffahd, better known as Cohen el Atthar, in Cairo in the middle of the 13th century. In his *Manual of the Dispensary—Menhadj Eddokkan—*, a book for apothecaries, he detailed the duties and rights of the apothecary indicating at the same time the techniques of recognition, preservation, measurement, preparation...After showing that pharmacy is the indispensable auxiliary of medicine in his preamble, Cohen el Atthar enumerates the qualities required for practising the pharmaceutical art. The pharmacist should be honest, virtuous, fearing God first and men afterwards.

"Be sure", he wrote, "that to have the right to accomplish this noble task and deserve the confidence it inspires, you must adhere to a line of conduct never to be abandoned. It will be ever-present and never for a single moment will you forget it nor will you pretend to have forgotten until you have drawn your last breath. Such a line of conduct will be traced in desiring for others what you demand for yourself..."

"Take this precious quality to be one of the most important chapters in your code; if you keep it in mind you will find a haven where disloyalty, lowness, frivolity and indecent or unseemly things may be avoided."

"My child, there is no greater fault than hurting your neighbour or depriving him of his belongings without the slightest justification, especially if he is weak, unfortunate or of feeble mind. When a sick man feels death approaching, he calls a doctor who is experienced, virtuous and soft spoken and whose sole aim in the practising of his art is to seek the august face of God the Almighty and his recompense. He prescribes for this patient whatever will bring rest to his exhausted limbs and put him on the road to recovery: it is on the pharmacist that the doctor relies for the making up of this prescription. All responsibility, therefore, comes back to you. Would it be a good thing, if you were sick, not to be concerned about yourself knowing that such thoughtlessness might lead both to the loss of your belongings and even of your life?...You are not unaware of the punishment reserved by God for the man who is guilty of this double sin nor of the lesson this punishment gives to the man with an intelligent and perceptive mind. Follow this advice every day, morning and evening and never forget it! And God is the most knowledgable!"

The *Manual of the Dispensary* is divided into twenty-five chapters. The first and twenty-third are deontological and in the twenty-third it is said that the pharmacist should weigh his words and especially his writings which bear the stamp of their author. The second chapter deals with beverages and the third with robs (thickened fruit juice). "The rob", wrote Cohen el Atthar, "is a preparation which, in principle, should have no sugar: it is better made in this way. "In Egypt fruits are generally too aqueous, their juice acquiring the right consistency only if a certain amount of sugar is added. The difference between the rob and the syrup is that the former contains more fruits than sugar and sometimes no sugar at all. In the syrup, on the other hand, the proportion of sugar is greater than that of fruit. The term *enrober* in French means to thicken or make more consistant. The *Manual* mentions the syrup of Cadhy, *Pandanus,* an Indian remedy for smallpox mentioned by Rhazès and which also bears the name of Cadar's syrup.

Chapter 4 treats of preserves. Here, for example, is the preparation of rose honey: "Take a pound of rose petals, mix them in a container with a pound of finely crushed sugar, then boil two pounds of honey until the right consistency is obtained. Add the roses thus prepared to the honey, stir and mix well together, add half a drachm of saffron and two halves of galangal and allow to settle."

The opiates, medicines kneaded in honey, are discussed in chapter 5 and electuaries in chapter 6.

Cohen el Atthar gave 37 applications for the theriac, and indicated the procedure to be used for discovering if it was good or bad, old or new. He thought Mithridates' antidote "effective for pains in the liver, stomach, spleen, kidneys and womb and also for dysmenorrhoea and colic. It is a purgative that causes no pain prescribed for nervous disorders and for residues of viscous humours surfecting the organism. It proves useful for amnesia, weak sight and dyspnoea and fights malignant, acid eructations. It tempers the organism getting rid of flatulence and relieves congestion of the liver and spleen. It soothes intercostal neuralgia, acts against respiratory weakness and a yellow complexion resulting from blood deficiency of veinal stasis after being in the cold and when ascites is to be feared as a result of malfunctioning of the liver. This antidote is even recommended for people in perfect health since it strengthens the organs and is a cleansing agent once it enters the blood vessels. It dissolves the humours which are evacuated in the urine and breaks up stones in the kidney and bladder. It acts against asthma, headache, elephantiasis, leprosy, phlegm, general paralysis, shivering, hemiplegia and epilepsy."

Chapters 7 to 16 deal with powders, pastilles, electuaries, pills, hieras, collyria, lozenges, ointments, oils and liniments. After making some general remarks on medicines for the mouth in chapter 17, Cohen el Atthar goes on to deal with dressings, suppositories, poultices, substitutes and synonyms in chapters 18 and 21. Chapter 22 is dedicated to weights and measures. We know the advice given to pupils: "Be pious. Clean the scales, its pans and stirrups, make sure it is true; clean the weights at least once a week. Don't cheat, substitute or give short weight Check the spoons every day and clean them so that they have no smell and wrap them in clean linen and be happy." After the advice for pharmacists (chapter 23), the work ends with a chapter on the gathering and preserving of simples and a chapter on the testing of simple and compound medicines.

In the 16th century Fez had an apothecaries' street containing 150 shops and Leo the African tells us: "These shops were very high and embellished with such luxurious cabinets that I think in all the world that no other apothecary's shop could equal this." For nearly eight centuries, the apothecaries' shops prospered in a world placed under Musulman domination despite the principle stated in the 13th century by el Akbary that the apothecary should neither amass wealth nor refuse to give medicines to the poor while demanding the correct price of the wealthy. An inspection of pharmacies was organized as early as the 9th century. Every week the *muhtasib* checks their plants and drugs, supervises their beverages and encourages apothecaries "with threats of sanctions and corporal punishment." The sale of toxic products was the object of special attention.

As far as the equipment is concerned, apart from weights and scales, the choice of the appropriate material (wood, iron, silver, glass, clay...) for all instruments used in the preparation of medicines, "the great innovation of the Arabs", as Mr. Bouvet remarked, "is the widespread use of stills enabling them to prepare alcohol, alcoholic extracts, essences and aromatic waters." Like the ancient Roman ophthalmologists, the Arab apothecaries began to stamp certain medicines. Gradually the lesson given by the Arab apothecary was transmitted to the Christian West.

Picking figs after Manfred Imperiale (14th century author, perhaps from Kaysersberg), *Liber de herbis et plantis...* B.N. Latin ms, 6823, fol. 69 V°.

Pharmacy jars at the centre of a group of characters : doctor, student and different patients in Joannes de Cuba, *Ortus sanitatis. De herbis et plantis...* (Strassburg). J. Grüninger (post 1500)

Teaching urology. The shape of the "matula," permitting the examination of urine, was not the same as the wicker basket used to transport it, from Joannes de cuba, *Ortus sanitatis. De herbis et plantis...* (Strasbourg). J. Grüninger (after 1500).

95

INFIRMIS SERVIRE
FIRMISSIMVM REGNARE.

Care of sick by the Order of the Knights of Malta (1588). B.N. Engravings.

Mandrake, famous therapeutic plant in the Middle Age (private collection).

a. *Mandragora foemina*, Schlaffäpfel.
b. *Mandragora Mas, Mandragore*, Alraun
c. *Mandragora flore subcoeruleo*, Hundsäpfel.

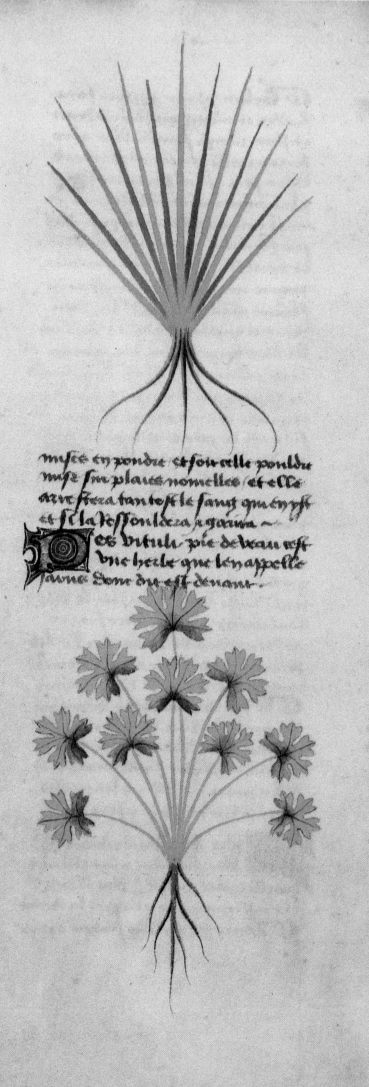

misee en poudre et soue celle pouldre
misse sur plaies nouvelles et elle
aresstera tantost le sang qui en yst
et se la ressouldera a garin ~

Pes vituli pie de veau est
une herbe que len appelle
iaune dont du est devant ~

Pes columbinus pie de colum
dest une herbe que aucuns
est appellee sletrio Elle a sur
les rondes endivisees e ressemble
au pie dung coulom et a les bran
ches ou les fueilles tenues rouges
et a fleur qui a couleur sur le temps
elle sespart pestent sur terre et
croist en roches en lieux sablon
neux et pierreux Len la dou
cueillir ou mois de may ou de iung
avec ses fueilt et la doit on seicher
en lombre len la peut garder par
ung an quant len trouve q len mete
en medecine or ces rostre appellez
rostre disarorcastis len y donne meint
les fueilles avec les fleurs
Contre les couillons se enflez de
fleume guils en velin set seront
broiez ensemble pur de colum a qui
lautre herbe set en sou faut emplast
sur ~

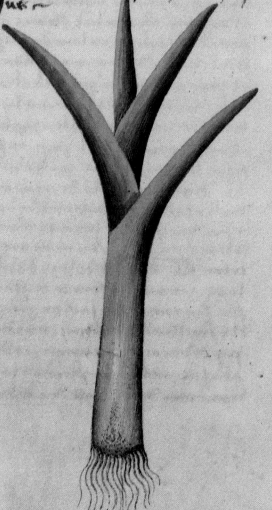

THE GREAT SCHOOLS AND THE FIRST DISPENSARIES IN WESTERN EUROPE

SALERNO

Salerno's position to the south-east of Naples is a happy one and, as Kurt Sprengel wrote, "the city's salubrious position with the sea to the south and, behind, a chain of mountains crowned with forests and covered with medicinal plants or balsamic shrubs and the excellent water with which it is abundantly privided greatly contribute to making a stay there as good for the health as Montpellier." The Romans had already esteemed Salerno as a place to relax. Perhaps, as Doctor Pierre Winter asks, was it "the affluence of the patients themselves coming in search of a restful climate which gave rise to this sanctuary of medical teaching?" Perhaps it was also the proximity of Monte-Cassino the famous Benedictine monastery or even the role that Byzantium continued to play in Southern Italy. What is certain is that at least from the beginning of the 9th century doctors of repute practised and taught at Salerno... The School where they were the first masters, only officially ceased to exist on the 28th November, 1811, its suppression being decreed by the Emperor Napoleon I.

Medicinal herbs after Platearius (family of doctors in Salerno in the 12th century). *Liber de simplici medicum* or *Circa instans* vellum manuscript. B.N. French ms. 1312, fol. 14 V°.

It is worthwhile quoting the legendary accounts concerning the origins of the School for two reasons: they announce all too clearly the future of Salerno and nothing precise has been put forward in their place. Some say Charlemagne founded the School of Salerno, others say it was the creation of the Saracens. Some declare that the real founder was Constantine the African and that the Salerno doctors had no reputation before him. The finest legend says that four princes of medical science founded it: Adela the Arab, Helinus the Jew, Pontus the Greek and Salernus the Latin. Thus, it is thought the four races converged who possessed all human knowledge. Later pills were to be made in the name of the four masters of Salerno. How could their power be doubted?

Despite «the distinctly secular tendency" soon to be shown by the School of Salerno, a tendency stressed by many authors, the idea that a health establishment founded on the shores of the gulf by the powerful Abbey of Monte Cassino could explain the origin of its therapeutic vocation is worth considering. We know that a doctor of Salerno was living in 904 at the court of the King of France and that in 984 the Bishop of Verdun, Adalberon, came to Salerno for treatment. We accept that at this time a college of ten doctors, paid by the students and granted certain privileges, taught the art of healing and wrote short medical treatises for the use of their pupils, but such was the success of these works that in the following centuries they were continually revised so that it is difficult to attribute the authorship of a text to the name of the author it bears. Much more than the others, the most famous treatise, the *Antidotaire,* has been constantly altered. This formulary, in its original form, has been lost and only the manuscript of the 12th and 13th centuries remains under the title of *Antidotario di Nicolo salernitano.* In a slightly different form and after a series of revisions, the *Antidotarium Nicolai Praepositi* was given this title, according to Sudhoff, by mistaking the master of Salerno for the French doctor Nicolas Prévost who lived in the second half of the 15th century and wrote an extremely useful *Dispensarium* for those interested in the apothecary's profession, but this was at Tours in the 15th century.

The *Antidotario* of Salerno, "father of all the following formularies and those inspired by it," as A. Castiglioni wrote, was for many centuries essential reading for all apothecaries. It went through many editors and was translated into the major European languages.

If Constantine the African, who lived in Italy in the second half of the 11th century only, cannot therefore be considered as the founder of the School of Salerno, his role in the development of the School's medical and pharmaceutical literature is important nevertheless. The story of this Carthaginian merchant, converted first to medicine and then to Christianity, remains as abscure as the first centuries of the School. His biographer Pierre Diacre claims that he went to Carthage (Tunis?), Babylone (Bagdad?) to study grammar, dialectics, physics, geometry, arithmetic, mathematics, astronomy, necromancy, music and the physics of the Chaldeans, the Arabs, the Persians and the Saracens.

He is then supposed to have travelled to India, Ehiopia and Egypt learning Hebrew, Syriac, Chaldean, Greek, Latin, Italian, Persian, Arab, Egyptian, Ethopian and Indian. All this knowledge he collected in a mere thirty-nine years. His learning seemed too great when he returned to N. Africa. He fled, secretly regained Salerno, was soon recognized as a master and magnificently received by the duke Robert Guiscard. Weary of honours, he was finally to retire to the monastery of Monte Cassino and died in 1087. It is difficult to separate truth from legend in this extraordinary life just as it is a delicate matter to distinguish between unsigned translations and personal observations. Modern criticism appears to place increasing importance on the latter as it accuses the translations of being awkward, hasty and confused. In the list of works by this doctor-translator given by Pierre Diacre, three directly concern pharmacy: *The Antidotary, Simple Medicines* and *Remarks on Plants.* The second of those works describes nearly one hundred and eighty medicines extracted from one hundred and sixty-eight different vegetables.

Daremberg observes that from the medical point of view "Constantine's influence as far as Salerno is concerned was not as great as is generally believed to be the case. It was not in the middle of the 11th century, but at the end of the 12th that Arab medicine replaced the Graeco-Roman in the School of Salerno and in W. Europe generally," but the important thing is that from the pharmaceutical point of view the pharmacopoeia was enriched by new formulas from the time of Constantine and, in part, thanks to him.

Arnaud de Villeneuve, professor at Montpellier at the end of the 13th century and at the beginning of the 14th century, author of the commentaries on the Salerno poem, *Regimen sanitatis Salernitanum,* B.N. Engravings.

ARNALDVS
Villanouanus.

B.R

Another even more mysterious figure from Salerno is the famous Trotula, this woman doctor who was perhaps practising before Constantine's arrival, but whose existence is contested by certain historians. She is supposed to have written not only a treatise on childbirth, but also to have provided numerous medical remedies: ointments, creams, fumigations, etc. She advised, for example, a preparation made from Virginia creeper macerated in honey to get rid of wrinkles. Other women also practised medicine in this most open of schools and the names of Abella, who wrote a treatise called *De atra bile,* Rebecca, Calenda, etc. are mentioned.

Historians agree that the School of Salerno reached its peak in the 12th century, but pharmacists especially would share this opinion. It was at this time that the *Liber de simplici medicina* and the *Regimen sanitatis salernitatum* appeared.

The first of these treatises, also known as *Circa instans,* was written by a certain Matthew Platearius who was born into a family of Salerno doctors. Matthew Platearius, who practised in Salerno between 1130 and 1160, had the famous Gilles de Corbeil among his disciples. The latter wrote in verse from his master's commentary of *Nicholas the Antidotary,* "I would like," he wrote in this poem, "Platearius to be alive today. How he would delight in seeing his works revived in my verses and his prose plying to their rhythm; the bonds of metre demand great precision and check the digressions of prose."

The doctor in the foreground prescribing the preparation of a remedy to the apothecary, telling the gardener at the same time the plants of be picked. Illustration from a collection (dated 1461) of manuscript treatises, one of which is the Antidotary of Bernard de gordon. B.N. Latin ms, 6966, fol. 154F V°.

"The mortar still semells of garlic", 16 th century drawing in a series of "Proverbs and figures) from a "collection of 131 pictures and figures" kent in the Arsenal Library, ms 5066.

The *Liber de simplici medicina* or *Circa instans* was intended as much for doctors and surgeons as apotl ecaries and herbalists. It met with immediate success and more or less precise copies appeared in great numbers, some of which contained considerable additions. One manuscript, for example, kept in the Breslau library has 432 chapters while the others only contain 276. The first editions, copied from some manuscript or other, added to the mistakes made in copying and grammar and to the lacunae as well. From the 13th century the work was translated several times into French and in the 15th century translations abound. The National Library prossesses 15 and all the great libraries generally have one manuscript to show. The first edition appeared without name, place, printer or date in Besançon or Lyon around 1490. The title of this folio of 213 leaves was: *Arbolayre contenant la qualitey et virtus, proprietey des herbes, arbres, gommes et semences, extrait de plusieurs tratiers de médecine, comment d'Avicenne, de Rasis, de Constantin, de Ysaac et Plateaire, selon le connun usaige bien correct. L'arboluyre* quickly became the *Great Herbal* and in the 16th century went through many editions.

In 1913 Doctor Dorveaux published the *Book of Simple Medicines* from a 16th century French translation kept among the manuscripts of the St. Geneviève library.

As well as being a treatise on medicine and therapeutics, this treatise is also a summary of drug adulteration. "What is written in this book on the adulteration of drugs," writes Platearius, "is not for those who want us to do it, but to prevent us being tricked by those who sell such drugs at the request of companions." In a prologue which begins *Circa instans,* which gives the work its title, the author defines "simple medicines," shows how "compound medicines" may be used and outlines his plan: "In treating each medicine, first its ingredients will be indicated, i.e. whether it is hot, cold, wet or dry. Then whether it is a tree or bush, herb or root, flower, seed, leaf, stone, juice or whatever. The different species, where they are found, the best species and how they are made into medicines and adulterated, how they can be recognized, preserve their different powers and how they should be administered." Classified in haphazard alphabetical order, the 273 chapters of the French translation published by Doctor Dorveaux include 229 chapters on drugs, taken from the vegetable kingdom, 14 from the animal, 28 from the mineral or chemical and 2 chapters on pharmaceutical preparations.

Furnace designed for the making of pitch resin and the thistle called "virga pastoris." Platearius (family of doctors in Salerno in 12th century). *Liber de simplici medicum* or *Circa instans,* manuscript on vellum. B.N. French ms, 1312, fol. 45 Vº.

Portrait of Albert the Great (1193-1280). B.N. Engravings

Mitra pedumq̃ oneri tibi quondam, Alberte, fuerunt.
Dulcius est Sophiæ delituisse sinu.

Still more famous is the poem written in the second half of the 12th century with the title *Regiment sanitatis salernitatum* or *Flos medicinae*. Like the *Circa instans* it has been greatly altered in the many copies made to the extent that the number of lines varies between 362 and 3520. The first edition published at Pisa in 1484 was followed by more than 300 others. This "flower of medicine" heterogeneous in nature was, according to Sudhoff, not only annotated by Arnaud de Villeneuve but enriched so as to gather together all the elements of Salerno teaching. After Arnaud, additions only increased. Daremberg observes: "However one might imagine the original form of the *Regimen,* whether as a medical consultation addressed *ex professo* to some great personality of the day or a series of crudely isolated aphorisms and proverbs, the fact remains that in essence it is exclusively dietetic in character as Arnaud de Villeneuve's *Commentary* illustrates..."

> Fatigue, ills, troubles, anger,
> Cut short the course of your days;
> Lively, playful spirit, flowers cover your path;
> Avoid the perfidious charms of pompous feasts
> Should you not want to die suffering from some painful discharge,
> Beware of the cold, drink and pleasure's intoxication.
> Eat, sleep and work in moderation:
> To overdo these would be against nature.
> Get up early and walk late in the evening
> And you will live to be a happy, cheerful man.

These lines taken from Charles Meaux Saint-Marc's translation published in 1860 are certainly of interest to the hygienist, but certain additions concerning medicine deserve more attention from the historian of pharmacy. Thus, in the same translation we find:

> *Mugwort.* It helps urinations and gets rid of stone.
> And promptly brings about abortion,
> In a pessary or drink the effect is the same;
> And crushed, applied to the stomach.

> *Chervil.* Chervil crushed and added to honey so sweet
> Relieves a cancer. Infused in wine,
> Crushed while green and applied as a compress,
> It soothes the pain in a weak side,
> Relieves the stomach by causing vomiting
> And keeps the relieved stomach free and esay.

> *Lupin.* Lupin ashes kill worms;
> Its juice destroy hairs and stops them returning.

> *Rose.* Leaving aside the seed and bark, the soothing rose
> Provides a good water for piles.
> It calms an irritating attack of colic;
> Treats both the head and mouth effectively.

Before explaining how effective the enema is, he gives the following advice:
> ...boil together
> Mallow, marsh mallow and mercury:
> To the gift of their juice which soon appears
> Add oil of violet, salt and bran
> To obtain quicker results

Against anthrax:

> For anthrax the best remedy
> Is the half of an egg with a little salt,
> Which when mixed together in poultice form and applied to the wound,
> Calm the pain. Should you be afraid of the pain,
> To kill its fire and bite and abate its violence
> Take the theriac with parsley and much praised honey;
> But be decisive and above all abstinent.

Certain recipes appear stranger today. The bitter urine of a dog is advised against warts. Pig's dirt placed in one's bed and trimming "the garment prepared for the night" protects against fleas. To make hair grow, prick the skull many times with a needle and sprinkle with honey for eight days...

Around 1100 a new solvent appeared in Salerno which was to have the greatest influence on the preparation of medicines and perfumes: alcohol. Its preparation was rapidly improved thanks to the use of dehydrators like potassium carbonate. It was generally used in two forms, one being the *aqua ardens* at 60° and the other *aqua vitae* at 90°. The expressions *soul of wine, burning, permanent* or *eternal water, vegetable mercury, animal air, light of mercury, prime spirit, quinte essence, subtle spirit*...were also used to designate the liquid obtained by heating wine and condensing its vapours by cooling. To credit, with R. J. Forbes, the practioners of Salerno with the honour of being the first to distil wine and condense its vapours remains one of the really crucial facts in the history of pharmacy. The discovery of eau de vie was for a long time attributed to Arnaud de Villeneuve because he was the first to write a special work on wine and its distillation. In fact, he merely studied it extensively and, in his search for the philosopher's stone, he observed certain properties of alcohol. His view of the world, dominated as it was by the *spiritus* doctrine or the vital force, an ethereal and cosmic fluid, led him to simplify the therapeutics of Salerno, restrict the use of medicines leaving much place to psychological cures. Hoefer's judgement of this astonishing figure is certainly too harsh, yet it is worthwhile considering: "All these claimed discoveries attributed to Arnaud de Villeneuve were already known before his time. He was an insolent charlatan who deftly used all sorts of phantasmorgia to exploit the credulity of his contemporaries. The preparation of eau de vie, essential oils and medicinal wines was known long before his time. Yet that does not shop him making a great secret of this in his Treatise *de Vinis*. He calls a tincture of rosemary drinkable gold and credits it with every imaginable power."

It was perhaps when the Hippocratic city of Salerno was at its very zenith that the first signs of decadence began to appear. In 1140 Roger of Sicily, protector of the School, had bestowed official status on it and in 1231, Frederick II of Hohenstaufen reglemented the duration of medical studies. This extraordinary man, "this prince of the Renaissance a century and a half before Quattrocento," to quote the formula of R. Grousset, even made the teaching of anatomy using a corpse obligatory. In 1267, Charles I of Anjou confirmed the rights and prerogatives of the doctors of Salerno, foreigners continued to come in great numbers to be taught by the members of the college and from 1266 to 1435 de Renzi counted more than one hundred and twenty doctors in Salerno. The control of medicines may, therefore, be given as an example. Druggists and apothecaries, limited in number, took the oath to make drugs according to the rules and had to sell them at fixed prices. The doctors, made responsible for watching over them, were fordidden to do business with them, nor keep stocks in their dispensaries nor own a shop themselves. Two imperial inspectors checked with the doctors the exact preparation of electuaries and syrups. The selling of poisons and love potions was strictly forbidden...though this trade flourished while the sick began to come to Salerno in smaller numbers and the teaching lost its vitality. Other schools were founded in Italy, France and throughout W. Europe. While the reputation of Salerno remained, its attraction diminished.

To share E. Desnons' judgement that Gilles de Corbeil (1140-1224) marked the glory of the famous School of Salerno at its peak, "even though it was in Paris that he acquired such reputation and anthority," is in no way paradoxical. This doctor of Philippe-Auguste with his poem on *Compound Medicines* did more for the pharmacy of Salerno than the doctors themselves.

The historically established facts in Gilles de Corbeil's biography are few in number. He must have been born in Corbeil (Seine-et-Marne) about 1140. After studying medicine in Salerno he went to Montpellier where he disagreed with the University teachers and was insulted "as if he had been a country yokel or clogmaker" and given a beating. Then he probably came to Paris where he taught medicine, was Canon of Notre Dame and Philippe-Auguste's doctor and there he finally died before the middle of 1224. In two passages of his *Hierapigra*, Gilles de Corbeil admits to being the "son of a peasant." In his *Compound Medicines* he recommends the taking of the remedy called *Diarrhodon Magnum* early in the morning when daily occupations begin and the illustrious city of Paris awakens to the sound of bells inviting its many citizens to go to church, which clearly shows that Gilles de Corbeil lived there. Some authors would have us believe he was a Benedicinte monk, but would he have spoken with the lack of seriousness he shows in enumerating the marvellous properties of an aphrodisiac, the electuary *Diasatyrion?* The young monks with ruddy faces and fat stomachs, he said, must make great use of it, the very excess of illicit pleasures resulting in eventual incapacity to pursue these and in the obligation to respect the continence of their vocation.

The two best known works of Gilles de Corbeil are his poems *On Urine* and *On the Pulse*. He also wrote a treatise *On the Signs and Symptoms of Diseases* and a satirical poem angainst the prelates, the *Hierapigra*. His poem *On the Virtues of Medicines* was printed for the first time in 1721 by Polycarpe Leyser in a collection of poems from the Middle Ages; C. Vieillard, however, sees it as "by far the most important and interesting of Gilles de Corbeil's medical works," yet admits that it is only "a poetical paraphrase of the properties and indications of compound medicines or, as one said at the time, the *Antidotes* of *Nicholas the Official."*

"In my opinion", wrote Gilles de Corbeil, "and without beating about the bush, I think that if those who want to practise medicine understood thoroughly what they had to do and were guided by an enlightened judgement, they would soon give up useless jumble of certain practises to restrict themselves to the study of the *Antidotary*. Here the doctor will find all necessary arms. If he is familiar with this work and follows it to the letter so that he adds to or reduces the formulas in each particular case or corrects the action of one drug with another, he will be able to relieve every infirmity and heal every disease of the human body."

The work, divided into four books, has 4663 lines and describes 80 medicines or antidotes. In the prologue to the first book, the author evokes his masters of Salerno: Musandinus, Platearius, Urson, Castalius, Romoald, Salomon Matthew and Richard the Elder. He could not be quiet and had to spread the pure doctrine of the great School. He has, as he writes in the prologue to the second book, rejuvenated this doctrine in his works and he hopes to make it popular once again since it was beginning to be unjustly forgotten.

Gilles de Corbeil is indignant (lke Symphorien Champier later) at somme uncrupululous apothecaries who replaced sugar with honey while preparing the electuary *Diaprunis:* "They should expiate their crime and themselves be exposed to the risk of dying the risk they subject others to with their frauds. They should pay with their own life the deaths for which they are responsible, these merchants of spices, aromatics and makers of paints. Don't they even go to the length of loading their weights, fixing their scales and changing at will the composition of drugs, adding honey where sugar is needed and selling as good products which they know perfectly well to be bad? With such behaviour they compromise the good reputation of the doctor, ruin the patient's health, prolong sickness, hasten the terrible hour of death and put wills into effect."

When he discusses the *Onguent Populeum*, such a virtuous attitude does not prevent Gilles de Corbeil advising the occasional changing of its greenish Colour by using sandalwood, madder, saffron, rose or camphor for the simple reason that "the patient eventually becomes tired of the same form of drug prescribed continually. He ridicules this stingy parsimony which undermines his confidence in the doctor who consequently loses his fee. Novelty is to be recommended in all things. By changing the colour of this ointment often, the doctor shows that he is anxious to heal the patient and ensures a generous fee for himself..." It is even more curious to see this author advising against the use of certain drugs which he simply regards as too effective and prompt: *"Acaristum,"* he writes, "means *no pay* for it is so effective and prompt that health is restored before the doctor has been able to benefit from the honour and profit his cure should have brought him and he is thus obliged to leave empty-handed. Health so rapidly restored seems to be the work of the nature and not that of the doctor. Thus the doctor is discredited in the eyes of the patient and makes his efforts worthless. On the other hand, a slow recovery gradually brought about at the price of pain and suffering in the good name of medicine is of much more use to the doctor to whom the patient is more closely attached. Such treatment bestows upon him honour and gifts. Thus the unwitting underestimate the very things they should, on the contrary, place the greatest value."

MONTPELLIER

Both from the medical and pharmaceutical point of view, historians agree on the outstanding importance of Montpellier in the Middle Ages. Arabs, Jews and Latins meet earlier and more intimately than elsewhere in this trading city. The influence of Salerno mixed with Arab science from Spain and the Hebraic tradition was profoundly felt. Economists have illustrated the role played by spices in international relations and we are aware of their importance for the apothecary, their links with drugs not only as far as their recognition and preservation was concerned but also regarding their sale by weight. Now Montpellier had a privileged position. Benjamin of Tudela, the Spanish traveller who passed through the city in 1165, observed that it was an excellent place for trade. Travellers come from Algarve (Portugal), Lombardy, the Roman States, Egypt, Palestine, Greece, France, Spain and England. There is, therefore, no need to be astonished by the fact that the hospital of Montpellier was highly esteemed in Asia Minor and that one of the oldest, if not the oldest bills of exchange is dated from Montpellier. Rare religious tolerance favoured the flourishing city of Languedoc where many pilgrims from Santiago de Compostela or the Holy Land stayed. The Jewish colony from Aragon or the East, which was relatively large in the 12th century, benefited from the division of powers between the Bishop of Maguelonne and the Guilhems, lords of the city. It counted in its ranks rich and philanthropic men, scholars and a great many doctors looking for pupils, Jewish or Christian who wanted "to know their secrets and recipes in return for payment," according to P. Delmas.

Georges Rivals wrote that in the first half of the 12th century, "under the Maguelonne bishops, the medical *Studium* was made up of sporadic elements, individual Scholars, as it were, who took free lessons from masters working at home and who had come from the most diverse places: Arabs, Jews or Christians from Salerno, Spain and Mainz. The episcopal authorities were slow to intervene." No doubt there were conflicts between teachers in the second half of the century, some of them wanting to enjoy a certain privilege for the act of January 1181 shows the reaction of Guilhem VIII against any restriction. He wanted independent teaching, free from any religious reserve: "Anybody, whatever his origin or his situation has the option of running a medical school." This idea which seems strange, to say the least, to us in the 20th century (healers excepted) can perhaps help us, once put it in its historical context, partially to understand the enigma of Montpellier. If the University Statutes, which are remarkable for their precision and tolerance, only date from the year 1120, we have to agree with the old dean Jean Astruc, doctor to Louis XV, who admitted that it is to the Jews "that the Faculty of Montpellier owes a large part of the reputation it enjoyed at its foundation, since in the 10th, 11th and 12th centuries they were virtually alone in Europe in possessing this knowledge which was passed on through them from the Arabs to the Christians."

Certain historians of medieval institutions, especially in the 19th century, thought that there was a link between the *collegia* of the Low-Empire and the communities of professions or trades in the 12th century, whereby the early traces of the spice and drug community in Montpellier would correspond to the reappearance of the Gallo-Roman organisation of Gallia Narbonensis. Others have seen a connection between the feudal organisation of the South and the birth of organised guilds. The most modern authors prefer to seek an explanation of the latter at the very time of its birth in the middle of the 12th century when the same phenomenon appears almost simultaneously throughout W. Europe. Such explanations would be of a social and economic nature.

The local lords were definitely interested in the creation of fairs and markets at this time, their revenues being increased by the taxes levied on the different trades and their justice holding a certain sway on the policy of these same trades, but basically the urban character remains fundamental and, as Mr. André Gouron writes, "during the second half of the 12th century, the organisation of the guilds in embryo form as it no doubt was, nevertheless provided the essential elements of the city's life both as far as its defence and its political institutions were concerned...In Languedoc the military factor appears essential to us for the formation of guild groups." Thus in the official collection of municipal acts of Montpellier called *Petit Thalamus* we see spice and drug merchants charged with the responsibility of guarding certain gates on Thursdays. The

Consulate was only founded here in 1205, but even before its creation a "common council" of Montpellier participates with the lord and bailiff in the reglementation of the trades, checking weights and measures and limiting prices and profits. It is remarkable that every monopoly and all attempts at securing exclusive rights of sale or production of any product whatever were forbidden and the guild organisation in Languedoc is marked by the freedom of its trades. "A double chronological process," Mr. André Gouron adds, "gradually establishes itself in which one distinguishes between the interior laws of the city where the practising of every profession remains free and an external law which sanctions the monopoly of the burghers vis-à-vis the foreigners."

This strange liberty of the especiadors of Montpellier—the grocer—apothecaries—as strange no doubt as that granted or rather confirmed in 1181 on all those who wanted to teach or practise medicine, was not really compromised by the oath taken before the consuls and which became traditional in the 13th and 14th centuries for all the people in the profession. In addition this oath little resembles the one demanded of the members of the Jurandes of Northern France and which really concerns fidelity to the profession. In Languedoc it "serves above all to establish that in practising his profession the new doctor will be a citizen devoted to the interest of his town" (A. Gouron). Furthermore, this oath of the Montpellier *especiadors* kept in the *Petit Thalamus* does not go back to the 12th century as has been said, but only dates from the end of the following century like most of the other traditional oaths of the city.

The *especiadors* committed themselves on two points: first to provide good drugs and secondly to sell them at the right price. Firstly: "To avoid suspicion and a bad reputation and to respect loyalty for which God protects the person and possessions of men who pay such respect as a duty and to observe, as far as possible, the meticulous execution of the agreements and wishes of the *especiadors* of Montpellier, both as far as they themselves are concerned and with regard to all those who have to deal with them by profession. So in their profession and preparations they act loyally, using no adulteration in accordance with the prescritions set down in the *Antrostaris* (books of antidotes) without innovation or the substitution of one thing for another unless it is approved by the consuls of the profession or two masters qualified in medicine and designated to that effect by consuls and without reducing or changing anything formulated by these masters. This should be observed concerning electuaries, medicines, plasters, syrups, powders and all things formulated or to be formulated by the qualified masters or their pupils regarding their profession. Nor should they purchase for the purpose of selling anything already prepared by those who have not taken the oath and are not resident in Montpellier, with the sole exception of gingerbread, rose sugar and violet or myrobolan preserves."

Secondly, "it is included in the said agreements and wishes that no master, pupil or hotelier is to sell anything at an increased price, but solely at the price fixed for the sale, this price being increased by no suggestion whatsoever and that these persons should neither be associated with any man for the sale or resale of articles of the profession nor provide harmful quantities or substances."

Consequently, "all *especiadors* are required to take the oath and observe all these rules while practising at Montpellier—and will have the same oath taken by those working for them in the profession. They will promise to observe each and every rule loyally without default, fraud, alteration or adulteration. All these aforesaid regulations I will strictly observe in good faith. And this before God who hears what I say and all the evangelic saints whom I touch with my body." In the 14th century, a crier was used to forbid those not in and approved by the profession to practise medicine, surgery or the selling of drugs and should such a person, whatever his position, be he Jew or Christian, dare prescribe or issue medicines then, the apothecaries jointly forbade him to prescribe and issue recipes not approved by the men of the art! The University statute of 1340 charges two of the oldest masters to warn apothecaries every year "not to sell any laxative to any citizen without the advice of one of the University masters or the opinion of those who have obtained from the Bishop of Maguelonne in accord with two-thirds of the masters the degree permitting them to practise medicine themselves." Twenty-four years later, Louis, Duke of Anjou, Lieutenant of Charles V of Languedoc, repeated this warning to apothecaries not to make up the prescriptions of those who practised medicine illegally, making it an offence subject to a 10 marc fine. On 3rd June, 1399 Charles VI was finally to confirm the Duke of Anjou's decision by stiffening punishment which tends to prove that the rules were badly kept.

Raymond Lulle, Catalon philosopher and alchemist, nicknamed *l'Illuminé* (about 1235-1315), author of *Ars magna*. B.N. Engravings.

B. RAYMVNDVS LVLLIVS PHILOSOPHVS
Doctrinam Pandit Raymund Lullius omnem, Cui Deus
infudit scibile quicquid erat. ex Vetustissimo prototypo
chamahistico authentico. I. mittann our. Moücornet ex.

THE FIRST WESTERN EUROPEAN DISPENSARIES

In ancient Rome, in Bagdad from the 8th century and a little later in other Arab cities, drug merchants no doubt carried on their trade in their shops, but in the course of the Middle Ages in W. Europe no apothecary would appear to have existed before the end of the 11th century. Doctors were to continue in the 12th and 13th centuries to be the most important preparers of medicine, yet they were not alone since the monasteries and the secular clergy and aristocracy also had an embryo of pharmacy intended for the sick around them.

We know that the bans of various councils (Clermont 1130, Montpellier 1162, Montpellier 1195, Paris 1212...) did not prevent the clergy from practising medicine and pharmacy. There was a strong tradition which wanted the care of the body to be entrusted to those who had the care of the soul. Fulbert, Bishop of Chartres (960-1028), for example, practised pharmacy. In a letter to Ebole the writes: "I am sending you three of Galen's potions and as much theriacal diatessaron. You will find in your books of antidotes their properties and how they should be taken. I am also sending the emetic you wanted though I don't want to tire you on account of your advanced years. However, should you need to seek relief with a medicine you can take frequently and without risk, use oxymel and valerian (Raphanus) which is more of a laxative for an old man and I would advise you to take it in pill form. I am sending you 90... 'If in a later note he says', Believe me when I say I have prepared no ointment since I became Bishop and the little I possess, I received from a doctor; I am doing without to give to you,..." he makes no reference to any apothecary but does mention a doctor who also prepares medicines.

In Angers at the end of the 11th century the *pigmentarri*, forerunners of the apothecaries, appear and in 1093, Count Foulques le Réchin forbids them "to practise their art outside the limits of the cathedral chapter." Their specialisation enabled them to supplant doctors, priests and doctor-monks by slow degrees. Concerning the latter, Pierre Rambaud gives a curious explanation of the successive bans issued by the councils: "The doctor-monks, used as they were to leaving the monasteries at will, gradually came to neglect the rules. They began to adopt the tastes and rules of secular life with which they were in constant contact. Love of wealth made them neglect the poor in order to treat the rich. Gilles de Corbeil, Philippe-Auguste's doctor, goes as far as censuring his book not only for charlatans but even for vagabond monks, who, protected by their religion, began to teach and practise medicine as well."

It is generally agreed that the preparation of medicines became a special trade in W. Europe after the universities were founded and began to teach medicine. Estienne Pasquier explains the separation thus: "The reason for this was that in this new arrangement the doctors found a place among the four faculties due to the importance of their work which was given full recognition, the manufacture of *scalpel*, pestle and mortar no longer being a part of it and from that time three different domains were distinguished, i.e. doctor, surgeon and apothecary." However, up to and even after the introduction of such statutes, many strangers to the profession continued to make up remedies. This 13th century poet lashes doctors for being:

> By no means do
> Doctor Sires heal,
> All the sick;
> Yet they sell heir pomegranates
> And bitter insipid blews
> For gold and silver...

Mylius (Johann Daniel) *Opus medico-chymicum... Basilica philosophia...* Francofurti, apud L. Iennis, 1618.

Rare indeed were the religious orders like that of S. François who forbade the practice of pharmacy except "for their own use" and who banned the selling or issuing of any medicine. Charlatans made remedies and we know how many there were until legislation successfully restricted their business. Finally there were private individuals who made them, convinced that they had inherited precious family secrets concerning balms, miraculous ointments...

The *pigmentarri* mentioned by Pierre Rambaud—a certain Arveux who signed a charter of Saint-Maixent in 1123, a Herveux who appears in a charter of Saint-Hilary in 1152—are spice merchants or "spicers of the pharmaceutical order" and their appearance coincides with that of the *medicus* or *fisicus* with the institution of a medical order. P. Rambaud thinks that they replaced the *apothecus* or doctor-apothecary, but we know virtually nothing of their business and, in particular, whether or not their shop was permanently open. Bernard le Provençal from Arles who, after studying in Salerno and Montpellier practised in his home town around 1150, must have practised the double profession. In his treatise on materia medica, *Commentarium Magistri Bernardi Provinzialis super Tabulas Salerni*, he indicates where plants of good quality may be gathered (Dodder in the neighbourhood of Montpellier, sumach in Jerusalem or Provence...) and draws our attention to the many fraudulent practices already carried out at this time: manna being prepared with debris of sugar cane, dried myrobolan with branches of asphodel, musk with the blood of a billy-goat, galangal with Cyperus coloured with saffron, ect. Bits of ebony were even sold as authentic fragments to the true Cross. Bernard le Provençal's work leads us to suppose that there were real apothecaries in Arles, but the real proof is provided by the article of *leges municipales Arelatis* dedicated to the *speciatoribus* (between 1162 and 1202) in which it is set down that apothecaries are forbidden to associate with doctors, give them presents or invite them to lavish meals. Thanks to Alexander Neckam, the English student who came to Paris around 1180, we know of the existence of several dispensaries grouped together in the Petit-Pont quarter. He writes: "The houses should have good windows facing East. Recipients and boxes are displayed there in the open air in which may be found: storax ammoniacum, opopanax, bdellium, euphorbia... *ungwentum populeum*, laurel-berry oil, etc." Similarly in Avignon at the beginning of the 13th century, merchants of spices and remedies were found living in the same street called *Carriera Pebrarie vel Speciarie*. They were named *speciarii* (from *species*, spices), *apothecarii* (from *apotheca*, shop), *pebrarii* or *piperarii*, pepper merchants or even *aromatarii*, merchants of aromatics. Henri Granel mentions the existence of a certain *Petrus speciator*, Peter the spicer, at this time whose will he found with several other solicitor's acts.

In chapter 36 of the Book of Statues of the City of Marseille (1200-1263), it is decreed that "all apothecaries are bound by a special oath to scrupulously prepare all confections, syrups and electuaries which they will make or sell or which another or others will sell in their name or in their place in their houses or dispensaries or in any place in Marseilles or on its territory and to the best of their knowbeldge and in all good faith have them prepared by their apprentices or attendants who will be bound by the same oath, the same applying to their boys who participate in any form whatever in the above-mentioned operations." The Statutes of Avignon in 1242 also require spicers and their servants to take the oath "to scrupulously practise their trade." They are forbidden to associate with doctors, do them favours, give them presents, make them promises "and all doctors, spicers or medical udents who have made agreements or pacts, enabling doctors to sell their remedies to spicers in return for presents or their pupils who have made promises to doctors will be punished by a fine of one hundred sols paid to the temporal court and whatever the doctor receives that is not due to him will be refunded for the benefit of the community and the informer will receive half the sum."

The doctor, the pharmacist (right), the patient and his servant (middle). Cosmes Camelos 1339, B.N. ms grec, 2243.

Next page : The master teaches the characteristics, properties and drawbacks (with the means to neutralize them) of the theriac, after Albucasis' *Observations* on the nature of different alimentary and hygienic products (Italy, first half of 15th century). B.N. Nouv. Acq. Lat., 1673, fol. 87 V°.

Page 113 : Jean de Ketham : "Fasciculus Medicinal". J. et G. Gregoire, 1495.

Triaca.

Nature. e. et f. melior ex ea. q̃ libera
mẽtur. rofias et egritudib; frigidis eciaxg̃ ncniment vigili-
remotio noct. cum infrigdantibus   ſeur aqua
ozti ꝯ ſimilia.

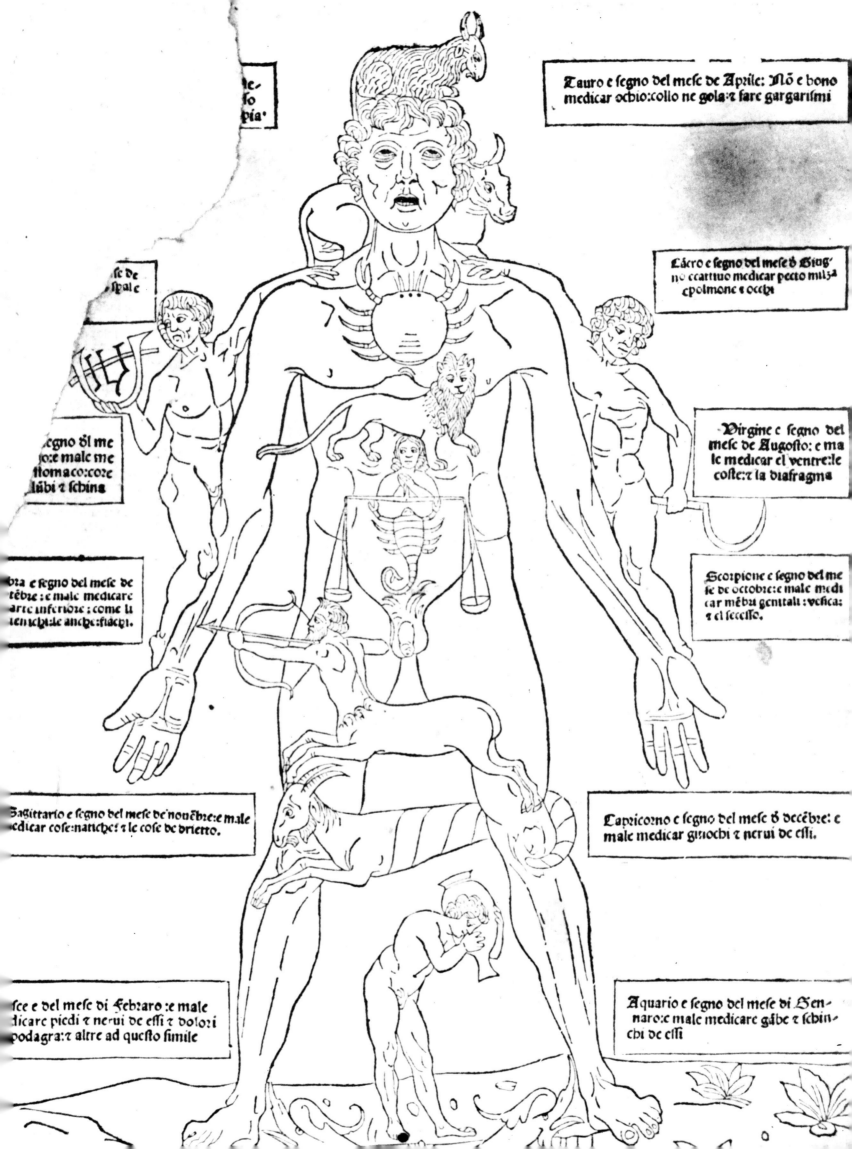

Tauro e segno del mese de Aprile: Nõ e bono medicar ochio:collo ne gola:τ fare gargarismi

Cãcro e segno del mese õ Giug'no ccattiuo medicar pecto milza e polmone e occhi

Virgine e segno del mese de Augosto: e male medicar el ventre:le coste:τ la diafragma

Scorpione e segno del mese de octobre:e male medicar mẽbu genitali : vesica: τ el secesso.

Sagittario e segno del mese de nouẽbre:e male medicar cose:natiche:τ le cose de drietto.

Capricorno e segno del mese õ decẽbre: e male medicar ginochi τ nerui de essi.

Aquario e segno del mese di Gennaro:e male medicare gãbe τ schinchi de essi

In the principal cities of France, the number of apothecaries grew throughout the 13th century. Mr. Bouvet mentions Eugene of Torre, a citizen of Barcelona, practising in Perpignan in 1207; Chandelier, a widow of Rouen in 1214; R. Laurentius, *speciarius* and H. Guillemus, *piperarius* n La Rochelle in 1224; Richardus, spicer in La Roche-sur-Yon and in 1255, Guillaume in Poitiers. Henri Philippi ran the Stag pharmacy in Strasburg from 1268. Finally in Paris in the same year. Etienne boileau's *Book of Trades* explains that apothecaries must only pay taxes if they sell at the market, but not if they sell in their shops. "All waxmakers, pepper merchants and apothecaries who sell in their shops pay nothing to the custom of the aforesaid taxes for they use the King's weight. All waxmakers, pepper merchants and apothecaries who sell their products at the market on Saturday must pay the customary obulus, but nothing while on their own premises as aforesaid." We know that the King's weight gave weight-controllers the right to weigh merchandise and keep a record. It was stricter for the products of the drugstore or spice merchant than it was for others. Three years later, in 1271, a statute of the Paris faculty of medicine accuses the city's apothecaries, surgeons and herbalists of overstepping the limits of their profession and unrightfully practising medicine. They had to take the oath, under pain of excommunication, to restrict themselves uniquely to their own preparations and to leave "the directions for their use to the masters of medicine alone and to those granted this right by the faculty." All they are authorised to issue in the absence of a doctor are "simple remedies like rose sugar, ordinary dragées, rose water, etc."

The apothecaries "who sell syrups and good electuaries "enjoy therefore professional independence from the 13th century, an independence soon to rival energetically with neighbouring trades.

Is it not a little strange to meet the word *corporation* for the first time in an official act from January 1776 when one of Turgot's memoirs presented to the King the edict which was to abolish mastership and guild mastership the following month, in other words, what we call corporations. To designate certain professional groupings, various terms had previously evolved over the centuries and particular to the region: trade, college, community, brotherhood, charity, fraternity, guild, hansa mastership, guildmasters...Each of these terms applying to a particular from of institution and each having evolved in the course of the centuries, the use of the word corporation to include such a diverse and often incompatible whole seems all the more delicate since it was borrowed from England where it applied to groups endowed with a Crown Charter or an act of Parliament of the "legal personality," like the Bank of England or the East India Company, institutions barely comparable with the community of cobblers in Rouen or the brotherhood of bakers in Troyes.

In France enormous family of workers' groups was also united under the name of corporation and one of the best specialists in this field, Emile Coornaert, considered that: "Among all the inextricable images that we are given, two features appear to be both essential and general: reglementation by custom or writing which guaranteed professional discipline, a formal act or tacit agreement of the authority which assures the existence and action of organized trades. Reglementation is a guarantee against the excesses of competition and a token of solidarity for the producers. The authority frequently made of it a guarantee for the consumers or the community. But it provided another token of security for the former by raising their communities above the confines of private law, endowing them with a legal personality more or less perfect as the case may be and by granting them a proper authority over its members."

Maurice Bouvet mentions the numerous traditions of the guilds or corporations before the 15th century and adds that from the end of the 12th century "the split between medicine and pharmacy resulted in attempts at reglementation whose traces are found in *Statuta sive leges municipales* promulgated in Arles between 1162 and 1202."

This apparent precocity may perhaps be partially explained by the fact that the apothecaries—sellers of products which were often harmful—found themselve classed with locksmiths—guarantors of the safety of houses—and barber-bleeders among the "dangerous professions." This idea that the drug preparers could make the populations run risks is found in the statues of the medical faculty in 1271. The statutes of Arles had already decreed that no doctor was to prepare any syrup, electuary or any medicine whatever on their premises (article 138), such preparations being made only "in the dispensary of the apothecary or in the patient's room." As for apothecaries, they could sell no drug without the advice of a doctor, their medicines had to be of good quality and without medical authorisation they were not allowed "to replace one thing by another in their preparations" (article 137).

After pointing out that the taking of an oath goes back to pagan antiquity, that the *collegia* existed in

Frontispiece of the *Thériaque d'Andromachus, dispensée et achevée publiquement à Paris par Moyse Charas.* Paris, Olivier de Varennes, 1668. Library of the National Order of Pharmacists.

Roman Gaul, that these *collegia* and the first *frairies* or *confréries* (brotherhoods) had things in common and finally that the worst upheavals hardly touched certain popular traditions, E.-H. Guitard sees the oath as the main element which kept the artisanal associations together. "In the beginning nothing was written down. One day the most usual oath was written down on a piece of parchment so as to be remembered easily. The first texts of this kind which have come down to us and are of interest to the associations of apothecaries (Marseille, Avignon, Montpellier) are transcriptions of sentences uttered at the beginning of the 13th century to take the particular oath of the profession." With professional obligations becoming more and more complex, the juror simply committed himself to meet the requirements set down in another text, i.e. the statutes. Yet the oath remained the base of the institution. It was to remain so right up to the end of the old order and continued to worry public authorities a little. That explains the reglementation of Parisian trades by Etienne Boileau in the reign of Saint Louis in the form the edict of François I in 1539 which ordered (to no effect) the immediate dissolution of all brotherhoods and also Turgot's attemps in 1776. The corporations were only temporarily defeated in 1791 by the voting in the revolutionary assemblies of 2nd March and 4th April. Thus as E.-H. Guitard observes "French pharmacists were the first to regain not only their right to hold meetings and establish their own schools, but also (not without setbacks, it is true) the practice of taking an oath stripped of its exclusively religious character."

E. H. Guitard recognizes the great importance of the oath in uniting the members of the brotherhoods at the very limit of the laws of the kingdom and of pure catholic orthodoxy and sees the particular utility of guild statutes for the so-called "dangerous" trades. He considers that the public authorities were logical in recognizing and reglementing those associations they could not destroy, which helps us to explain the evolution of professional communities. He writes: "The guilds, at first pious and mutualistic associations, were formed spontaneously." Yet this does not explain their origins.

According to one thesis, the guilds can be traced back to the professional colleges of the Roman world and this is an attractive idea, especially for the most Roman regions in Gaul. It is true that these colleges survived up to the 10th century in Italy and even longer in Byzantium.

Would that not also explain the astonishing complexity of the guilds of Provence and Languedoc when they appeared in the 12th century? North of the Loire, on the other hand, the predecessors of the guilds go back to old Germanic traditions brought into Gaul by the invasions. The piously preserved custom of banquets and other "gastronomic honours" offered to the masters of the trades by candidates reminds us of the ritual feasts and traditional drinking-bouts of the old *geldoniae, confratriae* or *caritates*. Thus, as E. Coornaert observes, "of the guilds one begins to see in the 11th century, several are things from the past, old relics remade both in the North and the South. The past lives on and becomes a part of their reality to an extent which, even if we cannot measure it precisely, was considerable nevertheless." However, we must consider the powerful revival in France of the 11th century which was to lead to the miraculous stability of the 13th century.

We must also take into consideration a fact fully recognized in the history of science and, in general, Western thought yet which is perhaps not sufficiently acknowledged in the history of professional groups or associations, i.e. the Arab influence and the role played by the Crusades in the economic and social development of the West. Though the life of Etienne Boileau the provost of Paris remains obscure, we agree with the *Histoire littéraire* which tells us that he "accompanied St. Louis on the crusade of 1248, was also taken captive with this prince in 1250 and only managed to regain his liberty by paying two hundred livres d'or in ransom money, a considerable sum which meant that the person asked to pay it must have been of a reasonably high position." Is it mere chance that Boileau took on the task of classifying in one collection the legislation of the trades on his return from the crusade and his time spent in captivity? The Arabs had already had active guilds for a long time. Despite the fact that the workers' communities interviewed by the provost in Paris claimed important prerogatives, the *Livre des métiers* still remains the first positive text outlining individual rights and for five centuries it was to be used to settle disputes. Thus, while recognizing the importance of Latin or Germanic traditions and the need for professional reorganization after the economic revival, it is significant, nevertheless, that many cultivated men in W. Europe wanted to see in their own countries certain institutions which they had already seen working well in countries of Arab civilisation. Perhaps this was another return to antiquity, but with the important difference that the old traditions had been enriched, without the slightest doubt, by the Arab contribution.

One problem remains. Etienne Boileau only mentions apothecaries in the second part of his book when he deals with tolls. This might be because there were few of them in the city or because their profession was not considered a proper trade, but we could reasonably assume that the sale of medicines was included in the art of medicine which went back to the Faculty and that the provost had the sole night regarding the drug merchants practising at public markets.

(Bottom) The laboratory of PP. Aignan et Rousseau, capuchins of the Louvre. *Mercure galant*, December 1678.

"The alchemist and his wife in a hermetic laboratory". Engraving taken from the treatise on alchemy published at La Rochelle in 1677, the *Mutus Liber* whose title refers to the thorough symbolic contents with no explanatory notes.

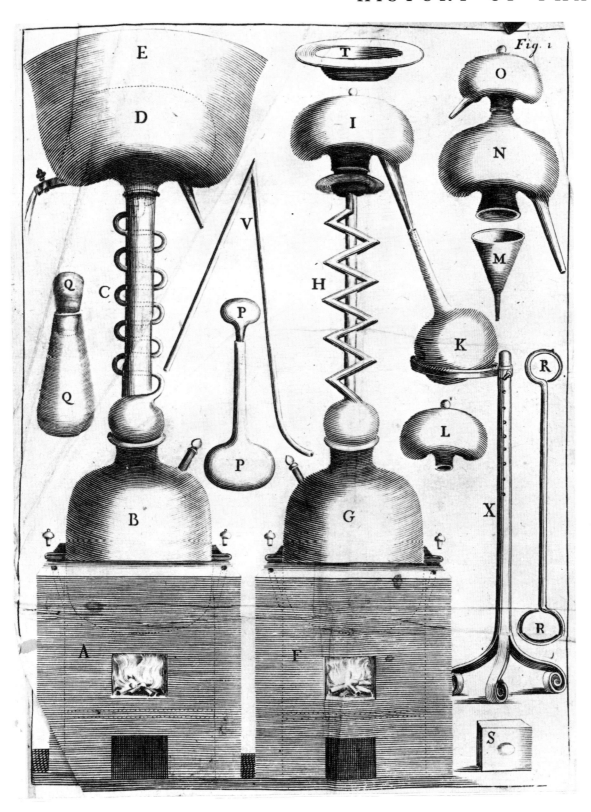

Description of laboratory material used for distilling spirits of wine from Moyse Charas, *Parmacopée royale galénique et chymique...* Published by the author in Paris in 1676. Library of the National Ordrer of Pharmacists.

II

THE APOTHECARY

DIFFICULT AND UNCERTAIN TIMES 14th-16th CENTURIES

Defining a sick man as one who needs a doctor and an apothecary, the number of sick people in 14th century Europe showed no great increase even if the number of deaths multiplied drastically. Even allowing for a certain degeneration of the medical and pharmaceutical knowledge acquired in the course of the preceding centuries, there is no reason to believe that it was impoverished, thus the explanation of all these deaths must be sought elsewhere. In the 14th century the population of Europe diminished and the mental health of a significant number appeared to be dangerously affected. Some have found the cause in the collapse of the feudal system and the France-England conflict which was just beginning and which was to last one hundred years; others talk about the economic crisis and the failure of religious ideals. All historians mention the famous Black Plague which originated in China and made its way west to the Black Sea and the mediterranean, striking Constantinople in 1347. Bagdad is thought to have lost five hundred thousand people in three months and Cairo ten thousand in a single day. The same year saw Crete, Genoa and the south of France affected and the following year over half of Europe. In 1350 the plague reached Scandinavia, the Baltic, Poland and Russia.

It is said that the population of England fell from three million seven hundred thousand in 1350 to two million in 1377. Certain Italian cities lost more than half these inhabitants. Crete had to be recolonised. In Alsace over three hundred localities were deserted and the surface area of arable land took until the 13th century to regain its previous dimensions. Around Avignon sixty thousand corpses were counted in three winter months...It has been rather rashly deduced from these facts that doctors were incompetent and pharmaceutical preparations were ineffective without stopping to consider the fundamental causes which seem to be the intensity of the Christian faith, the surprising range of international trade relations and the progress made by a civilisation typified by the excessive development of urban life.

Today everyone knows the role played by the rat in passing on the bubonic plague, capable as it was of carrying the flea, the vector of the disease, over great distances. Now the rat which was native to Central Asia and unknown in Europe appeared in the West in the 13th century after being brought from the Holy Land by ships of the Crusaders. It was not long before the rat completely invaded Europe and, always carried by ships, soon overran the world. It was the Christian faith therefore which enabled the plague to spread. The adventurous spirit of the traders of the Middle Ages is no less responsible since, as we have seen, the plague started in China. It would never have left the Far East without the collaboration of intrepid travellers in search of spices, silks and precious stones, etc. Finally the pest would not have spread in 14th century Europe with such lightning speed and claimed so many victims had the cities been less developed, less populous and less teeming with life. Do we blame doctors and pharmacists today because they are helpless before "the disease of the masses" and the weekly slaughter on the roads? They do what they can, but cannot prevent psychosis and the rising death toll every weed-end.

Such were the ravages of the epidemic, which lasted from 1347-1350, that some authors tried to see the Black Death as a disease without parallel in the past and which has disappeared since the 14th century. By stressing the effect on the lungs, they took the bubonic infection and the appearance of coal to be of only secondary importance. This scourge "which has killed a third of the world," Froissart said, and which eliminated twenty-five million people in Europe alone, was definitely the plague of the buboes, the real plague of the East. Today historians agree on this point.

What could the doctors do? The great Guy de Chauliac tells us: "The plague was something futile and shameful for doctors, all the more so since they dared not visit the sick for fear of being infected. Whenever they did visit them, the doctors were virtually useless and earned nothing, for all the sick died—except for some towards the end who escaped with mature buboes...I dared not refuse to visit myself for fear of being slandered, but living in constant fear I survived as best I could..." Yet Guy de Chauliac caught the plague "as the death rate began to fall" and escaped by the skin of his teeth.

In the year 1348 Philippe de Valois asked the College of the Faculty of Medicine of Paris to write a consultative work on the epidemic. This work found the cause of the plague in the conjunction of the stars and gave precious advice on hygiene useful in the fight against it. The last part of the work enumerates remedies which cured and prevented disease by using medicines.

The faculty recommended vinegar to be used at all meals "for it has the joint properties of countering putrefaction and contamination (decomposition)," eating garlic and sorrel, drinking sour milk and taking in the morning small slices of onion in boiled milk. Among the simple medicines, it accepts Armenian bole mixed with julep, tisane and vinegar, and sigillated clay which fights all poisons. The body may be purged with agaric and fortified with the great theriac, ten years old. "We also approve greatly of pills made from aloes, myrrh and saffron." "Aromatic perfumes should be used which are fragrant and fortifying...Those who are able should also have clothes made from woollen cloth or silk, their shirts being kept with aromatics. As for those travel in cloudy or sultry weather, they hould breathe in as little air as possible by trying as best they can to cover the respiratory canals. They should also take care to take with them artificially scented balls without which neither doctor nor any other person should have the temerity to approach those struck by this plague. "The Faculty gives numerous recipes for antidotes: pills to protect onself against the plague, lozenges which purified the air when burned, camphor lozenger to be swallowed, a ball of amber, cordial electuary, etc.

Let us take the formula of "the electuary which protects against polluted air, fever and stinking abcesses:" "Take a measure and a half of cinnamon and "alipte;" two scruples each of India Aloe wood, aloe flower, cubebs and white sugar; half a measure each of nutmeg, cloves, garingal, gen, two species of veronica and the great cardamom; one scruple each of "mard," leaves of "sedoair", saffron from the Orient, seeds of basil, balm, dried mint; different pearls, half a scruple of "jaconces," emerald, red coral, "karabe;" selected red woods roses, sandalwoods, stag-horn, calcinated ivory, ground ivory, all these in a half measure each; one scruple each of silightly acid seed, the four cold seeds of India, lemon seeds; one scruple of dyed silk cut into tiny pieces with kermes; half a measure grey amber; one scruple of musk and six grains of camphor; a

124

Care of the sick by the Order of the Knights of Malta (1588). B.N. Engravings.

measure and a half each of pine cones, some grapes or dried grapes without their stone; half an ounce each of rose, sycomore fruit and bugloss preserves; two ounces of incised lemon; two pounds each of sugar and camphor; prepare with rose—and bugloss-water. Cover the lot with leaves of pure gold."

The preparation of this antidote or others like it must have caused certain problems in getting all the ingredients and given some work to apothecaries, but the cost and sale price must also have curiously limited the possibilites both of making it up and selling it. However, a large part of the population was sick with the plague or afraid of becoming so and those not content with drinking vinegar or taking onions dipped in milk asked every Tom, Dick and Harry for less expensive antidotes. This was a great time for charlatans and sellers of cheap panaceas to the extent that the king had to intervene to stop the abuses. The misfortunes caused by the ravages of the Black Plague clearly explain the order of King John, in December 1352, concerning the sale of medicines and letters of patent and August 1353 setting down the rules governing apothecaries in seven articles.

Paradoxically the inability of the apothecaries to cater for all their clientele led to stricter controls and the number of drug-sellers being limited.

Despite the wars, famines, the Black Death, different epidemics and the charlatans who ruined, wore out, tortured and killed a large part of the population of Europe from the beginning of the 14th century to the middle of the 15th, it cannot be said that no progress was made. The discoveries of Leonardo da Vinci or Galileo carried on those made by the Parisian masters in the 14th century. Greek sicence became accessible to the Latin West by the intermediary of the Arabs; Christian thought, to a certain extent, took over from Islamic culture. Then, in the 14th century, "linen" began to replace the "swaddling clothes" of the Middle Ages, an important event responsbile for improving hygiene and successfully fighting leprosy. If we add that linen provided cheaply the raw material of the paper industry which had come from China in the 13th century, we may also say that the invention of the shirt and the button was to condition the printing industry, and we are aware of the consequences of printing...

In 1453 the Turks took Constantinople, driving out to the West the last Byzantine scholars. Twenty-five years before Gutenberg, the typography of mobile characters already favoured the book industry, but the rapid increase in the number of printing presses in the second half of the 15th century greatly accelerated the spread of knowledge and the exchange of ideas and profoundly influenced the progress of civilisation. In 1492 Christopher Columbus, while looking for the route to the Great Indies, touched land on the Antilles. In 1543 the *De Revolutionibus orbium caelestium* appeared in which Copernicus places the sun at the centre of the world and in 1616 Galileo's first trial began. In 1619 Harvey discovered the circulation of the blood. These few dates mark the brilliant period called the Renaissance which traditionally begins in 1453, flourishes in the 16th century and stretches into the first half of the following century.

The Hungarians took possession of the Carpathian Basin in 896. The conversion to Christianity and the subsequent founding of a kingdom created a link with Western culture. The first written pharmaceutic documents date back to the period 1192 to 1195. They were written by Benedictine monks of the monastery of Boldwa. Between the years 1244 to 1421, the professional activity of a pharmacist and the sale of medicines were regularized by the Ofener Decree. The first pharmacy was established in 1310 in Pressburg.

Thus the darkness of the Middle Ages disappeared and the shackles of scholasticism were broken. The great texts of Antiquity were discovered with the treasures of the New World, true Christianity and the beginnings of lifelike art. The earth was no longer one planet and man found in creation the role he had lost by the sin of his first parents. A link more intimitate than at any other period seemed to unite the different manifestations of human activity and some of the best men of the time dared to confront science and politics, religion, economy and art with the same serenity. The curiosity of painters made anatomy advance, the imagination of Utopians helped financiers, philosophers experimented, navigators were poets and certain state rulers had a taste for things of the spirit.

A century ago the Renaissance could be conceived of thus but today we see the best historians leaving it in semi-darkness. It has already been admitted that a genuine literary and artistic Renaissance had begun

---

The ideal French pharmacy at the beginning of the 17th century from the frontispiece of Jean de Renou's book - *Officina pharmaceutica seu Antidotarium dogmaticorum vetus, renovatum, auctum, illustratum...* Paris, Veuve Guillaume de la Noue and Denis de la Noue, 1606. Library of the National Order of Pharmacists.

Officina
Pharmaceutica
Seu

Iaspar Isac

before the fall of Constantinople. G. Beaujouan, historian of science and medievalist acknowledges that "the real scientific revolution did not begin until the dawn of the 17th century." If the Renaissance has long been considered as the secularization of the human spirit and the liberalisation of religious beliefs, paganism having awakened to triumph over Christianity, R. Le Bègue has shown, on the contrary, how the pagan authors were given Christian interpretations by Renaissance editors. Finally, from the point of view of literary history, C. S. Lewis declared that the Renaissance was "an imaginary entity given the task of meeting all the individual preferences of the 15th or 16th century."

Was pharmacy fortunate enough to be the exception? Apparently not. One sees more of an exhumation than a renaissance and the most certain thing seems to be the flourishing of new diseases among which syphilis was to figure prominently. Yet this abundance of misfortune with which man was struck helps us to understand better the hypersensitivity, aggressivity and the feeling of weakness manifested in this cruel and exciting time when the individual was quite definitely transformed. Chronically undernourished in the preceding period, frightened by dark traditions, helpless against the forces of nature, isolated from the rest of society by the very fact that he was more narrowly linked to a social group—parish, profession, family...—which was generally hostile to the others, Renaissance man entered the new world of uncertainty which made his position unbearable and out of which the great movements of faith and the wars of religion, the proliferation of the cult of the saints and outbreaks of sorcery, sexual disorders and the unquenchable thirst for knowledge, the will to reform and the taste for renaissance, all resulted.

The strange figure of Paracelsus (1493-1541) perhaps illustrates more than any other the split that took place in the thinking habits of the Renaissance. Philosopher, theologian, astrologer, alchemist, mineralogist, surgeon, doctor and pharmacologist, Paracelsus wrote on all subjects always expressing his own view vehemently defending this personal opinion in aggressive language even if this opinion was marked by a profound pacifism. No more Catholic than he was Reformed, but in favour of a community life that was Christian—even that conceived by the Middle Ages—this fiery doctor declared for example: "There are two sorts of war on the earth: one arises from stubbornness—since all power is evil in origin and illegitimate in birth. The other is that of the parts of our body—diseases. The former is caused by pride and its illustrious splendour; the latter takes place in the body and is an emergency in which pride has no place."

Though much has been said on the incoherency of Paracelsus' ideas, the incessant fluctuation between the study of nature and that of magic and a certain interior contrast which would explain his frequent obscurity, his personality seems, on the other hand, to be typified by a provocative and excessive coherence, eg. his general system of analogies and micromacrosomic correspondence between cosmology, theology, physics and medicine. Since man is the image of the world and reunites in himself all the elements that make up this world rather than contemplating exterior objects and reflecting on them, he may apprehend them by means of an affinity between the object and that to which it corresponds inside him. Walter Pagel, one of his most recent biographers, illustrates the theme thus: "Let us take a herb endowed with a specific *power*—purgative for example. This power is the *knowledge* of the herb—the knowledge relative to the means of carrying out the purge. In order to get to know perfectly this herb and its specific power, the physician (of nature) must find out what its internal mecanism is. In other words, there exists as a component in the researcher—"who is himself a microcosmic whole"—an element corresponding to the plant which should unite with it by an act of sympatho—magnetic attraction. Thus he apprehends the natural object in and through his own being, i.e. he apprehends intuitively and truthfully."

This is really a mystical form of research and if Paracelsus' system had very important consequences for science, it remains difficult to consider the theorist as a scholar such as we conceive today. While dispelling superstition, he believes in astrology and especially in the relation between the stars and drugs: "There are stars above and stars below, and since a remedy cannot act without the heavens, the heavens must direct it. Thus it behoves the heavens to render the drug volatile, in other words, to isolate it from its terrestial element; it is only on this condition that the heavens may direct it...Your would never say that balm is a herb for the womb and origanum for the head—only the ignorant speak like this. Their action is governed by Venus and the moon; if

---

A doctor's dress from the Lazaret of Marseille in 1720 form A.-B. Clot-Bey, *De la peste observée en Égypte*. Masson, Paris, 1840.

Imp. de P. Bineteau.

Costume d'un Médecin du Lazaret,
de Marseille en 1720.

Paracelius (1493-1541).

The Zodiak, illustration form Nicholas Myrepsos, *De compositione medicamentorum libri XXIV...* copied in 1339 by Cosmos Camelos. B.N. Greek ms, fol. 656 V°.

you like the heavens should act favourably... Can any nobler objective be imagined for a doctor than to discover the concordance of the stars. For it is in these that the fundamental essence of all illnesses is to be found."

The latter, which corresponded according to tradition to the equilibrium of the humours, became external objects for Paracelsus, "species" or "fruits" individually typified by a particular structure or function like metals and minerals. "Diseases grow in man like grass and bushes in the earth." To fight against them, therefore, specific remedies should be found and then the relation of man to the universe: man, his organs, their diseases and the stars, plants and minerals. The doctor's task is to know nature and ask it for remedies which correspond to the disease, and not those which are unlike it, an idea on which the homeopathic principle rests: "Arsenic cures arsenic, anthrax anthrax in the same way as poison kills poison."

While ancient pharmacy rested on the composition of medicines, the pharmacy of Paracelsus, on the contrary, was based on separation. It isolates the particular virtue which exerted a specific action on such and such a disease. It is chemical research and not a collection of traditions. It should "extract, not compose. It relies on the knowledge of what is interior and not on the composition and combination of a whole bric-à-brac of elements. What are the best trousers? Those made of a single piece of cloth; those made from different bits and pieces are the worst. Who would be stupid enough to imagine that nature gave so much power to this herb and so much to another and then asked your doctors to put them together?...Nature is the doctor, not you; it is from her and not men that you take your orders. She composes, not you. See to it that you learn where her dispensaries are, where virtues are written down and the places where they are stored..."

To cure stone, Paracelsus uses stones (crab's claws, stone of Judaea, aetites, selenite, etc.) first crushed to powder and dissolved *in vitro*; then crush and dissolve the stone *in vivo*. The doctrine of "signatures" gives useful information about the choice of remedies: the form and colour of a leaf, a flower, a root enabling its affinities with an organ, disease or star to be found. Since nettle leaves sting, they should heal sharp internal pains. Eyebright, or *Casse-lunettes,* looks like an eye and so will cure the eyes.

We are aware of the importance of uroscopy in Antiquity and the Middle Ages. The urine, indicating any sign of pathological change in the humours, was thought to enable us to recognize the disease. The urinal was divided into four parts corresponding to the head, chest, the abdomen and the urogenital system and should a granular deposit form at the top and descend towards the second level after shaking, this was symptomatic of "catarrh", i.e. a flux going down from the head into the chest. Paracelsus rejected this idea and held that the urine could give no useful information without examining it by "extraction," coagulation and distillation, i.e. by weighing and examining it chemically. The diagnosis would be made by studying the abnormal quantitives and the condition of salt, sulphur and mercury found in the urine. Yet it is true that despite their subtlety, Paracelsus' ideas on the interpretation of such deposits "turn out to be disappointing since they are no more than rehashes of uroscopy" (Walter Pagel).

Based on a "cosmological anthropology," the medicine of Paracelsus inspired the enthusiasm of his patients: "The only people I could please were my patients" and after his death, when the greater part of his work was finally published, the admiration of many disciples, notably J.-B. van Helmont, invested the master's ideas with a scientific form. The prudent—and innovatory—use of chemical products in therapeutics enabled him to bring about certain cures which were regarded as miraculous and the great intuitive aspect of his writing made of him the very picture of the genial precursor. He has been seen as the defender of experiment and reason against sterile tradition, the advocate of clinical teaching, the founder of iatrochemistry and chemotherapy, the advocate of mercury against syphilis, sulphur and antimony treatments, the use of tinctures and extracts in preference to tisanes, decoctions and electuaries, the defendor of crenotherapy and the inventor of the doctor for professional diseases.

All this and much more can be found in the strange universe of Paracelsus, but that is not why he is "modern." He remains the author of a theologico-metaphysical system in which his observations, once seen as premonitory, become part of a system like those of the Middle Ages. He denounced some of the dominating ideas of his time, yet believed that the power of the imagination could cause an epidemic of plague or contaminate the goods of a merchant unhappy with his turnover. He believed in amulets, nymphs and gnomes

---

Symphorien Champier, *Symphonia Platonis cum Aristotele et Galeni cum Hippocrate.* Paris, Josse Bade, 1516.

and such ideas do not comply with the notion one normally has of a precursor of contemporary science. Paracelsus was more a reformer than a founder and less a reformer than a brilliant mystic and an audacious doctor of great kindness and an impossible character at the same time.

In the 16th century as in the preceding centuries, the poor people used traditional remedies to fight the ills that befell them. Apothecaries were still rare, remedies very expensive and the enrichments of pharmacy could only be of benefit to the common people once they became the fashion. Yet the therapeutic arsenal was considerably enriched thanks to the voyages of discovery which turned the traditional idea of the universe upside down.

The trade in spices imported from Asia had contributed to wealth of Venice; form the 15th to he 17th centuries great navigators and intrepid explorers left Europe in the hope of getting rich in the same way. At the end of the 15th century Vasco de Gama landed on the Malabar coast and brought back spices worth a million ducats. In the 16th century the Portuguese became the main suppliers of spices in Europe and made enormous profit on the sale of nutmeg, cinnamon, cloves...which they had found in Asia. The richness of the vegetation of the Americas not only stimulated the curiosity of learned botanists but also started a profitable trade. The doctor Christobal Acosta describes mimosa, pineapple, cashew nut, tamarind, aloes of Soccrota...Filippo Sassati studied Black Catechu; Fernand Cortès mentioned vanilla, cacao and cayenne in his writings; Ribaut and Laudonnière write about Sassafras which grows in Florida. André Thevet brought back tobacco to Europe and only a few years later the French ambassador to Portugal, Jean Nicot, sent some grains of it to Catherine of Medici. Barbosa, the Portuguese navigator, added Malabar cardamom to European therapeutics. Hutten discovered in 1514 that guaiacum once heated gave out a blackish resin which rapidly *hardens*, but the wood of this tree, which grows in Santo Domingo, was used in medical practice long before the resin, since the latter is mentioned for the first time in the 1677 edition of the *London Pharmacopaeia*. The root of jalap, a herbaceous Mexican plant, played a very important role in Europe from the 17th to the 19th century as a purgative, but from the beginning of the 16th century considerable quantities of a convolvulaceous plant from Mexico were imported into Europe and this plant, called Mechoacan rhubarb, also a purgative, was sometimes confused with jalap. Sarsaparilla, considered an excellent depurative, was brought back from New Spain and was introduced to Seville in 1545. Then it was imported from the Honduras and later from the Equator...Up until the second half of the 19th century, Sarsaparilla root was thought to be one of the most effective weapons against rheumatism. Vanilla imported from Mexico and much used in flavouring chocolate and tobacco was only used in pharmacopoeia from the 18th century. Copaiba balsam, produced by trees growing in the hot regions of S. America was brought into European trade by the Porguguese in the 17th century. It was used for the tratment of wound but particularly to stop gonorrohoea. Gamboge from a tree growing in Cambodia, Siam and Southern Cochin China (Vietnam) began to be used in European medical practice at the beginning of the 17th century as a strong purgative and was generally mixed with other substances.

Two American vegetable medicines were to play a major role in European therapeutics from the 17th century, cinchona and ipecacuanha. Peruvian bark—which comes from trees of the genus *Cinchona*, growing originally on the West Coast of S. America in tropical, mountainous regions—was certainly used therapeutically by the natives before the arrival of Europeans, but the first Spaniards to settle in Peru only mention fever bark and we have to wait until the first half of the 17th century for the first cures by this remedy to be reported. This concerned a Jesuit missionary struck with fits of fever, a corregidor from Luxa, the wife of the vice-roy of Peru...The Peruvian drug was brought back to Spain in 1639. At that time, Seville monopolised the trade with America. Experiments having been concluded, the bark was sent to Cardinal Joannes de Lugo in Rome who belonged to a Seville family and who had under his control the medical college of Rome. From Rome the bark was taken to Belgium by Jesuits on their way to the election of a general. In 1649 Cardinal Joannes de Lugo, on his travels in France, himselft recommended to Cardinal Mazarin that Peruvian Bark should be administered to young King Louis XIV. Praised by some doctors and many Jesuits, but condemned by others, the febrifuge caused a long dispute in the second half of the century. *Jesuits' Powder* became famous throughout Europe. In 1678 Doctor Robert Talbor healed King Charles II of ague by using his own

Frontispiece from Pharmacopoia Wurtembergila, Stuttgart 1760.

preparation of the bark. In the same year he cured the Dauphin of France and several other prominent figures and received two thousand louis d'or from King Louix XIV and an annual pension of two thousand pounds for his secret which was the giving of strong doses of Peruvian Bark in wine. Though not accepted by everybody, especially the Jesuits' enemies, the remedy took on an official character, something it was to keep.

Ipecacuanha root, growing in the dark, damp forests of S. America and commonly used in Brazil, was not used in Europe until after 1672, the year in which Doctor Legras brought a certain quantity back to Paris. Though the first experiments, too strong in dosage, were hardly convincing F.-A. Flückiger and Daniel Hanbury relate that "in 1686 a Paris merchant, called Grenier or Garnier, became the owner of one hundred and fifty pounds of ipecacuanha. He experimented on himself and praised its action against dysentery to his doctor Afforty and Jean-Claude-Adrien Helvétius, a pupil of the latter. During his convalescence Grenier gave a small amount of this new drug to Afforty who did not take it very seriously. Helvétius, on the other hand, began to use it for cases of dysentery with great success. It is said that he had bills posted at street-corners proclaiming the success of his treatment by the new drug. He had it sent from Spain with the help of Grenier and sold it as a secret remedy. The fame of the cures brought about by Helvétius reached the French court and led to the drug being tried out at the Hôtel-Dieu. These experiments met with great success and Louis XIV granted Helvétius the exclusive right of sale of the remedy in France. Later when several prominent figures, the Dauphin among them, had benefited from the drug themselves, the King consulted his doctor, Antoine d'Aquin, and his confessor, P. La Chaise, and had their intermediary negotiate the purchase of the remedy's secret with Helvétius which he acquired for one thousand louis d'or and made public. Grenier took legal action against the rights of Helvétius to this sum, but the Châtelet of Paris upheld these rights. From this time the Brazilian root was used as an expectorant for catarrh, whooping cough and especially as an emetic or gastric upsets and haemoptysis.

Medicines originating from the animal kingdom which, until the 15th century were few in number, multiplied in the 16th century and were at the height of their popularity at the beginning of the 17th century. In 1608 Jean de Renou, Henri IV's doctor, wrote: "We make use of several animals, like for example cantharides, wood-lice, small worms, lizards, ants, vipers, scorpions, frogs, crayfish, leeches and some small birds. As far as their different parts are concerned, our doctors are convinced that they are endowed with several admiral virtues, and among these we may count the skull or the head of a dead man not yet buried; the bone in a stag's heart; the brain of sparrows and hares; the teeth of elephant and wild boar; frogs' heart; fox's lung; billy-goat liver; the guts of a wolf; the genitals of a beaver and a cock; pig's bladder; a stag's genital member; the skin and slough of a serpent."

"Ditto, human fat and that of pigs, geese, ewes, ducks, badgers, rabbits, goats, eels and serpents; the marrow of stag, calf and billy-goat; human blood and that of pigeon and billy-goat. In addition, all kinds of milk and related products like butter, whey and cheese; the horns of stag, deer and unicorn; the nails and feet of elk, goat and buffalo; the head of oysters and the pearls inside them and the shells of several fish.

"Finally, since the excrement of the aforementioned animals has also special virtues, it is not unbecoming for the pharmacist to keep it in his shop, particularly the droppings of dog, goat, stork, peacock, pigeon, musk deer, civet cat and the hair of certain animals."

The *mummy* in its true form "being nothing more than the dried skin of dead bodies" enjoyed a particular vogue. After being collected in the ancient tombs of Egypt, resembling as it did "a certain sweet-smelling liquid with the consistency of honey," it began to be sought not in the tombs of the great but in those of poor devils who had died "in misery or from plague." This kind of mummy was worthless and apothecaries began to make their own, both in liquid and dry form.

Among the medicines from the mineral kingdom, precious stones, those made from gold and medicinal clays are of particular importance. "The work of nature," wrote Jean de Renou, "has divinely invested every precious stone with some admirable virtue which obliges kings and princes to strew their crowns, jewels, etc. so that they may benefit from their spells, in order to heal several illnesses and keep their health." The doctor, therefore, only confirms an ancient tradition. The belief in the many therapeutic virtues of

---

Vipers and stag-tears number among the most effective remedies of the 16th century. Joannes de Cuba, *Ortus sanitatis. De herbis et plantis...* J. Grüninger (after 1500).

precious stones was widespread, and Jean de Renou is scathing in his criticism when he remarks on lapis-lazuli: "Once it is worn, not only does it improve the sight, lightens the heart but after being washed and prepared in the proper manner, purges the melancholy humour without risk. If I were superstitious, I would believe with several other writers that it makes the wearer agreeable, rich and lucky but, all the same, I don't believe it."

Apothecaries also possess a stock of fine pearls for they "are great tonics and warm the heart. For this reason, alchemists make a certain liqueur they call liqueur of pearls by means of which they promise miraculous cares for several diseases while, in most cases, they are nothing but smoke, vanity and charlatanism. A certain barber I used to know in this city of Paris, who was called by a sick man to apply two leeches, had the cheek to ask six gold crowns for his trouble with the excuse that he had fed the two leeches with nothing but the liqueur of pearls for a whole month."

Drinkable gold, recommended by alchemists, was still taken to be a definite cure for leprosy at the end of the 16th century. A man who fed himself on gold was supposed to be immortal. To administer the precious metal, the easiest solution was to cook a capon stuffed with gold coins; the stock restored vigour to the exhausted.

In "Le Médecin malgré lui" Molière has Sganarelle say: "Look, here is a piece of cheese which you must take.

Perrin: Cheese, sir!

Sgnanarelle: Yes. It's a special cheese containing gold, coral, pearls and many other precious ingredients."

Sigillated clay which, in theory, came from the island of Lemmos, could only be collected once a year and, could not, under pain of death, be transported from the country over which the Grand Turk reigned. It was in fact found most frequently around Blois and Saumur. In the 16th and 17th centuries it was used as a desiccative, fortifier, hemostatic and astringent. In the 20th century clay still has its followers.

Antimony and mercury, two metallic medicines, were of particular importance in the eyes of Renaissance man. The former is connected with the legend of Basil Valentin stumbling on the therapeutic properties for the body in the course of his research on the philosopher's stone. This monk, who lived in a monastery in Erfurt in the second half of the 15th century, allegedly threw some fragments of antimony, which he had been using to activate combustion in his alchemist work, into a pig trough. He discovered that this was a drastic purgative for the pigs which grew fatter and more vigorous. He then got the idea to try it out on his friars in the monastery. All fell sick, some died, hence the name antimony, i.e. "against monks." Unfortunately, this etymology is greatly questioned and the word "antimony" is most probably derived from the Arab athmoud, which became antimonium n Low Latin. This medicine was soon to have more advocates than Valentin: Paracelsus and the spagyric doctors, Louis de Launay, Bernard Palissy's friend, and notably Charles de Lorme, the son of a professor at Montpellier University and himself doctor to Gaston d'Orléans and then Louis XIII. Charles de Lorme, intendant of the mineral waters of France, brought the Bourbon waters into fashion and, it is said, managed to draw on a part of the profits of the apothecaries and surgeons to whom he sent his clients. This doctor became an enthusiastic advocate of antimony, a sovereign remedy for most diseases. He advised preparing it and mixing it with an equal portion of saltpeter and powdered tartar of Montpellier. Antimony was also administered in a pill-form called "perpetual pills." These metallic pills that the sick had to take as a purgative and which acted mechanically by making the intestine contract and chemically due to the slight layer of antimony oxide which coated them, were vomited virtually intact and so were used indefinitely and were passed on as heirlooms. Whoever wanted to treat himself with antimony could also use a goblet made of this metal and keep some white wine in it. The antimony oxide thus formed was dissolved in the wine to give an emetic and a purgative.

The critics of antimony were no less zealous than its advocates, and for more than a hundred years there was a war between them. On two occasions, in 1566 and 1615 the Faculty of Paris declared antimony to be a poison and banned its sale by apothecaries. The hostilities which had begun in 1566 with J. Grévin's attack in *Discours sur les vertus et facultez de l'Antimoine...* (Discourse on the Powers and Properties of Antimony) and Launay's reply, broke out again around 1630 and for thirty years pamphlets, judgements and insults were exchanged. In 1658 Louis XIV, sick in Calais, took antimony prescribed by an Abbeville doctor called Du Saulsoy and found it effective. Finally, on 10th April, 1666 a judgement by the Parliament of Paris

BALNEVM PLVMMERS. 299

The baths of Plombières in the 16th century from the work *De Balneis*, Venice, Junta, 1553.

reestablished the medicinal metal and permitted "all doctors of the Faculty to use the aforementioned emetic wine to cure diseases, to write about on and it debate."

Mercury did not meet with such resistance and soon enabled the spread of syphilis to be energetically countered. Ancient writers had already used it as a medicine to cure skin diseases and the first signs of syphilis were cutaneous. The metal, once mixed with pig fat and added to sulphur, myrrh and incense... made the fortune of numerous durg merchants who claimed to be the only ones who knew the real treatment and sold their mixtures expensively. They were said to be real alchemists who had resolved the transmutation of metals with that of mercury into gold.

If the succes of mercury made the fortune of numerous charlatans, the triumph of antimony's advocates was also that of apothecaries. For over a century there had been a running battle in France between doctors, surgeons and apothecaries. In 1532 the doctor Symphorien Champier criticized in his *Myrouel des Apothicaires et Pharmacopoles* these three bodies, but particularly the apothecaries who "often abuses and counterfeit medicine." In his *Déclaration des abus et tromperies que font les Apoticaires*, (Declaration on the abuses and tricks used by Apothecaries), the doctor Sébastien Collin showed in 1533 apothecaries cheating their customers by loading weights, falsifying medicines, fleecing the sick...A certain Pierre Braillier, a Lyon apothecary, retaliated in 1557 with his *Déclaration des abus et ignorances des Médecins*. (Declaration on the abuses and ignorance of Doctors). The doctors replied and the apothecaries reposted. After a certain calm the struggle continued in a different form in the 17th century. Disdaining the apothecaries, doctors addressed themselves directly to their patients, taught them how to be economic and effective how to prepare some medicines themselves. In 1623 appeared *Le Médecin charitable* (The Charitable Doctor) by Philibert Guybert, doctor regent of the Faculty of Paris. The work, which cost little, was a great success and new editions rapidly followed one another and were enriched in 1625 with numerous details on pharmaceutical operations. On 28th October 1631 Gui Patin wrote to his friend Falconet: "The apothecaries are in a rage about *Le Médecin charitable* and its adherents who have medicines prepared cheaply at home."

Yet it would be a mistake to imagine that apothecaries were all reduced to selling poisons despite the restrictions as was the case of the apothecary visited by the unfortunate Romeo:

"Sharp misery had worn him to the bones
And in his needy shop a tortoise hung,
An alligator stuff'd and other skins
Of ill-shap'd fishes; and about his shelves
A beggarly account of empty boxes,
Green earthen pots, bladders and musty seeds,
Remnants of packthread, and old cakes of roses,
Were thinly scattered, to make up a show..."

At the same time, all apothecaries were not rich merchants well installed in the best districts with the ideal dispensary described by Jean de Renou in his *Institutiones pharmaceuticarum* in 1608. If they already counted among the prominent city dwellers of the 16th century, some of their clients still took them to be spicers. They certainly came to the said of the sick, but in a junior capacity. Proud statutes like those of Besançon stipulate that they will have the task of "seeing, visiting and consoling their patients night and day to give them the heart, spirit and courage to recover." They were, in particular, to issue the medicines ordered by the doctor and administer the famous enema so dear to Molière.

The important thing, it would seem, is the fact that the European pharmaco poeia was enriched by medicines imported from Africa, Asia or America and that an interest was taken in new theories. Gardens of simples were laid out in Padua (1545), Pisa (1547), Leyden and Heidelberg (1577), Paris (Le « Jardin » of Nicolas Houel, 1578), Montpellier (1598), etc. and chemical medicine began to be taken seriously. At the same time, the exportation of European diseases and the use of remedies from distant lands did not result in a better knowledge of exotic medicines. Arab pharmaceutical art was certainly less known than was the case in the 13th century, even if India and China revealed some of their secrets and if the conquerors of the New World wonder at several Indian practices.

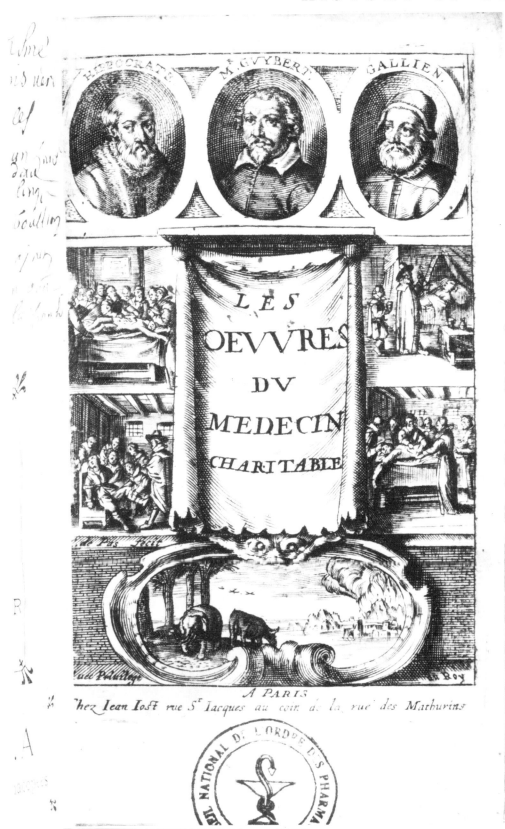

Frontispiece of *Oeuvres charitables de Philibert Guybert.* Paris, Jean Jost, 1629. In-12. Library of the National Order of Pharmacists.

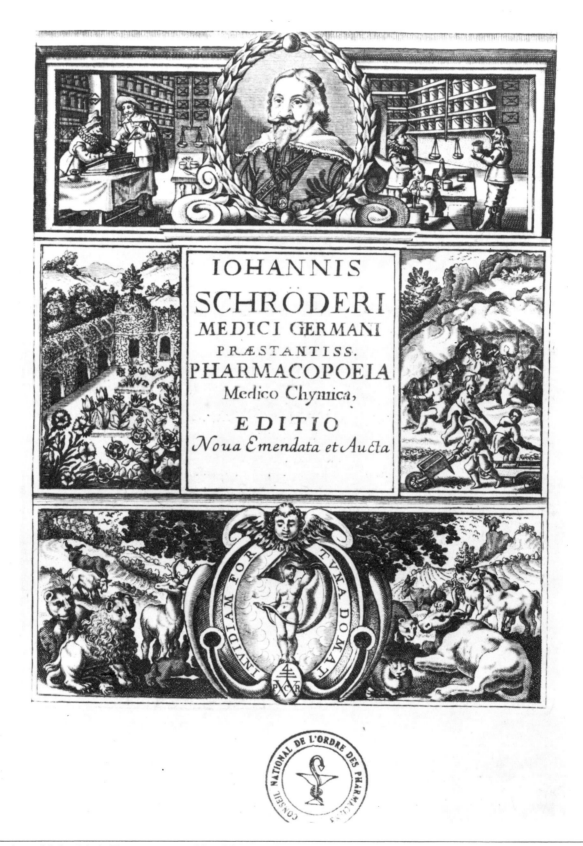

Frontispiece of Schroëder's *Pharmacopœia*. 4th edition, published by Pierre´Rigeaud, Lyon in 1656. Library of the National Order of Pharmacists.

THE CLASSICAL REVOLUTION 17th-18th CENTURIES

With the 17th century begins the "modern" world in which science provides a new conception of man and his place in the universe. The methods of reasoning and observation which were established were perfected and deepened but hardly changed until our own time. In setting down the universal law of gravity, Newton not only assured the final triumph of Copernicus, Kepler and Galileo but paradoxically consolidated man's position. No longer is he at the centre of the universe and the object of all divine preoccupations, but the earth is only one small planet in the immensity of the universe. Yet, in this new scheme of things, man acquired new responsibilites and, while Europeans were invading the Americas and making themselves feared in Africa, India and Japan and respected in China, the European spirit swelled with an excessive pride from which it still suffers.

Michel Servet was the frist to state that the walls of the heart are not perforated and Vesale only admitted it afterwards. André Césalpin used the word circulation for the first time in 1569 and more than another fifty years had to pass for William Harvey to formulate and demonstrate how circulation worked. The parallel discovery of lymphatic vessels by Aselli shed new light on physiology. The 17th century saw the birth of histology thanks to the microscope and Antoon van Leeuwenhoek observed red blood globules and discovered bacteria and protozoa. He confirmed the François Redi's experiments showing the impossibility of spontaneous generation. It was for the farmer general Antoine-Laurent Lavoisier to explain how the respiratory system really worked (1777), even though doctors and chemists had for a century established that air was necessary for respiration and combustion to take place.

The universal mechanism of Descartes: "I recognise no difference between machines made by workmen and the different bodies constructed by nature alone" led to the theory of animal-machines and the comparison of the human body with that of an automaton. During more than two centuries different medico-philosophical systems inspired by mechanics, physics, chemistry, mathematics, etc. and based on the discoveries made by European scholars tried to explain physiological and pathological phenomena without regard for external contingencies. Spiritualists like J.-B. van Helmont, Sylvius, Sanctorius, Borelli, Hoffmann, Stahl, Haller or materialists like La Mettrie, all were different doctrinarians who opposed each other violently and tore each other apart, but all proposed a certain idea of the man-machine. The mistrust of systems was slow to appear.

The discoveries made in the medical and pharmaceutical domain in the 17th and 18th centuries number among the greatest, the real men of science being numerous at that time, and it is unfair to see it as a period when the king was purged, bled and tortured continuously by his doctors, the poor hospital patients lying six in a bed, the privileged treated with oil of puppies, pastes prepared from spiders, theria and quack medicines, and all the sick subjected to the law of the pointed hats. From the beginnings of Greek comedy to *Knock,* doctors and the preparers of medicines have hardly been treated kindly by the theatre ; memorialists, writers of letters, novelists and philosophers have all been sceptical about the art of healing, and in this the 17th century occupies a place of his own.

There were more reasons for this scepticism than the particular mediocrity of medical practice, the most important being the growing middle class and the increasing worries of everyday life for the "honest man". To protect him, divine intervention is not neglected, but the doctor and the apothecary are needed. There are many of them now, lay people and bourgeois and the man who can pay is assured of being treated according to his social position. Their skill was no more doubted than it was at any other time, but they quarrelled among themselves and the very confidence placed in their science led those who served it to be mocked if they did not agree with each other.

Doctors and apothecaries, therefore, became familiar and important figures for the public of writers, particularly playwrights. Unlike the so-called devout and like the marquises, the *précieuses* and the cuckolds, "they suffered in silence what was portrayed before them and they pretended to find the way they had been represented as entertaining as everybody else." Curiously enough Molière is less ferocious with apothecaries than he is with doctors. However, he disliked medicines and is supposed to have said shortly before his death: "Everything which doesn't enter the body, I approve of willingly, but remedies which must be taken frighten me. I don't need anything to make me lose what is left of my life." No doubt he thought, like Béralde, that rest is the best medicine: "When we let it, nature itself gently reestablishes the order it has not been keeping. But our anxiety and impatience spoil everything and the majority of men die from their remedies and not from their illnesses." In his *Malade imaginaire,* Molière mocks the discount the apothecaries grant on the bills of their clients, but that was standard practice and he only exaggerated the amount of the reduction.

Was it for himself or his family that Molière had many prescriptions prepared towards the end of his life? The inventory carried out after his death from the 13th to 20th March details a debt of 163 livres 14 sols to Frapin, the apothecary, and 20 livres 10 sols to Dupré, another apothecary. It also mentions "a syringe with its case," valued at 20 sols in the home of the deceased and two red bronze stills with two furnaces valued at 25 livres which must have been used to prepare distilled waters.

As we hear in the oath taken by the apprentice doctor in the final fling of the *Malade imaginaire :*
Praeses: De non jamais te servire
De remediis aucunis
Quam de ceux seulement doctae Facultatis
Maladus dût-il crevare
Et mori de suo malo?
Bachelierus: Juro

Frontispiece from Docror R. de Graaf's book on the clyster, published in 1668.

R:
De GRAAF *Med: Doct:*
de
Virorum organis Gene
rationi *inservientibus,*
de Clysteribus *et*
de usu Siphonis
in Anatomia.

A

LUGD BATAV.
et ROTEROD. Ex Officina HACKIANA 1668.

143

PRACTISING OF THE PROFESSION

At first, the profession was practised in the shop (the word "apothicairerie" was rarely used and that of pharmacy alone applied to the profession).

"The apothecary who wants to set up a dispensary should first select a town where he may practise his art honestly with some chance of success. Jean de Renou gives the following advice on the subject:

"Just as all parts of the earth are not equally suited to the growing of good simples, by the same token all places are not equally fitting for the setting up of pharmaceutical shops where the compositions made up may be kept, prepared and sold, for there are very few places where all this can be done at the same time. Thus the majority of those who set up shop select the best towns to sell their merchandise and sell it at the highest price, though I am not of those who make much of mere charlatans (who fleece people for some little remedy not worth taking about and put up their little huts, or shops if you will, in the fields, in small villages or in stinking holes...)"

"The same J. de Renou recommends the choosing of a "well-lighted and aired place in a clean street far away from cesspools and sewers."

"Dusseau thinks..." every apothecary should select a convenient and fitting place, i.e. well-aired with its back to the South and sheltered from wind, rain, dust, smoke and everything which spoils or corrupts all kinds of medicines."

"Furthermore, the dispensary should be situated in a busy street near fairgrounds, squares, markets and churches."

"The dispensaries were usually grouped together in the best quarters from the business point of view. In Poitiers "from the Marché-Vieil to the Pilori;" in Niort "at the Herberie not far from the markets;" in Châtellerault "the Rue Basse or the Joyeux crossroads;" in the old town area of Nancy Rue du Petit-Bourgeois, Grande-Rue, etc. and later in the new town at la Carrière, Rue Saint-Nicolas, Rue des Cordeliers, etc."

"In the 16th and 17th centuries at least, the shop was mostly open to the street and the apothecary worked before the eyes of the public. At night it is closed by two doors, one being raised and the other lowered horizontally and often used for exposing certain drugs to the public."

"As examples illustrating this, there is the engraving of Jost Amman, reproduced by Moluçon, which does not represent one of our dispensaries and the passage from Dusseau's *Enchirid* where the author deplores the fact that "the dispensaries or shops of the aforementioned apothecaries" are not "closed like those of the barbers and goldsmiths." There is also the drawing inspired by N. Houel, representing "the apothecary's shop of the house of Christian Charity" (with the front open...letting us see the interior) and the illustrations reproduced for the different editions of Jean de Renou's book. In the 1624 edition, for example, the frontispiece shows the wall separating the dispensary from the street, a wall decorated with two pots of flowers and inside, near an opening, an assistant makes powders from the drugs while the master is speaking to a customer."

"Though glass panes were well known at this time, it would appear that glass doors were only installed in the 18th century. In any case, they were used to close the Baratte dispensary of Besançon whose front is reproduced in the *Bulletin de la Société d'Histoire de la Pharmacie* and that of the *Jambu* in La Rochelle, reproduced by Soenen after the reconstruction by E. Couneau."

"Since the houses were not numbered, signs were indispensable for recognizing both dispensaries and all other shops. They were generally very typical and reproduced:

"*Real animals:* lion, stork, bear, titmouse, etc., and many pharmacies in Alsace have retained names of this kind. Sometimes the sign only gave a part of the animal. For example, Jean Boursette was apothecary-

---

Pharmacoea, 1694, from Nicolas Debrigode.

Next page : Bartholomew, the Englishman. *The Proprietor,* translation by Friar Jehan Corbichon, reviewed by Friar Pierre Ferjet. On the left, the sick-room with the doctor at the patient's bedside examining his urine. The dispensary is in the foreground with the apothecary weighing out a remedy. B.N. French ms, 218, fol. 111.

Hæc Pharmacopœia
ad usum
NICOLAI. DEBRIGODE
A. Theod. DESCAMPS
Scripta
ANNO. M.D.CCXXXXII

pilon

spatule

NATIONAL DE L'ORDRE

Des remedes de la douleur du chief
Chappitre

Le chief a dedans soy une
douleur que les plusiacns
appellent migrayne et
ceste douleur est moult griefue sloee
du constantinrao il est admie aupariet
que on fiere et hurte toussiours dedas

Ainsi comme de petites clochettes. Derechief seesiues a aucune ssfoz aucun dehors
petites bubettes et poingnes dont il en
yst une orde humeur semble annel et
reste ordure est une humeur rhneuse
qui bient dedans le chief insques au
cur par dehors et passe par les pertuys
de la poitrine qui la est. Derechief il

An apothecary's boy by Watteau.

spicer in the Grande-Rue Saint-Jacques in Paris at the sign of "The Stag's Horn;" "Then there were the *fantastic animals,* like the phoènix and salamander in Poitiers in the 16th century, for example. In Schlestadt the pharmacy *of the Unicorn* was set up about the year 1650;

"Next came the *fruits* used is pharmacy, like the lemon at Fontenay-le-Comte (1509), the pomegranate in Poitiers (16th century), etc.;

"*Utensils* used by apothecaries also figured, like the *golden mortar* (Poitiers 1590, 1681), Bressuire (1622, 1623), La Rochelle in the 17th century, etc.); the *silver motar* (Poitiers, 16th and 17th centuries); the *golden vase* (Poitiers, 1651). Laboratory equipment (mortar, retort, wash-bottles among others) was shown on a sign from Vailly (Somme) dating from the 18th century;

"*Pharmaceutical scenes* were to be seen, like that depicted on the old sign in the Grande-Rue of Nantes, representing on one side an apothecary preparing a purgative and on the other the patient bringing up this purgative. The pulverisation of drugs was often depicted;

"Also shown were *objects having no connection with pharmacy:* the *green cross* at Niort (1607); the *red hat* in Paris (around 1641); the *golden bell* for François Clérambourg's dispensary in Paris (1724) or *the shield of France, the reaper, the crown, the black pillar, the white cross, the helmet,* etc.

"A resolution of 17th October, 1662 obliged privileged Paris Apothecaries to put hangings, signs, escutcheons or other marks of their choice outside their shops to distinguish them from each other and from the apothecaries' shops of the city.

"Thus on 12th April, 1668 one of them, Ch. Gamard, apothecary to the Grand Prevost, was authorized to hang at the front of his shop blue tapestries with fleurs-de-lys, marking his status as royal apothecary. This became obligatory and was confirmed for the apothecaries of the Grand Provost by the letters of patent if 19th October, 1925. They "were charged to decorate their shops and establishments with tapestries designing fleurs-de-lys and the ordinary device of the provostship of our Hospital..."

"Before the appearance of the bulbs which were to come with the arrival of gas lighting, the apothecaries placed *tripods* in their shop-windows though grocers were forbidden to use them.

"The Lieutenant General de Chauny extended this restriction to glass jars. The grocers had to take down "within a week their tripods and remove from their windows stills, retorts and other attributes of pharmacy which had not the right to be exhibited there."

"Despite this restriction, some Parisian grocers continued to use these jars. Finally, the very typical exterior of Mathieu-François Geoffroy's dispensary, as it appeared to Lister in 1685, is worth mentioning: "It is," he said, "in the Rue Bourgtibourg. The entrance to the yard is by a carriage entrance with *recesses where large copper vases are to be found...*"

"Yet it is Jean de Renou who describes the typical arrangement of the premises. He says:

"The shop should be sufficiently big, spacious and high so that its top floors may hold all the plants he requires and which may best be stored here, the driest and airiest place in the house. In the lowest part, which is the cellar, many things are placed which demand a moist and humid atmosphere, for example black cassia, wine and suchlike things.

"Between the cellar and the attic of the aforesaid house, there should be several floors, at least one where apothecary and his family live, and immediately below this the pharmaceutical shop should be found, large, pleasant, square and bright, but without being over-exposed to the sun's rays in case too many of the apothecary's compositions and other simple medicines are dried, melted or heated or, even worse, at the mercy of the thirty-two winds which would be too much of a nuisance.

"Now, in this shop there should be two doors, one at the front opening on to the street and providing the entrance to the shop and the other at the back and through which one passes into a low kitchen adjoining the said shop where the good and well-advised apothecary will stay most of the time with his family to drink, eat or sleep so that he is always on the spot and can spy, by means of a little glass window set for this purpose in the common wall, on his apprentices and servants, to see if they are at their work, receiving customers amiably and scrupulously, distributing and selling his drugs and compositions.

Preparation of the theriak. Anonymous drawing from the 17th century. B.N. Engravings.

"Once again, in one of the corners of the aforementioned kitchen adjoining the fireplace, the pharmacist should keep a little pan in which he conserves his sugar, dragées and his solid confections. If the place is big enough, he should also have a little store and back-shop in which be puts away fruits, seeds and many other commodities and simples which should not be bought in large quantities, like almonds, rice, prunes, honey, several seeds, roots and wood. However, he will always remember to keep in his shop his compositions and the majority of the rarest and most precious simples he has and which he is in the habit of using, for example tamarind seeds, dried grapes, liquorice, common polypody, senna and the like."

"*Furniture* mainly consists of sets of *compartments, cupboards, show-cases, tables, chairs* and *lighting material.*

"Jean de Renou advises the *Sets of compartments* to be set up like this;

"So that his medicines may properly be arranged in the apothecary's shop, it should be equipped with several different shelves, most of which are equidistant from each other and made from planks nailed to big pieces of wood likewise fixed to the walls. Thus by having a variety of these, there will be room enough to keep all pharmaceutical vessels in their proper places, should they be big or small, made of wood, clay, glass or pewter, nor will he, at the same time, neglect to arrange them near at hand or at a greater distance depending on their frequent or occasional use."

"The same author allows for certain vases and sachets to be hung from the beams of the roof of the boutique.

"Such primitive installations in the shops of well-off apothecaries were completed by closed *cupboards,* sometimes called dressers. So in the inventory of David Heli of Poitiers in 1656 we find: "Three pairs of painted cupboards with key locks" valued at twelve livres.

"On the premises of the same Helie, we find two great monstrosities to be put in the shop and two small monstrosities in the shape of stepladders."

"These *monstrosities* were occasionally decorated or gilded and used for displaying boxes or vases.

"Rambaud also gives precise information concerning the seating arrangements. Behind the counters "is the straight bench or *"doussier"* on which the master sits to supervise his pupils and receive his clients. He has often a case near at hand which can be locked and where he keeps medicines. At his side "the gossiping chair" was found, intended as it was for doctors or friends of the family. Apart from this seat, in itself rare, no others are mentioned in the inventories. Clients did not tarry long in the shops since custom had it that medicines needing a long time to prepare were always delivered to the patient's home."

"*Tables,* of course, very greatly in size. Wecker wanted at least two wooden tables, one for sieving and the other to carry the different utensils and the "Antidoraire;" a marble table with its slab for crushing precious stones; a stone table for preparing plasters and cerates; two large tables or counters for making up preparations and setting the required material. Obviously these tables should, as far as possible, be provided with drawers.

"Tallow candles were normally used for *lighting.* In 1553 L. Simon had a table with candles and Lapesse had two candelabra in 1597.

"Certain dispensaries, especially those kept by monks and nuns, often had a definite artistic character (eg. the pharmacies of the hospitals of Burgundy studied by Baudot; the pharmacy of the Jesuits in Toulouse, etc.)

"The Feuillants dispensary in Paris has been enthusiastically described by many authors. It is "the most symmetrical and curious in the Kingdom," said Sauval. Caryatids carved in the wood support the carving of the cupboards and "on the doors of each cupboard there are bas-reliefs representing the miraculous cures of the New Testament."

"Certain apothecaries, however, decorate their shops with pictures, tapestries, etc. As early as the year 1522, we find in Robert Caillier's shop in Paris "a picture of Notre-Dame on wood, encased in glass." Gervais Honoré, who died in Paris on 24th June, 1530, possessed:

"A wooden carving of Notre-Dame with its spire of gilt lead in a wooden case on which two angels were painted, LX s.t.; a tapestry of the Passion of Our Lord and a small picture of Our Lady of Mercy;...two large tapestries representing several great figures of the 15th century.

Title page of a medical thesis published at Strasbourg in 1734 on the medicinal powers of petroleum (de Pechelbronn). Museum of Pechelbronn.

I. N. I.

HISTORIA
BALSAMI MINERA-
LIS ALSATICI SEV
PETROLEI
VALLIS SANCTI LAMPERTI

Germanice

Der Hanauische Erd-Balsam/Lam-
perslocher Oel-oder Bächel-Brunn/

QVAM

AVXILIANTE SVMMO ARCHIATRO

EX CONSENSV GRATIOSIS-
SIMÆ FACVLTATIS MEDICÆ
PRO LICENTIA

SVMMISQVE IN ARTE SALVTARI HONORIBVS
AC PRIVILEGIIS DOCTORALIBVS MORE MAIORVM
RITE OBTINENDIS

SISTIT

AVTOR

IOHANNES THEOPHILVS HOEFFEL
Woerthensis.

Ad d. 1. Octobr. Anno M DCC XXXIV. Horis locoque consuetis.

ARGENTORATI,
LITERIS Heredum JOHANNIS PASTORII.

"Finally, Lépinois has reproduced the inventory of the numerous "objects d'art" collected by Nicolas Houël, the learned artist. We find, in particular:

"An oil painting done on wood and without frame of the Raising of Lazarus valued at 72 livres; 'The Last Judgement,' a black and white brush painting, encased in wood with a glass cover valued at 72 livres; a landscape by Lucas, oil on wood with frame, valued at 4 livres 16 sols and a 'Last Judgement' by Micael Lange on paper, gilt-framed and worth 6 livres.

"Wecker points out that the apothecary needed a garden 'in order to find fresh herbs whose juices are frequently required, grow rare plants and choose a place there that gets plenty of sun to dry, blanch and prepare everything doctors require to be left in the sun." Rambaud has shown that the apothecaries of Poitiers were cultivating such gardens in the 16th century. Mathurin Dutertre, for example, rented one in 1568 and another in 1596."

The dried plants are conserved in wooden boxes which often had artistic decorations, while other drugs were kept in containers made from horn, pewter, tin, white cast iron lead, glass and especially clay: stoneware and earthenware pots first imported from Damascus, Italy or Spain and later made in France at Nevers, Rouen, Moustiers..., porcelaine pots at the end of the 18th century. Most of these post were:

"*Spouted drug jars,* 'for syrups, honeys and oils.' They were the perfect pharmacist's pot. Their forms and dimensions varied; 'they have only one handle on one side so that they may easily be taken in one hand and on the other a little spout for emptying out their contents. The hole at the top is wide, thus enabling them to be filled easily...' Apothecaries alone have the right to use them;

"*Bottles,* 'for distilled waters.' There were two models 'both of which had a flat bottom. One model had a spherical belly or one which was a slightly flattened sphere...the others with a flattened belly were provided with rings through which a string or strap was passed...;'

"*Jugs,* 'for syrups and distilled waters', particularly used in the great hospitals;

"*Ointment jars* 'for ointments, opiates, confections, electuaries, balms, etc.' They were so called 'because of their form;'

"*Jars* 'for pills and extracts,' similar in form to the ointment jars but smaller;

"*Theriac vases* and vases for the *larger galenicals.*

'These different containers frequently had inscriptions, sometimes drawings and the arms of noble families."

The equipment necessary for practising as an apothecary included mortars made from iron or bronze, but also in marble, agate, alabaster, copper, pewter, ivory, glass and wood...distilling apparatus, iron or wooden mallets, screens and seives, presses, funnels, bottles, pill jars...and, of course, scales and their weights.

The packaging of drugs remained extremely rudimentary, and it is Mr. Bouvet's opinion that the first specialists designed packages with better presentation and trans port in mind. He mentions the wooden boxes for Belloste' pills, pewter containers for the theriac, tin boxes for the tea of the Alps, paper packets for Sedlitz salt, earthenware pots for creams, glass bottles for the Queen of Hungary's water, etc. While handwritten labels remained in use in the shops to avoid mistakes, again it was the specialists who were the first to use engraved and often illustrated labels.

The most reputed medicines of the 17th and 18th centuries often seem to be out of step with be undeniable progress made by chemistry and pharmacology and the considerable growth of the apothecary's profession. If we were not afraid of giving a too cursory and, therefore, false idea of this evolution, it would be easy to distinguish two movements, one scholarly, whereby medical therapeutics becomes more and more of a science, and the other popular, in which some of the greatest prejudices of the Middle Ages and the Renaissance not only continue, but are taken more seriously. At the same time, this second tendency was perhaps not as harmful as it was in the 19th century. It bestowed stability on the materia medica which, incidentally, conformed to traditions as old as antiquity and permitted the theories, however ingenuous, of chemists, doctors and pharmacologists to be carefully tested and widely applied once the first enthusiasm had passed. In this way many excesses due to the usual belief in the universal properties of the new medicine were avoided.

The clyster, engraving by Abraham Bosse (1602-1676), B.N. Engravings.

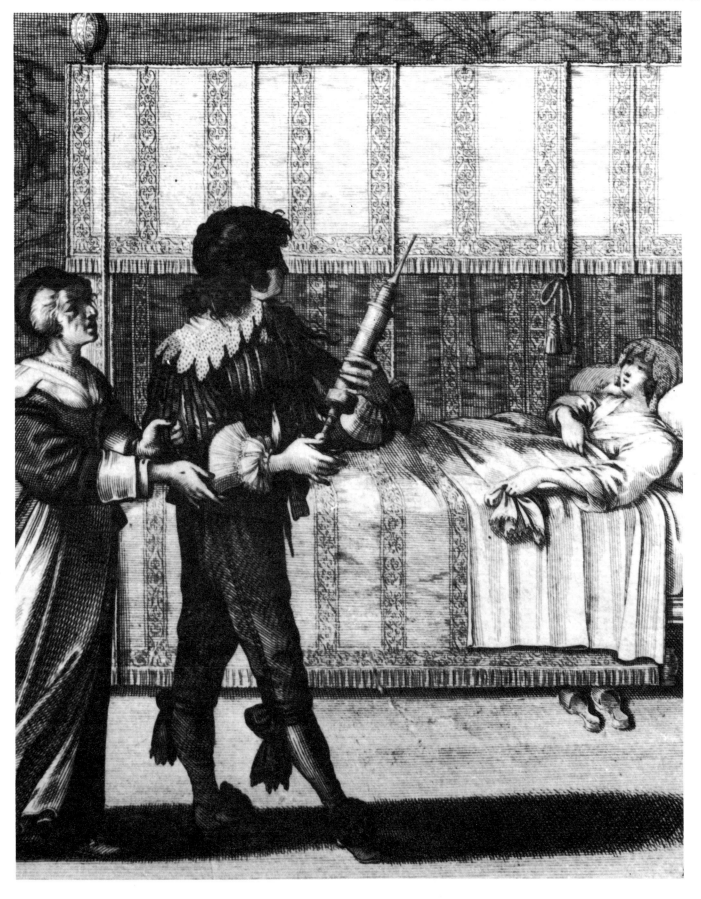

Apothecaries continued to retail, as pharmacists were to do in the 19th century numerous indigenous plants whose virtues, better-known perhaps at that time, had been esteemed from the Middle Ages. However, the stock of exotic plants rapidly increased thanks to navigators who had been crossing the seas from the 16th century.

To guaiacum, tolu balsam, sarsaparilla, vanilla, copaiba balsam, cardamom, chinaroot or cherry laurel was added guttapercha, a sample of which was brought back from China in 1603 by the Dutch admiral Van Neck. Opium-based medicines became more familiar thanks to the propaganda Sydenham spread in their favour, and for a short time opium was considered a kind of panacea. Tobacco, coffee, tea and cocoa gradually became familiar in Europe and were often accused of having ill effects on the organism.

The importation of Cinchona into the old continent started a veritable revolution in the history of medicine. Juan del Vego, doctor to the Spanish governor of Peru, had cured the latter's wife of tertiary ague with this remedy. He brought the new medicine to Spain in 1640 and it spread rapidly. The English doctor Talbot popularized it in France around 1678. Great disputes immediately broke out throughout Europe: on the one hand, the galenists violently opposed this irrational drug while, on the other, the devoted advocates of Cinchona used it as a powder, macerated in wine and then in pill form. The healing of numerous sick, the Duke of Burgundy and the Duke of Anjou in particular, enabled the remedy's advocates to triumph, but it was a hard fought battle with a religious quarrel added to the medical one, since the Jesuits imported large quantities of Cinchona from South America and made considerable profits.

About 1687 Adrien Helvétius, the Dutch doctor, popularized the use of ipecacuanha in France. The struggles concerning ipecacuanha root were much less violent in nature than those caused by Cinchona, yet the new remedy was of almost equal interest. In curing the Dauphin of dysentery with the aid of ipecacuanha, he was on his way to earning a quick fortune.

In the 18th century some new exotic plants, particulartly quassia, were introduced to therapeutics, but the interest was really focused on the physiological properties of indigenous plants. Darwin (1780) recommended digitalis, used in the 17th century against scrofula, for the treatment of dropsy. Henbane, colchicum, valerian and arnica are found numerous therapeutic uses.

Among the mineral medicines, gold, precious stones and pearls continued to be favoured by the public. Doctor Valot prescribed tablets made from gold and pearls for Louis XIV. In the 18th century the *golden drops of General de La Motte* were in great fashion like many other medicinal waters having a gold base. In 1616 Henry Wicker discovered magnesium sulphate in Epsom water. Nine years later, Glauber made his preparation of soda sulphate, *sal admirabile,* and about 1630 Jean Beguin popularized the use of calomel and Glaser, the apothecary, was preparing fused silver nitrate, saltpetre or *sal prunella* (fused potassium sulphate) and *antifebrile salt* or *Rochelle salts of Glaser* (impure potassium sulphate).

Alchemical pharmacy, therefore, triumphed. As Moyse Charas wrote: "Chemical pharmacy, like the galenical, acknowledges the legitimacy of animals, vegetables and minerals as material for preparing medicines. However, while galenical pharmacy eliminates by normal means those parts it finds negative or useless and is content to hull, wash, infuse, cook, crush or mix as required those elements if finds superior, chemical pharmacy goes much further into the heart of natural bodies to isolate, by artificial means, the parts of which they are composed separating them from impurities imperceptible to the senses."

The antimony dispute, in particular, illustrates the opposition between apothecaries and doctors. Despite the ban on the sale of antimony (1615), apothecaries aided and abetted by some doctors continued to supply it. They triumphed in the end after an exchange of pamphlets, decrees and insults which lasted for over thirty years. Their enemies, especially Guy Patin, managed to ban practically all medicines, imagining that all diseases could be cured with the syringe and lancet, cassia, senna, rose syrup and peach tree flowers. In 1623 Philibert Guybert, doctor regent, published *The Charitable Doctor, teaching how remedies for all sorts of diseases could be prepared at home easily and cheaply...,* a book costing "one or two sols" which met with considerable success. He advised that the raw materials for the remedies should be purchased "from spicers and drug-sellers, since they have been selected by the doctor while roots, herbs, seeds, flowers, etc. can be bought from herbalists at the market pole, Maubert Square or elsewhere, all inexpensively."

This advice was followed and Guy Patin wrote to his friend Falconet (1631): "The apothecaries are in a mad rage at *The Charitable Doctor* and its advocates who have medicines prepared at home and cheaply."

Besides, Guy Patin had also published a supplement to Guybert's book *Le Premier Traicté de l'apothicairerie du médecin charitable,* a book of popular pharmacy in 1625. Two trials followed which the apothecaries lost. On 14th March, 1647 the doctor of Montigny presented a thesis inspired by Guy Patin and which turned out to be a long diatribe against apothecaries. Guy Patin cried victory, writing: "We have ruined the apothecaries of Paris...They are only needed by foreigners in furnished rooms and apart from that, I can honestly tell you that they should take no apprentices for their trade is so bad that nobody wants to bother with them today."

All the same, Dusausoy, the empiricist doctor of Abbeville, had cured Louis XIV of scarlet fever at Calais thanks to emetic wine, and many doctors went over to the antimony side. On 29th March, 1666 the Faculty of Paris admitted emetic wine "to the purgative remedies" and twelve days later permitted "all doctors of the Faculty to use the said emetic for healing the sick and write and debate on the subject." Guy Patin bitterly declared: "These gentlemen say that poison is not a poison in the hands of a good doctor. They go against their own experience, for the majority of them have killed their wife, children or friends. In any case, they speak well of a drug which they wouldn't take themselves, so as to favour apothecaries... When the wind begins to change, all these champions of antimony will disappear like the smoke from their furnaces." The wind did not change, but *The Charitable Doctor* and other works which followed had dealt a serious blow to the apothecary's profession nevertheless. If, in the 18th century, new chemical products like alum, which Helvétius popularized, kermes or *Carthusian Powder,* magnesia (discovered in 1770 by Thomas Henry, a Manchester apothecary), limewater (used by Marat to treat tuberculosis), arsenic (prepared as a solution by Thomas Fowler), potassium chlorate discovered by Berthollet in 1787...offer serious guarantees, we may comprehend Guy Patin's antipathy to *Arabian trifles,* among which he included bezoar, tonic waters, theriac and mithridate, confection of hyacinth or alkermes, powdered vipers, etc.

In fact, it was in the first half of the 17th century when a craze for strange medicines from the animal kingdom profited, but in 1690 Lémery was still writing about the preparation of mummies or the virtues of human excrement which was "digestive, resolvent, soothing, good for anthrax and for bringing the bubos of the plague to suppuration point and for inflammation of the throat. Some advise it to be swallowed dry, in powder form for swelling of the throat, epilepsy and recurrent fever. Its Latin name is *oletum vel stercus humanum.* The dose varies from a scruple to a dram."

Cod-liver oil made its appearance at the end of the 18th century (1782) and was to be unanimously accepted at the end of the following century.

Bezoar—calcareous concretions found in the head or stomach of various animals, in particular a type of billy-goat living in the East—was reputed to be "the surest and most effective antidote for all sorts of poisons and contagious diseases," but Ambroise Paré partly demolished this reputation. However, in 1741, Savary

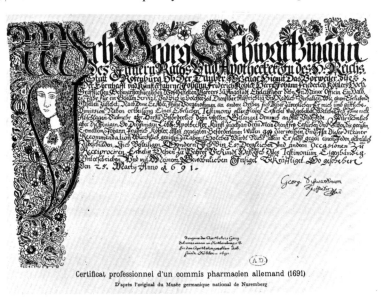

Certificat professionnel d'un commis pharmacien allemand (1691)
D'après l'original du Musée germanique national de Nuremberg

Professional certificate of a German assistant apothecary, 1691. Library of Decorative Arts.

153

observed in his *Dictionnaire du Commerce:* "Whenever these bezoars arrive from Amsterdam, they are bought for up to three or four hundred livres each and even more. They are not purchased by merchants to be commercialised later, but by the wealthiest bourgeois either as prospective presents for important persons or for keeping in their own families as a most valuable treasure to be handed down to their children."

The tear of a stag, a unicorn's horn and serpent's tongue continued to be esteemed, but what other remedy could win more public confidence than the theriac? This electuary, which was so solemnly made up in all the great cities of Europe until the Revolution, enjoyed universal respect.

If, before Scheele, organic acid salts (ammonium acetate discovered in 1616 by Doctor Minderer, sodium and potassium tartrate which Seignette the apothecary isolated in 1672, and potassium borotartrate or flux of Lassonne [1755], etc.) figured greatly among the organic medicines, thymol was discovered in 1719 by Newmann. Scheele was to make known glycerine, citric acid, tartaric acid...

Yet, from the 18th century on, the real forerunner which announced the advent of modern pharmacy was the existence of many *specialities,* then called secret remedies and whose history has been under taken by Mr. Bouvet. The list of them would be almost interminable. Among the most famous, we may mention Eau de Cologne (around 1650), "Eau de Rabel (aromatic sulphuric acid) (around 1678), "Baume tranquille" (around 1680), Belloste's pills (around 1681), Garrus elixir (before 1719), the Regent's cream (1767), etc. The *secret* remedies led to a whole new legislation and literature. They were rarely the work of apothecaries although Elie Seignette was given a patent for his *Rochelle salts* (1673), Lémery announced his *"huile de talc"* (1680), Clérambourg manufactured his *seeds of life* and Baumé launched his *antivenereal syrup.* It was only accidental if apothecaries themselves kept stores of secret remedies. Once the plague and leprosy had stopped raging in Renaissance Europe, other contagious diseases like exanthematous typhus, the English fever (malaria) and especially syphilis took their place. After trying theriac, the mithridate and prayers requesting the intervention of the saints, the therapeutics of syphilis entered a definitive phase with the introduction of mercury. Still in the 18th century it was the most vital element in numerous remedies intended for "the poor victims of the pox." We may mention, for example, the fortifying cakes made from mercury by Mr. Bru (1789), the chocolates, dragées, tablets, antivenereal ratafias and the "antivenereal underpants" of Lefebvre of Saint-Ildefont. Thanks to such precious medicines, the errant husband could, for example, "take his chocolate in the presence of his wife without her suspecting any mystery; she may even take it herself without for a moment thinking she was drinking an antivenereal, and by such innocent means peace and harmony prevailed in the home."

The history of antivenereal *"eau fondante"* of Guilbert de Préval is perhaps the most significant. Guilbert de Préval, "doctor regent and professor of matiera medica at the Faculty of medicine at the university of Paris, consultant doctor and correspondent to His Majesty the King of Denmark," having made up an antisyphytic *eau fondante* sold it at the price of one gold louis a flask without first obtaining the Faculty's permission. He even went as far as demonstrating the efficacity of his water in 1771 before the Duke of Chartres and the Prince of Condé...and the experiment, "which even the least sensitive person would not bear hearing about, never mind seeing," was a success.

The Faculty got angry. Trials made on the order of the lieutenant general of police were thwarted!

Préval's battle with the Faculty began and was to continue for more than five years. Despite the support of Rétif de la Bretonne and seventeen lawyers, Préval finally had to admit defeat. On his death, his friend Rétif wrote as an epitatph (in *Nuits de Paris*): "Here lies Doctor Guilbert de Préval who cured sixty thousand people between 1777 and 1788."

As Rétif de la Bretonne ironically remarked, Guilbert's water had the drawback of being given before and not after the disease had made its appearance. Now it is through illness that we appreciate health: "...if you allow the disease to became established...if you wait until a good pleurisy... a good, putrid fever or a good syphilis have taken a patient do death's door, what glory may be found in restoring him to health as if taking him by the hand! What delight the doctor takes in seeing a man so proud a week before, stretched out on a bed, a pale heap of skin and bone! Or this imperious beauty with a thousand despised conquests in her train!"

All politicians agree that a state cannot survive without finances. The doctor is like a state whose members are like lice, bugs and fleas; the difference being, however, that these animalcules suck the blood of the healthy, while doctors live off the sick; medicine is a necessary state... But would this great necessity not be abandoned if it did not feed...those who practise it? What could be more disagreeable good salaries being what they are, than cutting short or preventing diseases!"

Mineral waters were only to be seen in dispensaries in the second part of the 17th century. Some found that water, even taken at the source, had no effect. "We depend more," wrote Diderot, "on the voyage than the remedy," and according to Voltaire: "Going to take the waters has been invented by women bored at home." Yet, Louis XV was to organize the sale of mineral waters and granted Alleaume and Delage in Paris exclusive rights for the transport and sale of French and Foreign mineral waters. They had to pay the sum of 40,000 livres to the Treasury every year, which is quite a good indication of the extent to which the use of mineral waters in the home had developed. In France there were many dispensaries with stocks of waters from Sainte-Reine, Forges, Vals, Plombières, Vichy, Spa...

As in the 16th century, the apothecary not only gave out medicines from the dispensary, often indulging in numerous prohibited quid pro quos, but also went to the patient's bedside and the *Déclaration royale* of 15th May, 1724 even recognized this right to visit in the absence of a doctor. This, however, was to give rise to rivalries since the principal duty of the apothecary towards the patient was the administering of clysters. This operation cost at least fifteen sous and was a delicate one: "The patient should remove any garment that gets in the way. He will turn over on his right side, bend forward his leg and do what he is told without shame or false prudery. The person carrying out this operation should be a skilful tactician and never approach the spot as if mounting an attack, but instead should be more of an infantryman who stealthily advances, pushing aside or treading down the grass or undergrowth that gets in the way, then stop, look around and after making out the enemy, take aim and fire. Thus, he will be both skilful and circumspect in making no movement without first having found the target. Then, kneeling down carefully and taking the instrument in his left hand without the silghtest haste or precipitation, he will take down *amoroso* the force pump and push smoothly and discreetly, *pianissimo*." The possibility of practising as a doctor and apothecary at the same time was permitted when the same person had both diplomas, and such cases were quite common.

While doctors were forbidden to prepare medicines themselves, special cases apart, they did have the right, like everybody else, to prepare patent medicines, eg. Helvétius and his *Remedy* (ipecacuanta), Garrus and his *elixir*, Bellet and his *syrup of mercury*, Marat and his *artificial water for lung disease*, etc. As in the past, they were forbidden to associate with apothecaries. The surgeons, who were in an awkward situation, issued drugs everywhere and were constantly involved in legal battles with the apothecaries. The same applied to spicers, and it was not until the College of Pharmacy was founded by the declaration of April 1777 that their attributes were clearly defined.

"The spicers will continue to enjoy the right to sell simple drugs wholesale though only at the trade and not at the medicinal weight. Nevertheless, they may retail manna, cassia, rhubarb and senna (at the medicinal weight) as well as woods and roots all in their natural state without being prepared, altered or compounded, punishable by a 500 livres fine for first offenders and harsher measures for habitual ones."

"We forbid the spicers and any other person to make or sell any salts, compounds or preparations intended to be taken by the human body in the form of medicine, punishable by a 500 livres fine or more as the case may be."

This Declaration of April 1777 was limited in its effect to Paris and its immediate surroundings. In Pontoise, for example, the guild of apothecaries continued to legitimately confer the title of apothecary up until the beginning of the 19th century, and the fight against the spicers went on in Pointoise itself, Etampes and Versailles without the text of this Declaration being heeded.

Charlatans, who were particularly numerous in the 17th century, were to be found in the Pont-Neuf district of Paris, selling balms, ointments, rosaries, oils and marvellous waters. Tabarin sold an ointment for burns. Then the merchants of orvietan took over. Molière's opératear sings (*L'Amour médecin*):

"The gold of every country bound by the sea
Could never buy this vital secret
With a rare excellence my remedy cures
More ills than one could count in a year:
Gall, bad temper, ringworm, fever,
The plague, gout, pox, prolapse,
Measles, O great is the power of orvietan."

This nostrum, orvietan, an electuary analogous to theriac, but only found at the beginning of the 17th century, was supposedly invented at the end of the preceding century by Lupi from Orvieto, a town in Tuscany. It figures in the pharmacopoeias of 1665 and 1818 alone and was in great fashion in the reign of Louis XIV thanks to the Contugi family. Depending on the author, its formula varies between nine and fifty-four compounds, but theriac appears in every preparation. In the 18th century the apothecaries also prepared orvietan and, in so doing, tried to compete with the charlatans.

Louis XV and then Louis XVI introduced methodical regulations governing the sale of secret remedies and managed, to a certain extent, to limit the success of itinerant drug merchants. Royal declarations and various regulations did not get the same results with the religious orders. Not only did the latter possess large dispensaries, but they also sold important specialities, like the *balm water of the barefooted Carmelites, baume tranquille of Father Aignan, Carthusian powder, red water of the Jacobins, lavender water of the Benedictine nuns of Trainsnel,* etc.

The Bordeaux apothecaries wrote in 1762: "There are a dozen pharmacy shops in the monasteries which do virtually everything without respecting any restriction set down to this effect, either by the church or by the King and his parliament...; so the only wages left to the master apothecaries for their efforts and care for the sick is the privilege of paying the city taxes and rates and dying of hunger."

Le Curieux, by Baudoin. B.N.

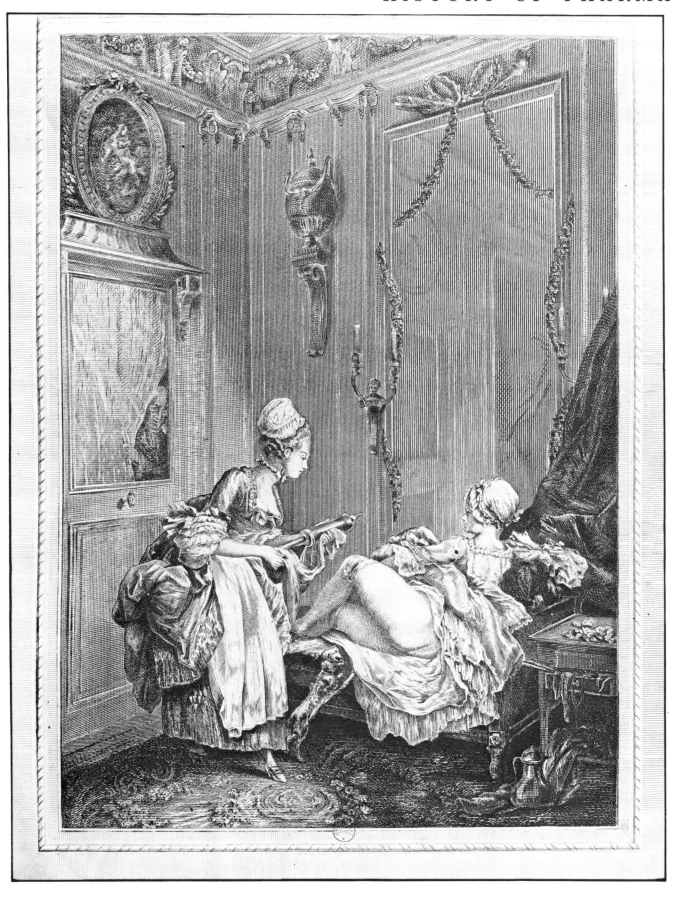

The scientific application of cupping glasses.

Man's first intravenous injection. Johannes Elshal, Clysmatica nova, 17 th century. B.N.

The apothecary (drawing by Engerbascht, 1735, collection Bouvet).

Next : Still for herbs distillation, 19th century, collection Ducommun, Genève.

III

MODERN TIMES

IMPACTS ON TWO
FATEFUL CENTURIES

XIX-XX Pharmacy in the 19th century was not merely an extension of the 18th. It was rather a series of thrusts into the 20th century. Each new thrust was a breakthrough that changed pharmacy fundamentally. And most of the time it was not even pharmacists who caused the changes—situations somewhat similar to those of the present time. Today, after more than 7000 years of consecutive change and progress, 20th century pharmacy again finds itself at the crossroads of its new existence. It must in our 20th century make decisions that will make pharmacy stronger, or else destroy the profession beyond recognition within the 21st century.

LAVOISIER

What exactly were some of the crises that affected pharmacy in the 19th century? One was the phlogiston theory, whose proponents were still active even though their main spokesman—Georg Ernst Stahl—had died in 1734. Phlogiston, meaning inflammable, was supposed to be a component found in all substances that burn. As the substances burned, phlogiston was given off, thus making the burned substances lighter. It sounded logical—one could almost see phlogiston given off when an open container of water boiled and its vapors twirled upwards into the sky. Or when a piece of burning charcoal glowed brightly in the dusk. It had to be true, it seemed that as a substance burned it decreased in weight. But when metals were calcined (smelled), the calx was heavier than the original metal. The process was reversed. Unfortunately phlogiston was invisible—if it existed at all—and weightless, or nearly so. At any rate, no weight could be assigned to phlogiston. Otherwise it would have been easier for Georg Ernst Stahl to present tangible proof of his beliefs. As it was, Stahl and his group did provide a lot of examples and many of them were valid. Stahl was a physician. He was born in Ansbach Germany in 1660 and studied medicine at the University of Jena. Soon after the founding of the University at Halle, G.E. Stahl was appointed to the staff there. At Halle, he taught natural sciences and thus found many advocates among his students. During some of this time, he also taught medicine and acted as personal physician to the governing personalities in Berlin. He died there in 1734. But his Phlogiston Theory of Chemistry lived on until deep into the 19th century. It was overthrown by a French chemist whose demeanor, training and outlook were just the opposite of Stahl's.

The French scientist was Antoine Laurent Lavoisier, who was born in Paris on August 26, 1743. The chemistry he knew was a pitifully disoriented collection of empirical information of all types. The chemical composition of substances could not be known with any amount of precision because most of the elements had not yet been isolated. Classes of chemical substances, such as acids bases salts and metals were known, but the gases were not. A lot of work was being done on combustion, especially the "fire matter" known as phlogiston. A standard nomenclature was not available. The arguments made by Lavoisier against the Phlogiston Theory can be mapped out in a very simplified manner.

The phlogiston advocates believed that phlogiston was given off when substances were burned. Lavoisier pointed out that just the opposite was true—something in the air combined with the substance being burned. He could not know that it was oxygen; it had not yet been discovered.

Because it was known that ores of metals subjected to calcination showed an increase in weight, the phlogiston advocates thought that phlogiston was transferred by the charcoal to the calx, or oxide. Lavoisier showed that the increase in weight was due to combination of the metal with air, or with something in the air. It was also recognized by him that rusting iron and calcination of metals were combustion processes. It was also Lavoisier's belief that respiration of animals is slow combustion. Animals and humans breathe in oxygen and give off carbon dioxide.

Before proceeding with his other scientific accomplishments, it might be interesting to review the life of Antoine Laurent Lavoisier—chemist, economist and public servant. He was independently wealthy. Thus, he could afford to set up his own private laboratories to indulge in his hobbies of chemistry, mineralogy, geology and botany. He enjoyed a superior education. One reason was that Lavoisier started to study law—as did his prosperous father—before he turned to the sciences.

As a private scientist he published on an almost continuous basis on subjects of interest and utility. Papers on mineral waters. The chemical aspects of gypsum. Improved systems of street lighting in Paris. And later, of course, on combustion. In 1768, Lavoisier was elected to the Royal Academy of Sciences when he was only twenty-five years old. But Lavoisier was not only a scientist. He felt that he should do some public service.

Antoine Lavoisier was liberal in his political views. He believed in social reforms and took an active part in the political activities during the years preceeding the French Revolution. For example, he joined a committee whose main activites dealt with social and agricultural needs. There it was Lavoisier who made far reaching suggestions concerning pension systems and tax reforms. Since he understood financial matters,

Lavoisier was asked to make statistical studies of the economic resources of France. This was during the French Revolution. He also was made Director of the Caisse d'Escompte, or Discount Bank.

No doubt some of these activities were due to Lavoisier's father-in-law who was a Farmer General, a member of a small private group that collected tariffs and excise taxes for the government. Naturally, Lavoisier also became a member of this group. As the French Revolution intensified, so, too, did the accusations made by radical journalists against group members. They were accused of manipulations against France, of blackmailing and exploiting the population, of adulterating tobacco, of helping themselves to the state finances, of charging interest rates of six per cent to ten per cent instead of the legal four per cent and of many other irregularities.

The result was that Lavoisier and 28 other Farmers General were imprisoned in December 1793. On May 7, 1794, the group was incarcerated again, and the next morning the charges against them were read and sentence was pronounced: immediate execution by guillotine. As fourth on the list, Lavoisier could see the execution of his father-in-law just before the drums rolled for Antoine Laurent Lavoisier.

It is said that during his trial, Lavoisier asked for postponement so that he could finish a scientific investigation. Supposedly the presiding judge answered that "La république n'a pas besoin de savants, il faut que la justice suive son cours."

Better authenticated is the statement made by the famous astronomist and mathematician Joseph-Louis Lagrange: "It took only an instant to cut off that head, and a hundred years may not produce another like it."

Thus ended the life and works of a truly great man. Although he himself did not find new substances, he was nevertheless the chief architect of the newly emerging science of chemistry. Lavoisier made fundamental contributions such as pointing out that the weight of the products of reactions must equal the weight of the reactants. To him, scales and measuring techniques were more important than reagents. He liked to confirm and consolidate the experiments of others. Thus Lavoisier, who did so much to explain the role of oxygen in combustion, left the discovery of oxygen to Joseph Priestly of England and America, and to C.W. Scheele of Sweden. The composition of water was discovered by Henry Cavendish of England with James Waitt in 1781, and it was Cavendish also who discovered hydrogen.

Lavoisier's own publications included a joint effort with his disciples on a book, "Elementary Treatise of Chemistry," intended to introduce the new chemistry. And "Method of Chemical Nomenclature" was intended to unify the nomenclature. All these efforts led Lavoisier to formulate a new unified theory of combustion, calcination and respiration, and the role of oxygen in such processes. Thus, the groundwork for events in the 19th and 20th centuries had been laid down one or two centuries earlier.

F. W. A. SERTÜRNER AND THE OPIUM

An event of the early 19th century still exerts an impact upon pharmacy. It was the isolation from opium of what today we designate as morphine and classify as an alkaloid. The man who developed the method of isolation was a pharmacist of Neuhaus near Paderborn in northern Germany who was baptized by his father J. S. Sertürner (a surveyor in government service), as Fridericus Wilhelmus Adamus on June 19, 1783. But today we know of him as Friedrich Wilhelm Adam Sertürner.

At the age of 16, Sertürner was apprenticed for four years in a pharmacy in Paderborn. He was a valuable student and was encouraged to absorb as much theoretical and practical knowledge as possible. He could even use the pharmacy laboratory to carry out some experiments on plants of all types—especially opium—in an attempt to find the active principles. Pharmacists of that time were concerned with plant drugs. Was the whole plant necessary? Or just the roots? Or leaves? Or seeds? A major question was why one dose acted in one manner, on one patient for example as a sedative, while the very same amount might exert no action at all or could turn out to be fatal for another.

As was the custom of the times, research investigators sent their reports to Dr. Johann Bartholomäus Trommsdorf of Erfurt to be published in the famous "Trommsdorf Journal—Journal der Pharmazie." Only two years after his apprenticeship, the young Sertürner already had sent Trommsdorf two reports concerning the acids in opium. These were followed up by a long summary of 57 studies he had carried out before leaving Paderborn. Trommsdorf published this report in his "Journal der Pharmazie" in 1806. At least one of the 57 studies described the isolation of morphine. The report was titled "Characterization of pure opium acid and a chemical study of opium in relationship to a newly isolated substance." Sertürner named his preparation a "sleep-causing principle," while today we say hypnotic, sedative, anodyne, pain killer, and many other such terms. What is important is that Sertürner gave the medical profession one of its most indispensable drugs—morphine. But let us see why this is so important. What is opium? What is its relationship to morphine? What else did Friedrich Wilhelm Adam Sertürner investigate?

Probably the pharmacopoeia of each and every country of the world includes opium as an official drug. There may perhaps be an exception or two in some of the newer countries, but this diminishes neither the enormous widespread use nor the popularity of this historical drug.

By definition opium is the juice obtained from the unripe capsules of *Papaver somniferum* by incision and spontaneous evaporation. Besides opium, the whole plant or other parts of it may also be official in some countries as are *Semen papaveris* in Germany and Russia, *Folium papaveris* in Spain and Portugal, and *Fructus papaveris maturus* in Portugal.

The plant itself—Papaver somniferum var. album or other species or varieties—grows all over the world, including, in Norway up to the Artic Circle. It has a growth period of only 120-140 days. The capsules produced by the various species of plants are not uniform. They may be round or somewhat long and slender. They may be small or unusually large. The capsules may hang downward or rest horizontally. Some capsules terminate in a pointy end while in others the ends look crushed. The colors of the leaves also vary rather widely. And the seeds may be obtained in blue, white or black.

By manipulation of the various aspects, the capsules may produce somewhat more milky fluid, but the amount of morphine found is neither increased nor decreased.

The nearly ripe capsules of *Papaver somniferum* are called papaver or poppy. It is mostly the capsules alone that yield the opium, but these capsules must be incised by hand. A good worker can fracture or incise 2000 capsules per twelve hour day.

Since the milky fluid is found in the capsule under strong hydrostatic pressure, any small cut or incision will cause the fluid to ooze as soon as the capsule is wounded. Thus, some use the tip of a knife, or a curved knife. Some a small cleaver. Others put up to seven blades in a special structure so as to get parallel incisions. And some use a pair of tongs in a ringlike instrument. It seems not to matter which instrument is employed. More important is that the milky fluid oozes and gets hardened by evaporation.

Antoine Laurent de Lavoisier (1743-1794).

Friedrich Wilhelm Adam Sertürner (1783-1841).

For this reason, several methods are used to get a good opium. Some growers incise the capsules in the late afternoon and evening, at about the period the capsules begin to ripen. Others cut at various times from two to four weeks after blooming, depending on the area concerned. The milky juice is then picked the next morning. Only now it is not milky anymore—it is brownish due to oxidation. The amount of opium obtained from each capsule varies from 15 mg to 20 mg and occasionally up to 60 mg. Of this amount approximately ten per cent is morphine.

Because a rainstorm or even a shower can literally wash away the harvest, various other schemes are employed to win opium. Some growers incise once and collect the milky fluid on the finger of the worker. Others let one person, usually a woman, make several incisions whereupon a second woman passes by with a glass and collects whatever has seeped out and begun to dry. The yield is greater but the owner has the expenses of a second employee. It is all a question of economics. Other poppy farmers attempt to get a good opium by collecting it on cotton, which absorbs the water. At any rate, a lot of these variations are based on logical facts. Thus it has been found that after one incision, the opium obtained contains more morphine than that of a second incision and in turn, a third incision contains much less of both opium and morphine. Growers have to take into account the commercial facts: is it cheaper to take a decreased yield but have fewer workers? Is it better to try to get secondary products from the seeds of the poppy plants, since seeds normally ripen long after incision? Or a tertiary product—the sliced pieces of exhaused poppy capsules? In the end, all that counts is that opium containing at least ten per cent of morphine is made available to meet the pharmacopeal and manufacturers' standards.

Opium as a legal drug is needed in quantities of over 500 tons yearly. Since it is available in quantities of 10 to 20 mg per capsule, there will be much scope to plant Papaver and prepare it for market, both legally and illegally.

Special laws concerning opium have always been necessary. Usually they were ignored, whereupon still another treaty had to be formulated. From 1840 to 1842, Great Britain and China had an opium war. The cause was China's attempt to stop illegal importation of Indian opium by the English and other foreigners. England wished to make importation legal because of the high fees it would collect as duties. An agreement was reached whereby England succeeded in opening the ports of Amoy, Canton, Fu-tschou, Ning-po and Shanghai. Regulation of the opium trade was better enforced by the Treaty of Tientsin in 1860.

The Chinese Opium Edict of September 20, 1906, dealt with the prohibition of further planting of poppy and the prevention of opium smoking. The International Opium Conference in Shanghai in 1909 praised China for having as its goal the elimination within its borders of opium production and smoking, and it encouraged other countries to do the same. They did not, and opium abuse was widespread in London from about 1820 to 1910. In France, the city of Toulon could count 963 opium dens in 1913. China and England made another treaty in 1911 and promised to stop the shipment of opium to China and the cultivation of poppy by December 31, 1917. In spite of all the broken promises, much progress was made in this period.

The texts of The Opium Conventions of February 23, 1912, and October 4, 1919, were printed in the Swiss Journal of Pharmacy. The International Opium Agreements of January 23, 1912, in Den Haag, took force as of January 1, 1921. In the United States of America the Harrison Bill was passed. It promised to maintain control of all narcotic drugs. Pharmacists became involved immediately. When ordering narcotic drugs from wholesalers they had to complete special forms. The wholesalers in turn had to complete their part and send the goods and forms in a separate container, not with other packages. The drugs were to be stored in a separate closet or in desk drawers, again with other narcotics only. Pharmacists of today are in the same dilemma as those of that time. As pharmacist, he must obey the law and do what little he can, such as reporting false prescriptions. As only one person, he cannot do much against big-time operators dealing in tons of illegal merchandise, whose trails often lead to high-ranking politicians and businessmen in deals involving millions of dollars.

By reviewing the botanical aspects of opium, we could see the difficulties met with in growing and handling this unusual plant. Let us now briefly review the chemical aspects. For only in this manner can we appreciate the genius needed to uravel the riddle of morphine—the genius supplied by Friedrich Wilhelm Adam Sertürner.

At the time of Sertürner, chemistry was still new and undeveloped. Lavoisier had only just begun to formalize the new science. As they had done for hundreds and even thousands of years, pharmacists had treated drug plants with water, wine, honey and other easily obtainable substances, mostly liquids, to make syrups or other drinks. The new chemists were isolating elements.

As for the poppy plant, it was known that the capsule contained a milky product that could be collected by incising the capsule's coat and letting the viscous milky fluid seep out. It was also known that the hard but malleable caramel-like substance would cause the user to sleep.

As for its chemistry, it was known that opium always gave an acidic reaction. Thus it was confusing for Sertürner to have a substance in his hands that was basic, or a alkaline. Sertürner realized then that he had isolated from opium a completely new compound that was strongly basic with beautiful silk-like needle crystals or robust rhombic prisms. This was the first plant base to be discovered. Later Joseph-Louis Gay-Lussac proposed that this new substance should be named morphine, for Morpheus, the god of sleep. More important, morphine was found to be a prototype. It was the first plant base found, but there were many others. It was the pharmacist Wilhelm Meissner of Halle who gave such plants—those containing nitrogenous organic bases as active principles—the description alkaloid. Meissner had begun investigations in 1818, and in 1819 had isolated a base from Sabadilla seeds. He published his findings in February 1821 in Trommsdorff's Neuem Journal der Pharmazie 5, 1 (1821) 3, where for the first time he employed the name Alkaloid.

In spite of doubts about the efficacy of morphine, priority claims and even plagiarism, Sertürner prevailed and was awarded the Prix Montyon on June 27, 1831, "pour avoir reconnu la nature alcaline de la morphine et avoir ainsi ouvert une voie qui a produit de grandes découvertes médicales": for having recognized the alkaline nature of morphine and for having opened up pathways that promise to lead to great medical discoveries. The promise was kept. Pharmacist after pharmacist, chemist after chemist, started investigations, and all obtained alkaloids, some of which were extremely valuable for the medical profession and others that are still being investigated. We need think only of belladonna, ergot, quinine, cocaine and many others. Later a different prototype was to be found in some plants—the glycosides that are present in digitalis, for example. What made the alkaloids difficult to isolate was that in most plants, the main principle is accompanied by secondary alkaloids. In opium, there are at least 25 secondary alkaloids. When we think that some have teen given several names by several investigators, we can understand the difficulties pharmacists encountered. Listed here are some of the alkaloids found in opium.

Morphine: found in amounts of ten to fourteen per cent in opium. Exerts full effect as anodyne against pain and as hypnotic to cause sleep. Isolated by Sertürner. Used widely in therapy.

Narcotine: Opian Opianine Aconellin Anarcotine is less narcotic than morphine. Probably found by Derosne who had impure substance of narcotine or morphine or both. Up to four per cent may be obtained from opium.

Codeine: primarily anodynic; it stops pain. As hypnotic it is less active than morphine. Found in less than seven per cent quantities in opium. Morphine can be converted to codeine. Codeine can also be synthesized. Used widely in therapy.

Thebaine: Paramorphine. The most poisonous opium alkaloid, it causes tetanic-like cramps. Found in opium in amounts up to one per cent.

Papaverine: as a narcotic it is not so strong. Its effect is between that of codeine and morphine. It is present in opium in proportions up to one per cent. Used widely in therapy.

Narceine: Inactive. Found in opium up to 0.5 per cent.

Protopine, Landanine, Landanidine, Landanosine, Lanthopine, Inoscopine, Hydrocotarnine, Oxynarcotine, Pseudomorphine, Rhoeadin, Kryptopine, T topin, Pseudopapaverine, Meconidine, Pavaveramine, Xanthaline, Codamine, Tritopine and Porphyroxine are Additional minor alkaloids have no useful effects. Some are very poisonous in that they induce tetanus. Other may not even be present in opium but are produced as a result of the chemical manipulations.

The impact on pharmacy was obvious. New alkaloids led to new pharmacological testing which led to new types of therapy. But pharmacists were also limited in that they could no longer use their prescription departments as a place of manufacture. They were forced to establish commercial laboratories or even small factories.

The impact on Friedrich Wilhelm Adam Sertürner himself was also profound. We can only speculate if any pharmacist of today could withstand the pressures placed on him. Even when he was very young, he had to cope with the very little space available to him in his parents' house. His life became even more modest after his father died. His discovery of morphine did not bring Sertürner sudden fame. Some doubted his discovery. Some claimed they were first. Sertürner had to defend himself, by carrying out still more laboratory investigations publishing more and more reports on the same subject: morphine. Its properties. Its crystalline nature. His life was working in his pharmacy and then rushing to his laboratory and writing up reports and rushing back to his two pharmacies. He was frustrated. Moreover, he longed to get married but could not because, besides helping the sick and poor as a practicing pharmacist, he was totally supporting his mother. Then he started supporting his sister also. Thus he was forced to postpone his marriage to Eleonore von Rettburg several times. But by 1821, Sertürner thought he now could finally enjoy life. Honors were being bestowed upon him, such as honorary degrees from Göttingen and Jena and honorary memberships in scientific societies. His wife bore him four daughters and two sons and they had a happy life together. However, a series of vexations then started to manifest themselves. Probably the first hint of real trouble came when his permission to practice pharmacy was withdrawn. As we recall, after Sertürner had left Paderborn he practiced in nearby Einbeck. In addition to receiving permission to manage a pharmacy there, the French-Westphalian authorities granted him permission to manage a second pharmacy, too. Now the succeeding Hannover government cancelled both licenses. But he was able in 1820 to purchase his own pharmacy in nearby Hameln of Pied Piper fame.

Friedrich Wilhelm Adam Sertürner surely was deeply frustrated when the editor of the Journal der Chemie rejected one of his reports. It was to anounce that Sertürner could demonstrate for the first time that the corrosive bases were a union of metals with oxygen. Sertürner was correct, but only a short time later the famous English scientist Humphry Davy announced this fact, after verifying the work of Sertürner. Davy previously had discovered potassium and sodium. He proved that hydrogen plus chlorine formed hydrochloric acid' and that chlorine was an element. Davy also showed that water broke down only and always to hydrogen and oxygen. This was advanced work for the early 19th century.

In carrying out some research his father had begun on ballistics, Sertürner described a new alloy of lead and antimony that was supposed to exert a greater penetration power. He also built a new type of rear-loading rifle. Because he complained that the scientific journals were too slow in printing and that too little attention was paid to the results obtained, Sertürner printed leaflets at his own expense. He even established his own journal. It could not be called a success.

When Europe was hit by an epidemic of cholera in 1831, Friedrich Sertürner again printed leaflets at his own expense to warn his fellow citizens to be on guard. He described the disease and its therapy at that time. It is remarkable that almost fifty years before Louis Pasteur and Robert Koch, when bacteria were not yet known, Sertürner described the cause of cholera to be, in his words, a poisonous and animated being which can reproduce itself or cause itself to be reproduced. His pamphlet was mockingly ignored.

Likewise Sertürner kept warning all who would listen that morphine should be taken with care, that it did not only ease pain, that it dit not merely cause sleep, that it did have side effects, and did cause addiction. All these were shouts in the wilderness. Friedrich Wilhelm Adam Sertürner grew more and more frustrated as he became increasingly immobilized due to gout. Death finally put an end to his suffering on February 20, 1841.

L'AN 1820 LES
PHARMACIENS
PELLETIER
ET
CAVENTOU
FIRENT
LA DECOUVERTE
DE LA QUININE

Memorial in honor of the pharmacists Pelletier and Caventou, in Paris, Boulevard St-Michel.

CAVENTOU AND PELLETIER

The floodgates Sertürner opened caused a cascade of new research leading to new products in medicine, new industries and new processes of utmost importance. The 19th century was quite prolific. Pharmacists were still at the forefront of these activities. Most still worked as individuals such as these performed but joint research investigations were also being reported, by Caventou and Pelletier.

These two pharmacists were born in Paris, and this was probably one of the very few things they had in common. Otherwise they came from opposite sides of the social and financial scale. Nevertheless, they were called the Siamese twins of pharmacy. In writing about them one could not be mentioned without the other. They did their best work together and their discoveries were numerous.

Pierre Joseph Pelletier, born March 22, 1788, had a grandfather who was a pharmacist. His father was also a pharmacist—one famous for discovering arsenic, developing new methods of manufacturing phosphorus, processing ethers, being a member of the French Academy of Science, and for being a professor.

Joseph Bienaimé Caventou, born June 30, 1795, had a father who was a hospital pharmacist living in modest circumstances. Whereas Pelletier could study under the great Louis Vauquelin, poor Caventou had to work in a pharmacy while attending school. Caventou then worked in a hospital. When Napoleon returned from Elba, Joseph Caventou became an army pharmacist. He returned to Paris after the Battle of Waterloo to work in the Hôpital St. Antoine. Here he met Pierre Pelletier. The two became fast friends even though Pelletier nail a famous pharmacy in Paris that assured his material needs and Caventou had to live on his army pay. He was attempting to write a book on chemical nomenclature in order to earn some money. At any rate, the two pharmacists started collaboration.

Their first report announced their isolation of emetine in 1817. They then reported their isolation of strychnine in 1818 and of brucine in 1819. At first, the team proposed the name vauqueline for strychnine in honor of the renowned chemist who had been Pelletier's teacher. However, the Academy of Sciences refused to accept the proposal because "un nom chéri ne pouvait être appliqué à un principe malfaisant": a cherished name should not be applied to a noxious substance. It was overlooked that the secondary alkaloid in *nux vomica* was named brucine after the explorer Jacques Bruce. Or perhaps the name Bruce was not so cherished.

In 1818, the pharmacy twins reported their preparation of carmine from coccinella and crotonic acid from the seeds of the plant. They also coined the name chlorophyll (from the Greek *chloros* meaning light and *phyllon* designating leaf) for the green coloring matter of plants. In 1819, they announced the preparation of veratrine from several different plants. Then, in 1820, they prepared colchicine from *Colchicum autumnale* and caffeine from coffee in 1821.

This two also announced in 1820 their greatest achievement, the isolation of quinine and cinchonine, in reports titled "Recherches chimiques sur les quinquinas." Caventou and Pelletier wanted to honor their friend Marcellin Berthollet by giving his name to the new substances. He declined, however, by saying that new substances from plants should be named after the plant itself or after a property of the plant. No matter what the name, quinine was an immediate success.

To cover demand, Pelletier built a factory (he could afford it) in Neuilly on the outskirts of Paris. The twins remained twins. Both believed that all of humanity should profit from their discovery and thus both published their process so that other factories could also manufacture quinine from cinchona bark, and so they could keep the price low. After only six years, they could report that two factories in the Paris area alone—their own and a competitor's—processed 160 tons of cinchona bark to produce 60,000 ounces of quinine sulfate. In 1827, the Academy of Sciences awarded Caventou and Pelletier a joint prize of 10,000 French Francs for their discoveries. Thereafter the pair was somewhat less Siamese, which does not mean that they relinquished their activities.

Pierre Joseph Pelletier built a new factory for the manufacture of pharmaceutical and chemical substances. He became a Professor of Natural Sciences in the School of Pharmacy and carried out research with several collaborators. In 1832 he obtained narceine from opium. In 1833 he obtained impure thebaine, which he obtained in a pure state in 1835. Also in 1835 he prepared pseudomorphine and in 1836 tolnol by the dry distillation of resin from ine trees. On July 24, 1842, Pierre Joseph Pelletier died in Paris at the age of only 54 years.

As for Joseph Bienaimé Caventou, he preferred to refrain from all commercial activities, except one. This was his pension. He was happy to receive a generous and substantial settlement for the rest of his life. Caventou could keep up with scientific activities by becoming Professor of Toxicology at the School of Pharmacy, the same Institution where Pelletier also taught. At age 83, Joseph Caventou joined his friend in death when he died on May 5, 1877.

During their lifetimes both were awarded prizes and honors, including membership in the Academy of Sciences. After their death the city of Paris erected a monument to them in close vicinity to the Ecole de Pharmacie. But perhaps the greatest monument of all is that their quinine, emetine and caffeine after 160 years are still prescribed every day by grateful physicians and pharmacists.

FRIEDRICH WÖHLER

The discovery of urea in 1828 exerted an on pharmacy and indeed on the whole world of chemistry as well as on the world itself that is still being felt by all of us. The chemist (not pharmacist) involved was Friedrich Wöhler. This was the first time ever that an organic substance produced in an animal body could be synthesized in a laboratory. Organic chemistry as a new discipline was born. Today chemists are still attaching, exchanging and removing units in their structural formulas. Thousands of new synthetic compounds are being produced yearly. The possibilities are endless. So long as atoms can provide space for up to four attachments, there will always be a new synthetic compound, either as a long chain or rings or both, for organic chemistry is essentially the chemistry of carbon. And yet Friedrich Wöhler was not even looking for urea. He was interested in inorganic analytical chemistry. In fact, only two weeks before he had announced his discovery of aluminum.

Urea is the main product of animal protein metabolism occuriny primarily in the liver. It is found in the urine of mammals, fish and amphibians, but not in birds and reptiles, where uric acid is found instead. Humans excrete up to thirty grams daily. This was the substance that in 1799 was named "urée" by Vauquelin and Fourcroy, and announced by Wöhler in a humorous letter to his friend J.J. Berzelius on February 22, 1828. It read: Berlin, 22ten Febr. 1828. Lieber Herr Professor! Obgleich ich sicher hoffe, dass mein Brief vom 12. Jan. und das Postscript von 2ten Februar bey Ihnen angelangt sind, und ich täglich, oder vielmehr stündlich in gespannter Hoffnung lebe, einen Brief von Ihnen zu erhalten, so will ich ihn doch nicht abwarten, sondern schon wieder schreiben, denn ich kann, so zu sagen, mein chemisches Wasser nicht halten und muss Ihnen sagen, dass ich Harnstoff machen kann, ohne Nieren oder überhaupt ein Thier, sey es Mensch oder Hund, nöthig zu haben. Das cyansaure Ammoniak ist Harnstoff . . .

Berzelius also displayed some humor by answering: . . . und sollte die Quantität der artifiziellen nicht genügen, so kann man leicht mit ein wenig aus dem Nachttopf supplieren.

Friedrich Wöhler was appointed Professor soon after. Pure aluminum and synthetic urea within two weeks deserved such an award, to say the least.

Gez v. l' Allemand   Lith u. gedr bei Hanfstaengl in Dresden

F. Wöhler

Friedrich Wöhler (1800-1882).

FRIEDRICH KRAFT

The 19th century saw one of great expansion in pharmacy and chemistry. And a lot of this was due to one-man laboratories. Of course, these scientists were not really alone.

Some professors, for instance, whould have thirty or forty or more assistants for a semester or two. Many pharmacists and chemists rotated from laboratory to laboratory. Berlin. Munich. Frankfurt. Halle, Strasbourg. Göttigen. Even Paris and England. The result was that they all knew what was going on and were kept à jour by the various Annalen. Some pharmaceutical research workers were really alone, however. Such was Fritz Kraft of Brugg, Switzerland.

His background was a commercial one ; his grandfather and father were successful negotiants and his wife the daughter of a prosperous dairy farmer. There was nothing unusual concerning the training of Carl Friedrich Kraft (the full name of Fritz Kraft) other than always being at the top of his classes. Thus, schooling was normal in Brugg and Baden. And his study of pharmacy was routine in Zurich, with practical semesters in Basel and Geneva. After he was graduated, he returned to Basel to work as a research pharmacist in a large chemical firm. But he gave this up after one year because he could not stand to have superiors looking over his shoulder all the time. He wated to be independent. Therefore, he purchased a pharmacy on the outer edges of Basel. There he did some research work. However, this time it was his customers who bothered him and interrupted his experiments, so Fritz Kraft returned to Brugg in 1901. There he built for his bride a rather large house in the middle of an apple orchard and, for himself, a private laboratory on the ground floor of his new home. He decide to investigate *Dryopteris filix mas* or male fern.

Male fern is a very old plant dating back to antiquity—to Dioskurides, Galen, Plinius and many others. It was used successfully against taperworm, always by drying the rhizome and then grating or dicing it and mixing it with honey before taking it with a laxative. Kraft tried to isolate the active principle. He thought he had it in Filmaron ® which C.F. Boehringer & Soehne in Mannheim Germany brought on the market in 1904. Filmaron quickly became world famous especially in the leading harbors and port cities where tapeworm infestation was a major problem. It was quickly adopted by many pharmacopeias.

At first it was thought that Filmaron was a single substance, but analytical methods show that Filmaron is a complex of aspidinol and filicin—aspidinolfilicin. Male fern, or aspidium, as it is called, contains at least eight or more components which individually or collectively exert to various degrees an anthelmintic effect. Some of the other components in male fern are filicin, filicinic acid, filix acid, aspidin, aspidinin, albaspidin, aspidinol and others in related species of Dryopteris.

That a product put on the market in 1904 could still be obtained up to a few years ago demonstrates the efficacy of Filmaron. Actually, the tapeworms are not killed illed. They are paralyzed by the Filmaron and then expelled by the action of the laxative. Since Atabrine works in the same manner it has taken over from Filmaron. This does not detract from the fact that Fritz Kraft alone was first in analyzing a drug plant used empirically for thousands of years.

Another old drug that intrigued Fritz Kraft was ergot. Even though this drug plant had been used by midwives for hundreds of years to stop obstetrical bleeding, it defied chemist who tried to isolate its secrets. It was only in 1875 that Charles Tanret could isolate two substances from ergot. One was crystalline, so this pharmacist from Troyes France named it "Ergotinine cristallisée." The other substance was amorphous so he named it "Ergotinine amorphe" because he found it identical to the crystalline portion. Tanret thought that the substance was amorphous because of impurities that prevented crystallization. Since it was rather difficult to make salts of these two substances and since the pure crystallne alkaloid had no useful clinical effects, few pharmacists investigated ergot further.

Then in 1906, George Barger and F.H. Carr published in Chemical News (*94*, 89, 1906) on August 24 an abstract of a report they had delivered a short time before at a meeting of the British Association in York.

Death spares nobody during an epidemic; the demons wait to attack their prey and the succour of faith cannot stop the divine will being done (Petrach). *Remedies of fortune,* French translation, B.N. French ms, 225, fol. 202 (1503).

They announced the isolation of a new amorphous alkaloid out of Tanret's Ergotinine amorphe. Barger and Carr named their alkaloid Ergotoxine. It was not difficult to make salts of ergotoxine. Thus it could be studies both pharmacologically and clinically on a larger scale.

Meanwhile, Fritz Kraft on August 3, 1906, had sent his manuscript "Ueber das Mutterhorn" (On Ergot) to the German pharmaceutical journal Archiv der Pharmazie (224 336-359 1906). Kraft reported that the Ergotinine amorphe and the Ergotinine cristallisée of Tanret were interchangeable. Simply by heating the amorphous form with alcohol he could obtain Ergotinine cristallisée. And simply by treating the crystalline form with acid he could obtain Ergotinine amorphe. Fritz Kraft gave the name Hydroergotinin to his compound because he considered it to be hydrated ergotinine.

Then on October 10 of that year George Barger and Henry Dale sent Archiv der Pharmazie (244 550-555 1906) their comments concerning the claims of Fritz Kraft. They said that although many of Kraft's findings were the same as their own, they could not accept as fact that hydroergotinin and ergotoxine were the same. Many other investigators soon took sides and after many pros and cons they all agreed that Kraft was correct, and that ergotoxine was indeed hydroergotinin.

In a notice appearing in the Archiv der Pharmazie (245 235, 1907) titled "On Ergot Alkaloids-Rectification" George Barger pointed out that he had assigned the wrong formula to his ergotoxine and that he could verify that Kraft's method of boiling Tanret's amorphous alkaloid in methylalcohol gave ergotinine cristallisée. Thus Hydroergotinin and Ergotoxine were one and the same. However the name Ergotoxine won out and Hydroergotinin dropped by the wayside. It was only in 1926 that Geoffrey Timmis in England could make Ergotoxine in crystalline form, and it was 1943 before Arthur Stoll and Albert Hofmann in Basel, Switzerland, could show that Ergotoxine was in reality a varying triad of three other alkaloids and that none of these was Ergotamine, the pure initial alkaloid of ergot as by Stoll in 1918. But Ergotoxine in its hydrogenated form, as prepared by Stoll and Hofmann, is a valuable addition to the physician's armamentorium, thanks to Fritz Kraft, who opened up the field and showed the way.

In his small private laboratory in Brugg, Kraft worked on another old drug, Digitalis. After being introduced into medicine by William Withering in England, physicians were forced to use the dry plant in therapy. Later they were able to use the tincture of digitalis. These dosage forms were not satisfactory. Fritz Kraft then started his investigations on digitalis and soon had the first good clinical form of a digitalis glycoside. He named it Gitalin. It could be patented and subjected to clinical trials. He then could crystallize a second glycocide that he named Gitoxin. Kraft's early deatsh put an end to this project.

Fritz Kraft died of a stroke on April 28, 1914, when only fity years old. But with his Aspidinolfilicin, Gitalin Gitoxin and Ergotoxine, Fritz Kraft will live on in the annals of pharmacy as one of the greatest pharmacists of all time. He was probably one of the very last successful researchers with a one-man laboratory.

Today we can only admire a shy pharmacist who could work in his own home on three of the most important drugs in medicine: Ergot, Digitalis and Male Fern.

CLAUDE-ADOLPHE NATIVELLE

Prior to Fritz Kraft was Claude-Adolphe Nativelle, who was also a one-man researcher in the field of digitalis. He, too, is one of the most neglected heroes in pharmacy.

Claude Nativelle was born in the vicinity of the Cathedral of Notre Dame in Paris on June 25, 1812. His father was a butcher while his mother supplemented the family income by selling herbs and flowers along the streets of Paris. Since Nativelle's father died when Claude was only eight years old, the youngster was taken out of school in order to help his mother. In the very early hours, mother and son gathered their flowers in the fields on the periphery of Paris and then peddled them to passers-by or delivered them to certain customers by prearrangement. One such customer was a Parisian pharmacist who had ordered some herbs. The youngster was attracted by a certain plant that the friendly pharmacist described in full. Young Claude was told that the dark green plant with the long ovate leaves and purple campanulate flowers grew in the Vosges mountains of eastern France and that the plant was named digitalis. Persons with heart disease were given an infusion of the leaves. This was a lesson which Claude never forgot, especially since his mother soon there after died suddenly of a heart attack.

His guardians were not understanding and apprenticed him to a brush factory and then to a hat maker. The 15-year-old orphan who was so well read on botany, had even built up a large herbarium and had read Jean-Jacques Rousseau preferred to peddle the flowers and herbs he liked so much. But at last a Paris pharmacist took on as an apprentice this self-willed, undernourished orphan.

Apprenticeship at that time lasted eight years. This Nativelle should have been finished long before his 25th birthday. Instead he finished at age 29. The main reason was that he changed pharmacies several times and sometimes gave up apprenticeship for a while to do some private research work. Moreover, he was involved in the revolution of 1830, as well as acquiring cholera in the epidemic of 1832. Thus it was only in 1835 that Nativelle could submit his first publication. It concerned a new method of isolating quinine sulfate. But because his employer objected, surely because of the time and materials involved, Nativelle terminated his apprenticeship. The same thing occurred in 1836 and in 1837 as well. But finally he received his Diploma in Pharmacy in 1841 for his research investigations on cinchona bark, resin of jalap and the blessed thistle (Chardon bénit), from which he isolated cnicine.

Upon learning that an expedition was being formed to set sail for Colombia in South America to search for cinchona trees, Claude Nativelle succeeded in joining of the group. The expedition penetrated the Colombian jungles in 1843. Soon thereafter Nativelle returned to Paris alone. He, nowan expert on cinchona, returned from South America and never again uttered word or mentioned the quarrels on board. And he never again worked with the substance. He turned his full attention to digitalis, the dark green plant of his boyhood;

Because Friedrich W.A. Sertünner had been so successful in isolating an alkaloid (morphine) the whole pharmaceutical world turned to phytochemical investigations of other plants and other alkaloids. The Société de Pharmacie in 1844 offered a prize to anyone who could isolate the active principle of digitalis, it being thought that it would be an alkaloid too. At any rate, Claude Nativelle made many tests and reactions and isolated a substance that surely was not an alkaloid. He presented his report and the new substance to the Société in applying for the prize. With hindsight we now can say that the Société de Pharmacie was wrong in awarding the prize to Homolle. Of course Nativelle was angry. He was disappointed and frustrated.

Nativelle wrote a letter of protest that he had printed and distributed. Tenacious as ever, he purchased a pharmacy as his bread and butter and erected a laboratory for his research investigations. It galled him to think that Homolle's preparation was enjoying more and more commercial success at the same time that his own substances were being acclaimed as better by pharmacological and clinical studies. Nativelle's frustrations soon turned into obsessions. For the next 28 years after he closed shop, he went to his laboratory. Or to his room to read his books. He had no family and no friends. He was attached to his guardian and visited him periodically, usually wearing a poncho he brought back from South America. Of course he was looked upon as an eccentric.

Claude-Adolphe Nativelle was not the only one seeking new substances in digitalis. Many pharmacists vied for the prize, suchas Homolle, Schmiedeberg, and Walz. Some researchers found seven or eight substances. Nativelle could obtain three distinct fractions. One was his famous, highly active Digitaline Nativelle or Digitaline cristallisée. The less active second fraction was named Digitaléine Nativelle. The third fraction was inactive but was gien the names of Digitaline passive, Digitine Nativelle and Substance cristallisée inerte anyway.

All this work in refining the processes of isolation and reisolation brought its own rewards. In his 28-year running fight with Homolle and the Société de Pharmacie, Nativelle threw down a challenge in 1869. He published all the details of the methods he used in obtaining his famous Digitaline Nativelle, and had his report printed in the Journal de Pharmacie et de Chimie. During the next year, 1870, Nativelle sent his report and crystalline substance to the Académie de Médecine which had offered a prize to anybody who could isolate the active principle of digitalis. Needless to say this time it was Claude-Adolphe Nativelle who won the Orfila Prize in 1872. As a result, the French Pharmacopea accepted Digitaline Nativelle an official drug. Right up ot the present, it is still official along with several other pure glycosides of digitalis.

Today we know that what Claude Nativelle had isolated was digitoxin, the initial crystalline, almost pure, digitalis glycoside. It was the almost pure glycoside because it was extremely difficult to remove the five to 30 per cent of gitoxin which was always present in the digitoxin isolated. Even the United States Pharmacopeia allowed up to ten per cent gitoxin as an impurity. All this does not detract from the fact that it was Claude Nativelle who first isolated pure digitoxin and to this day still keeps millions of people alive and active, and grateful to a somewhat unhappy pharmacist.

Whatever the reason, Claude Nativelle received no recognition apart from the rather modest Orfila Prize of 1872. When he died of the flu in Paris on March 25, 1889, he was 77 years old and all alone, with no family and no friends. Only one pharmaceutical journal published a short biographical notice. It was only in 1937 that Albéric Cahuet published a more substantial biography. And it was only on November 7, 1948, that a bronze plaque commemorating Claude-Adolphe Nativelle and his work was unveiled at the Faculté de Pharmacie de Paris. There was a five-line notice in the January 1949 issue of France Pharmacie reporting this event. With such treatment perhaps Claude Nativelle would not be surprised at all, if he were to come back, to learn that there are certain groups that advocate dropping the use of natural digitalis glycosides altogether in favor of purely chemical compounds known as Beta Blockers. Only time can tell.

As for us today, we can say that Claude Nativelle with his one-man laboratory showed the way. Later phytochemists worked hard to unravel the mysteries of digitalis to show us that the plant species themselves varied. For example, as Arthur Stoll and his group in Basel could report, Digitalis lanata contained three substances named A, B and C, whereas Digitalis purpurea had only A and B, but all of them had precursors. At any rate, physicians have at their disposal a whole variety of cardiac glycosides. There and those that have a longer onset of action and last a long time such as digitoxin. There are those with a rapid onset of action such as lanatoside C and digoxin that last an intermediate period of time, and those with very fast onsets of action. And so on; the doctor has a large choice of preparations, thanks to Claude-Adolphe Nativelle.

ALFRED BERNHARD NOBEL

Not all chemists of the 19th century were phytochemists. Not all were German or French. One chemist with great impact, literally and figurative, was the Swede, Alfred Bernhard Nobel. Pharmacists and physicians employ his product in drop doses or in tablets or in gelatin capsules triurated to prevent or relieve angina pectoris. Engineers and builders use nitroglycerine by the ton in the form of dynamite.

The Name Nobel conjures up the words "Prizes" and "Explosives." Yet of course with just those words we do not and cannot know the real Alfred Nobel. We must first study his family background and character as well as the character of his times. Perhaps we can in this manner untangle the riddle of why Alfred Bernhard Nobel is known as a benefactor of manking, a merchant of death, an atheist, or as a deeply religious man. As an uneducated boor. Or as a poet, writer, linguist, scientist and inventor. As an unrealistic idealist. Or as a hardheaded pragmatic businessman. As a melancholy pessimist. Or as a witty optimist.

In the 19th century, in the southern tip of Sweden, the ancestors of Alfred Nobel earned their living as Scandian farmers. It was the custom then that the first member of a family who had somehow acquired a university education had the privilege of choosing a family name. So did it come about that one Petrus Olavi who was born in Nöbbelöv and could study at the University of Uppsala exercised his privilege and named his family Nobelius. Being especially talented in music, Petrus Olavi Nobelius soon came to the attention of Olaf Rudbeck, who was the founder of musical activities in Uppsala, and who had a daughter Vendela. Petrus Olavi Nobelius finished his education, became a judge in the Swedish province of Uppland and married Vendela Rudbeck to found the beginnings of the Nobelius family. It was one of the grandsons of this marriage who shortened the family name to Nobel.

Immanuel Nobel, the father of Aldred, was born in 1801 in Gävle, in Northern Sweden. He had no formal education and could hardly read and write and knew no foreign language. However he made up for this by having a keen intelligence brimming over with ideas of all kinds. At the age of 14, Immanuel Nobel was sent to sea as a cabin boy. After spending three years in the Mediterranean Sea he was apprenticed to builders in Gävle and Stockholm. Part of the training was to attend school for courses in mechanics and architecture.

In 1825 Immanuel Nobel set up his own business as architect and builder, but he was bankrupt by 1833. His projects were too ambitious. He then left Sweden for St. Petersburg in 1837. In Russia he was quite successful, as were his sons Robert helped develop the petroleum industry in Baku. Ludwig founded a famous arms factory in St. Petersburg. Emil was too young for anything. And Alfred, born on October 21, 1833, studied chemistry and languages. He was fluent in Swedish, Russian, German, English and French. Literature interested him most and he wrote poetry in various languages. All went well with the Immanuel Nobel family. But then disaster struck each member.

The commissions promised Immanuel Nobel by the Russian government for boats, mines and other equipment to reinforce the coastline did not materialize. The over-expanded factory remianed idle. Thus once again Immanuel Nobel went bankrupt and had to return to Sweden in 1859.

As for Alfred Nobel, his fiancée died. This shattering emotional experience led him to write a long poem whose last stanza read:

"From that hour
I have not shared the pleasure of the crowd
Nor moved in Beauty's eye compassion's tear
But I have learned to study Nature's book
And comprehend its pages and extract
From their deep love, a solace for my grief."

Another disaster was an explosion in 1864 caused by nitroglycerin in the laboratory of a factory built by Alfred and his father, in which the youngest brother Emil was killed along with four other victims. This was followed a few weeks later by a stroke suffered by Immanuel from which he never recovered. The Nobel family had cause for its grief.

Claude Adolphe Nativelle (1812-1889).

Alfred Bernard Nobel (1833-1896).

Bibliothèque Universitaire, Basel.

Alfred Nobel then turned more of his attention to his experiments. Nitroglycerin was fascinating. It was first prepared in 1847 in Italy by Ascanio Sobrero of Torino. Professor Zinin of St. Petersburg brought it to the attention of Nobel who introduced it in 1867 as dynamite. What exactly is nitroglycerin?

Because even when administered by mouth it acts very rapidly—within two minutes the blood pressure begins to fall and the effect last half an hour—nitroglycerin has been accepted as an official drug by many pharmacopeias. It has only one effect: to lower blood pressure. Thus it is valuable in treating angina pectoris as well as asthma and threatened stroke. It may be used many times daily if required in emergencies. At any rate, millions of persons stay alive each day thanks to Glyceryl Trinitrate Spirit or Glyceryl Trinitrate Tablets, as the pharmacopeias list it. Nitroglycerin is also known as Glonoin or Trinitrin. It is an oil-like liquid of specific gravity 1.6, insoluble in water but soluble in alcohol and extremely sensitive to shock. Thus it is hazardous to transport.

The U.S. pharmacopeia points out that the spirit form is a one per cent alcohol solution of nitroglycerin for which extremely great care must be taken in dispensing, packing, storing or transporting the spirit. Dangerous explosions may result if the spirit is spilled, or if some of the alcohol is evaporated. If some of the spirit is spilled, then a solution of sodium hydroxide or potassium hydroxide should be poured over the spilled portion in order to decompose the glyceryl trinitrate. The spirit should neither be tasted nor put on the skin because it will cause severe headache. And yet there are now available adhesive pads used as 24-hour skin patches for transdermal therapy. Supposedly a slow, steady stream of nitroglycerin is released over a full day—just enough to exert a prophylactic effect.

It was this substance with which Alfred Nobel experimented. He found that nitroglycerin could be adsorbed on siliceous earts such as kieselgur or diatomite in amounts ranging from 25 to 75 per cent. If so treated, the result was a solid substance that was safe and easy to handle and could be molded into bricks, for example, for easy transportation since it was reasonably insensitive to shock. He named his solid substance, his nitroglycerin-kieselgur mixture, Dynamite. Soon every builder, mine owner, factory establishment and so on clamored for dynamite. He built factories in many countries. Alfred Nobel became wealthier and wealthier while his character grew stranger and stranger. Or at least more complex and more difficult to fathom. The impact on him of his own invention was tremendous.

Greedy and dishonest individuals tried to infringe on his patents Well-meaning groups berated him for manufacturing explosives that might be used in wars. Alfred Nobel himself was a complete pacifist who loathed war and also was afraid that his dynamite might be used for non-peaceful, non-building purposes. He refused, however, to speak at peace congresses and to make contributions to peace groups. He once said: "My factories may make an end of war sooner than your congresses. The day when two army corps can annihilate each other in one second, all civilized nations, it is to be hoped, will recoil from war and discharge their troops." It is to be hoped.

With factories all over Europe and America, Alfred Nobel spent a great deal of his life in trains, boats and hotels. But he had few friends and preferred to be alone. He brooded. He dreamed. As he once wrote: "I want to live among trees and bushes, silent friends who respect the state of my nerves, and I escape when I can from both large cities and deserts." Additionally, he once said: "I drift about without a rudder or compass, a wreck on the sea of life." He also hated pretentiousness. When asked for autographs or photographs of himself, Nobel would say: "In these days of conspicuous and unashamed publicity, only those who are specially adapted to the purpose ought to let their photographs appear in a newaspaper."

As for religion, his views were complex. Suffice it here to say that Nobel claimed that religion had value only to the extent to which it expressed itself in love for all mankind. As for literature Nobel once claimed that literature was a source of health for humanity as it progressed evermore into the future.

With this short review we perhaps can form an idea of Nobel's viewpoints of life in general, of literature, of peace and of science, all of which blended into a concept resulting in what today are known as the Nobel Prizes for achievements in the fields of physics, chemistry, medicine, literature and the furtherance of peace. We can certainly agree with Alfred Bernhard Nobel that progress in these fields can only result in happiness for future generations.

On December 10, 1896, Alfred Nobel died in San Remo, Italy.

Louis Pasteur in his laboratory (1885).

LOUIS PASTEUR

Of course there are many many photochemical drugs other than the ergot, digitalis and quinine described here along with others. But with few exceptions, such as atropine, their impacts were or are of small dimensions. Also, there are many plant drugs which are not plant alkaloids but nevertheless exert a great impact on us. Of the men or events which have exerted or still exert an impact on us of the 19th and 20th centuries, perhaps the greatest of all was Louis Pasteur.

This founder of the microbiological sciences has an interesting background. Louis Pasteur was born on December 27, 1822, in Dôle, in the Jura region of France. His education was scientific, and all of it was received in the Ecole Normale Supérieure in Paris. He was graduated in 1847. He then became Professor of Physics (1848-1849) in Dijon, Professor of Chemistry (1849-1854) in Strasbourg and Professor of Chemistry and Dean of the Lille Faculty of Sciences. In 1857, Pasteur returned to the Ecole Normale Supérieure in Paris as Director of Scientific Studies. Finally in 1867 he became Professor of Chemistry at the Sorbonne in Paris. The reason for all these changes was that most of the time the had to organize or reorganize the departments concerned.

ISOMERISM

One of Pasteur's first findings was made while he was still a student: he discovered isomerism by manually separating the two crystalline forms of tartaric acid and demonstrating their opposite effects on polarized light. Pasteur also showed that natural substances always are found in one of the two isomeric forms, levorotatory or dextrorotatory, but that substances produced by chemical synthesis are mixtures of both, or racemic forms. He also pointed out that as regards their chemical action on isomeric forms, all living things exhibit selectivity, a chemical selectivity of living processes. The findings were only preliminary to his general germ theories. In this development he was helped along by a factory owner in Lille.

ALCOHOL

The industrialist asked Louis Pasteur for help, because in making alcohol by fermentation of sugar by yeast he often obtained unwanted and undesirable secondary products. At that time, scientists thought that yeast was merely a non-living catalyst for the fermentation process. Pasteur's studies on the chemical selectivity of living processes led him to think that yeast was a living organism with its own characteristics, and that its conversion of sugar into alcohol was one of its characteristics, its chemical selectivity. The only difference here was that yeast was a very tiny substance, a microbe. Louis Pasteur reported this to the Lille industrialist and pointed out that his alcohol contained not only yeast but other microscopic living organisms which co-existed with or overcame the processes expressed by yeast. Later, Pasteur could change, by fermentation methods, sugar into alcohol or butyric acid or lactic acid, or alcohol into acetic acid and other fermentations. Pasteur believed that each specific fermentation process was effected by a specific microbe, or germ (as he named it), acting on a specific substance to produce another specific substance, such as yeast acting on sugar to produce alcohol. Thus was the germ theory of fermentation evolved.

GERM THEORY OF FERMENTATION

In 1857, Louis Pasteur published his first paper on the germ theory of fermentation. It is now a classic. It was titled "Mémoire sur la fermentation appelée lactique." Pasteur said that the various types of microorganisms could be separated from each other by proper techniques, could take advantage of the nutritional needs of the microbes and their degrees of response to antiseptic substances. Louis Pasteur then claimed that just as each type of fermentation was carried out by a specific germ, so it was with many diseases. Each type of disease was caused by a specific germ. This short report was only the beginning.

Continuing his studies of microbiological life, Pasteur discovered that some microbes could live without oxygen, that they could derive energy from actions that did not employ oxygen, and that this type of anaerobiosis demonstrated that fermentation is the metabolic equivalent of respiration when life is sustained without oxygen.

Pasteur's next accomplishment was to squelch the idea of spontaneous generation. Scientists of that time occupied themselves with the origin of microbes. Some thought they derived from souring milk or putrefaction of meat or fermentation of the juice of grapes. Pasteur demonstrated that each microorganism is derived from a preexisting microorganism. He showed, too, that perishable products could be kept fresh by killing the microbes present, that is, by sterilizing the products, and that they could be kept sterilized by keeping contaminants away. Pasteur's method involved the use of heat and in his honor is called pasteurization. It is used widely for milk foods and beverages.

GERM THEORY OF DISEASE

Because wounds could not be heated, could not be pasteurized, the English surgeon Joseph Lister reasoned that if microbes caused putrefaction, they also could cause wound infections. Thus he tested compounds that would kill germs without heat. Carbolic acid solution was his answer. Lister applied it to dressings and instruments and as a spray in the operating theater. And by employing steam under high pressure, Lister could sterilize instruments, gowns and drapes, and thus practice aseptic surgery.

SPORES

Meanwhile, Louis Pasteur in 1865 was asked by the silk industry if he could solve its problems. The silkworms were diseased. Pasteur found that they actually had two diseases, one caused by a parasite and one due to bad nutrition, and developed techniques to treat them. Another finding by Louis Pasteur was his discovery of highly resistant structures he named spores. This was the answer as to why the anthrax bacillus, for example, could survive in the soil or in the carcasses of animals for lengthy periods of time.

IMMUNIZATION

Still another contribution to the microbiological sciences was immunity. Pasteur showed that birds infected by old cultures of chicken cholera were not affected by virulent cultures. Therefore, he proposed that such attenuated forms, altered by any of several methods available, could be used to immunize persons. This then was the reason why injection of cowpox material protected humans against smallpox. And why sheep and goats were protected against virulent anthrax. Pasteur himself suggested the terminology by proposing the word vaccine for the attenuated cultures and their employment as vaccination.

The resistance met with by Louis Pasteur as late as 1881 can be seen in a passage that appeared in the September issue of Scientific American for that year:

"So long as smallpox vaccination stood alone, the alleged prevention of a malignant disease by the voluntary production of a mild disease of a similar type being a fact unique and unexplained, the anti-vaccinationists had a shadowy ground to stand on. How is it possible, they asked, to protect life and health by inviting disease? And when they boldly disputed statistics and pronounced the theory of vaccination a delusion, not a few intelligent people were confounded and prejudiced against a practice that has reduced to comparative feebleness one of the worst of the plagues of former days. The discoveries of the past year by Professor Pasteur in connection with chicken cholera made vaccination a fact no longer unique, and they gave a most promising clew to the rationale of its operation in making the system less vulnerable to smallpox. That distinguished investigator of microscopic life demonstrated the living virus of chicken cholera, and he proved that by suitable cultivation it could be so attenuated or shorn of its malignant quality that it would produce only a feeble disturbance of the animal organization, which yet sufficed to protect the animal as thoroughly from the more virulent disease as the latter could in case it was not fatal."

VIRUSES

In 1882, Pasteur expanded his work on viruses by commencing his studies on rabies. He could show that this terrible disease of animals was transmitted by a microbiological agent so small that it could not be seen, even under microscopes. Louis Pasteur thus definitely uncovered the world of viruses. In developing his vaccine against rabies, he infected rabbit spinal cord tissues and attenuated the material to vaccinate dogs against the disease. He also prepared a vaccine for humans bitten by rabid dogs, foxes, rabbits and other animals in contact with humans.

This time the whole world took notice and funds both private and public poured into Paris to build the famous Pasteur Institute in 1888. Its first director was Louis Pasteur. That its staff numbers among its members several Nobel Prize winners is an indication of the high order of research carried out there still.

The Paris School of Pharmacy (1885).

INDUSTRIAL MICROBIOLOGY

ANTON VAN LEEUWENHOEK

When we think of Louis Pasteur working with test tubes, pipettes, Erlenmayer flasks and microscopes, we can only marvel at the results he and his predecessors accomplished. Anton van Leeuwenhoek in 1676 had established the fact that there were numerous living organisms in one drop of water. "No more pleasant sight has met my eye than this of so many thousands of living creatures in one small drop of water."

C. LINNAEUS

Thus the Dutchman, two hundred years before Pasteur, had discovered protozoa and bacteria. One hundred years before Pasteur, Carolus Linnaeus of Sweden in the mid-1700 s made a classification of all animals and plants: Kingdoms, Phyla, Classes, Orders, Families, Genera and Species. Contemporary with Pasteur in 1858, the German Rudolf Virchow suggested that living cells all derived from other preexisting living cells. The Englishman Charles Darwin in 1859 published his now classic book, "The Origin of Species."

C. DARWIN

The book was based on the voyage Darwin started in 1831 on H.M.S. Beagle. He marveled that the Galapagos Islands off the coast of Ecuador should have so many different species, and that many anatomical features conformed with the tasks to be carried out. Finches, for example, displayed special feeding habits by cracking hard seeds and yet each one had a different beak. It took Charles Darwin almost three decades then to formulate his theory of evolution by natural selection, now most popularly known as survival of the fittest. As Darwin wrote: "Can we doubt that individuals having any advantage, however slight, over others would have the best chance of surviving and procreating their kind?" Or, as Darwin further proclamed, that "any variation in the least degree injurious would be rigidly destroyed." As Charles Darwin stated, Nature employed this principle to control life and its development.

GREGOR MENDEL

Another 19th century scientist contemporary with Pasteur was Gregor Mendel of Austria. As a monk almost secluded in his monastery, Mendel worked quietly and inconspicuously in the monastery gardens to develop the laws of heredity. By crossbreeding yellow and green peas, he showed that traits were always in a three-to-one ratio, as, for example, three yellows for every green pea. He called the yellow ones dominant and the green one recessive. Further, Mendel suggested that because these traits always reappear in later generations and in the same ratio, then it must be that characteristics that are inheritable are passed on by discrete factors. Today we call these genes. Because he published in an obscure journal and because scientists ignored this simple monk, the work of Gregor Mendel was forgotten. It was 1900 before his work was discovered, sixteen years after his death in 1884.

T.H. MORGAN

Carrying on the work of Gregor Mendel in an effort to unravel the details of inheritance was an American of the 20th century, Thomas Hunt Morgan of Columbia University in New York City. Besides elaborating on Mendel's theories, T.H. Morgan extolled the use of the fruit fly Drosophila. Because this fly has only four pairs of chromosomes and multiplies rapidly, it is ideal for tracing how specific traits are transmitted from one generation to another for numerous generations. Thus Morgan could make mutations of the Drosophila by stunting the wings or mismatching eye colors or by making the fly bodies asymmetric. In 1926, Morgan published his book "The Theory of the Gene." This established genetics as an independent field ot its own.

HISTORY OF PHARMACY

J.D. WATSON/F. CRICK

How independent was shown by an Anglo-American team that solved one of the most difficult biological problems—the molecular structure of DNA. The American, James D. Watson, was a post-doctoral student in England, and in 1951 teamed up with Francis Crick, a British physicist. Some eighteen months later, they showed that the chemical DNA had the structure of a double spiral staircase—a double helix—which demonstrated the mechanism employed by the DNA of cells to store genetic imprints and transmit them further. The full story of DNA remains to be told.

With his Germ Theory of Fermentation and Germ Theory of Diseases Louis Pasteur exerted a great impact on pharmacy, medicine, nursing and all paramedical disciplines. He opened up to us a broad pathway and left ajar the doors to the new worlds of viruses and genetics and their allied sciences of molecular biology and immunology. The profession of pharmacy has wonderful new opportunities to exploit. Its pharmacognosy now embraces back-room disciplines whereby pharmacists such as Fritz Kraft, Claude Nativelle, and others could again do research work in the prescription room or most likely a laboratory annex.

NEW HORIZONS

Pharmacists also have a golden opportunity in manufacturing the new medicines by new methods. Pharmaceutical drugs can now be manufactured by microbiological production. What started out with Pasteur and was furthered by bacteriologists like Robert Koch, A. Calmette and C. Guérin and others to treat diseases by means of vaccines has developed into microbiological manufacture of substances such as antibiotics, hormones, vitamins and alkaloids, and research substances such as interferon, antitumor drugs, and other drugs of all kinds. But most of the emphasis is on cheaper production. Here again pharmacists can profit because it is they who must work out the substrates. Who must keep track of the microorganisms employed. Who must be in charge of modifications and of numerous other activities.

PENICILLIN MOLD

Microbiological manufacturing received its greatest impetus only after World War II, when penicillin was in such great demand. But its dramatic story started before the war. About 1870, Pasteur, Tyndall and Roberts actually observed the antibiotic antagonism of one microbe upon another, and Pasteur even suggested that this phenomenon could be exploited therapeutically. For the next four or five decades, microbial preparations were given to animals, but they were either poisonous or had no effect at all. In his laboratory in London, in 1929 Alexander Fleming had made cultures of *Staphylococcus aureus,* but he noticed that a mold had contaminated his cultures. Fortunately for us, Fleming did not merely throw away his ruined cultures. Instead he grew the mold—*Penicillium notatum*—in a liquid medium. Then he separated the cells from the fluid. His cell-free fluid was tested on various microbes, and Fleming found that it inhibited the growth of many different kinds of bacteria. He gave the name penicillin to the active ingredient in the cell-free fluid. Ironically, he did not follow through and stopped testing his self-styled penicillin. His fellow British scientists continued work along the same lines.

INDUSTRIAL PENICILLIN

Penicillin was a very unstable substance and thus British researchers throughout the 1930's were stumped.

The 1940's were different. Ernst B. Chain, Howard W. Florey, Norman G. Heatley and others at Oxford University in 1939 began a search for a stable penicillin. They found it in a mold called *Penicillin chrysogenum* that is closely related to *P. notatum.* They marveled at its antibacterial action in animals and man and eagerly sought an industrial process for its manufacture. Since World War II was raging, it was almost impossible to work toward this end. Accordingly, it was agreed in 1941 to approach the United States for help. Soon the United States Department of Agriculture and five American pharmaceutical companies (Abbott, Merck, Pfizer, Squibb and Winthrop) started building large vats for fermentation of penicillin. It was not easy because in the beginning deep cultures were not available. Only surface cultures in large flat pans were

Charles Robert Darwin (1809-1882).

available until engineers could solve the problem of sterilization of such large silos. Today, fermentation columns hold up to 200,000 liters of culture.

STREPTOMYCIN

After penicillin came streptomycin. It was discovered by Selman A. Waksman at Rutger's University in New Jersey, U.S.A. Waksman was a soil microbiologist at the University and succeeded in obtaining several new antibiotics from a class of organisms named actinomycetes. The best of these by far was streptomycin; it started off the long list of new fermentation products and processes that are still available to us now.

ANTIBIOTICS

It can be seen that penicillin not only was the start of a new era clinically but also commercially and industrially. The highest sales are in five antibiotics groups: penicillins, cephalosporins, tetracyclines, erythromycins, and the aminoglycosides, which include streptomycin. Of the 5,000 antibiotics known, only 100 have been marketed. Over 20 per cent of the prescription value represents sales of drugs produced almost solely by microbiological manufacture.

Besides the antibiotics, other drugs for the pharmaceutical industry are being made by microbiological processes, or at least by both biological and nonbiological means. One such group of drugs is the steroids, which include cutisme.

STEROIDS

In working on the hormones secreted by the adrenal glands, Professor Tadeus Reichstein of the University of Basel, Switzerland, and Edward C. Kendall of the Mayo Foundation isolated several hormones in the early 1930's. One of these was named cortisone. Then a decade later, Philip S. Hench, also of the Mayo Foundation, gave it to patients and found that it relieved the pain of rheumatoid arthritis. The demand for cortisone was tremendous. Naturally, every drug house started immediate research to increase yields.

Chemical synthesis involved 37 steps, which was much too elaborate, and too expensive. The key to a cheaper synthesis was that a hydroxyl-OH group had to be inserted at position 11 in the four-ring steroid nucleus. Many chemists worked on this problem because the rewards were tremendous. Finally, in 1952, two Upjohn Company scientists, D. H. Peterson and H. C. Murray, reported that a strain of bread mold named *Rhizopus arrhizus* could hydroxylate a different steroid hormone named progesterone which in turn could hydroxylate cortisone by microbial hydroxylation. This meant 11 steps instead of 37 and a price only 20 per cent that of the totally synthetic drug. As for the other steroid drugs, some are also produced by microorganisms, at least partially. These are the corticosteroids: cortisone, hydrocortisone, prednisone and dexamethasone, as well as the androgen, testosterone, and the estrogen, estradiol, and the diuretic, spironolactone. Such steroids are now available at reasonable prices not only due to microbes but also because simple manufacturing practices can be used: water as a solvent with fermentation carried out at 37° C at atmospheric pressure.

SEMISYNTHETICS

However, from the practical point of view in industrial microbiology at present, semisynthetic approaches are employed. This is so for penicillins and cephalosporins, collectively known as betalactam antibiotics, in which new side chains are attached, exchanged or removed by chemical synthesis after fermentation methods have been employed. During a screening program, Merck Sharp & Dohme and Eli Lilly and Company found new betalactam antibiotics in the fermentation broths of streptomycetes. They named these cephamycins. They are similar to cephalosporins.

MUTASYNTHESIS

Another new method of making antibiotics is called mutational biosynthesis, or mutasynthesis for short. This genetic method consists of inducing a mutation in a gene that codes for one precursor of a microbe's

190

natural antibiotic. The original active antibiotic leads to the synthesis of an incomplete and inactive antibiotic. But when the missing precursor is again added to the medium, the result is again an original active antibiotic. It can be seen that if, instead of the original missing precursor, a precursor or a series of precursors with different characteristics is added to the medium, then the result is a new active antibiotic.

UNCONQUERED FIELDS

It may be wondered why, after four decades of antibiotics research, the chase after new ones is greater than ever. The reason is that most antibiotics to date are antibacterial, and that they are more effective against Gram positive than against Gram negative bacteria. Thus the search is still on for substances that would be effective against viruses and against fungi as well as against tumors.

The new agents would have to be selective. As it is, the few now available act against normal human cells as well as diseased or cancerous tissues. The antifungal agents can be applied topically but are toxic if swallowed. Viruses may be conquered one day, but it took Merck Sharp & Dohme thirteen years to develop a new hepatitis vaccine made directly from human blood. And up to now the antitumor agents are damaging to the heart or have other toxic effects. Here is another chance for pharmacists to become active in these fields.

Jonathan Pereira (1804-1853).

Interior of an Italian pharmacy, 18th century, Museum of Health, Rome.

David Handbury (1825-1875).

Advertising for a syrup for children, end of 19th century (courtesy of American Institute of the History of Pharmacy).

NINETEENTH CENTURY
PHARMACOGNOSY

Pharmacognosy in the 19th century was dominatoo by four pharmacists. Jonathan Pereira, Daniel Hanbury, Friedrich August Flückiger, Alexander Tschirch.

J. Pereira

Jonathan Pereira of London (1804-1853) beyan his career when only 15 years old when he was apprenticed to a ship's surgean. Twe years later he was studying surgery at St. Bartholomew's Hospital. At the same time, he studies pharmacy and chemistry at Aldersyate General Dispensatory. From 1827 to 1832, Pereira taught students pharmacy and prepared them for their pharmaceutical examinations. It was during, his period that Jonathan Pereira translatee the London Pharmacopeia of 1824 into english. Moreover he adapted it by prividing scientific descriptions of its preparations and his comments on their uses. Thus, this was the forerunner of all subsequent "extra" pharmacopeias such as Martindale's and ispensatories such as the U.S.D. or United states Dispensatory. Soon Pereira started to print his lectures on materia in the London Medical Gazette. They provec to be so popular that they were translated into German. At the same time, Pereira used his lectures as a base for his now classic book "Elements of Materia Medica and Therapeutics..." This was first printed in 1839 and was out of print by 1848. It was also translated into German. Meanwhile, he had written other books such as "A General Table of Atomic Numbers with an Introduction in the Atomic Theory." Another publication was "Selecta e. Praescriptis" which had elevea editions within thirty years.

In 1842, the Pharmaceutical Society of Great Britain put all its facilities for research at his disposal. Pereira took full advantage af the offer. His famous research on Peruvian Salsan was honored by namting the plant from which the balsam comes Myroxylon Persirae. Also well known are his investigations on microscopic plants in pharmaceutical preparations, as well as his use of polarizetion to distinguish between ethereal pils and balsams.

Naturally, Jonathan Pereira received many honors: being named a Fellow of the Royal Society, Curator of the Museum, Pharmacopeial Commission Doctor honoris causa, and many others. After all, it was Jonathan Pereira who put pharmacognosy on a scientific level. Following his death on January 20, 1853« the Pharmaceutical Society and London Hospital had a marble bust sculptured and erected in his memory. But perhaps an even greater honor was the re-publication of Jonathan Pereira's "Elements" two decades after his death.

D. Hanbury

The life of Daniel Hanbury can be described in one word: harmony. He was in harmony with himself and with the pharmaceutical world. As Professor Flückiger pointed out, "... dividing his time between the two poles of practical and scientific occupation, Hanbury's life was spent outwardly and inwardly in undisturbed harmony".

He was born on September 11. 1825 in London. To understand his life style better, we should know more about his background. The Hanbury family tree dates back to the twelfth century when even then the family members were landowners in Worcestershire. In 1806 Hanbury's great-aunt Charlotte married William Allen, a Quaker philanthropist and pharmaceutical factory owner.

En 1808 Allen took into his factory two new apprentices, Daniel and Cornelius Hanbury, his wife's nephews and the first Hanburys to enter pharmacy. The two nephews and their uncle, together with some friends, founded the Pharmaceutical Society of Great Britain on April 15, 1840. Mr. Allen became its first president.

Daniel Hanbury, jr., was born on September 11. 1825, in London as the first of six sons and one daughter. He was educated at a private school and very early displayed his precocious intelligence. He continued taking private lessns even after leaving school. His favorite studies were classical studies and water

Friedrich August Flückiger (1828-1894).

color painting. He spoke French fluently and was able to get along in German and Italian. His hobby was reading the Latin works of early Spanish, Portugese and Dutch explorers. Daniel Hanbury enjoyed travelling and writing, resulting in travel comments with sketches or paintings of what he thought or saw. Surely he must have derived much pleasure in laying out a botanical garden on land his brother Thomas (Sir Thomas) purchased on the Italian Riviera. Many guests were entertained in the Palazzo Orengo (the ruins of the castle having been renovated), including Queen Victoria. Empress Fredericka of Germany and her daughter enjoyed sketching the garden. The Prince of Wales, later to become king Edwards, the future King George and Queen Mary, and other royalty, were also visitors. This then was the one side of Daniel Hanbury.

In the meantime, his other side had also developed. At age 16 young Hanbury was apprenticed to his father and uncle at their firm in Lombard Street in London. Later one of his colleagues said of Hanbury that "... he was a good assistant though a scholar..." In 1844 he entered the school of the Pharmaceutical Society at Bloomsbury Square. There he met the great Jonathan Pereira, of whom he became a close friend and colleague. In fact, it was under Pereira's tutelage that Hanbury could make his contributions to pharmacognosy, about seventy of them. The first paper (on Turnsde) was printed in January 1850 in The Pharmaceutical Journal. Later monographs were on Cinchona, Balsam of Peru, myrrh, Chinese Materia Medica, and of course the Pharmacographia—A History of the Principal Drugs of Vegetable Origin which he co-authored with professor Flückiger.

Even though they had corresponded for three years, it was only in 1867 that Friedrich. A Flückiger and Daniel Hanbury net personally. They soon became fast friends. Both deplored the fact that there was no comprehensive work in English on pharmacognosy. The result was a joint venture, the "Pharmacographia" by F.A. Flückiger and D. Hanbury. Both dug deep in their work and contacted all sources of information: libraries, collections, warehouses, London docks and drug auctions. Hanbury even retired from business, at age 45, to devote all his time to "Pharmacographia." His father had also retired to help his son edit the various monographs. Both travelled extensively. Notwithstanding all this work, Daniel Hanbury was asked by the government to help establish and publish the Pharmacopoeia of India.

Although he had at his disposal ample financial means and all the luxury money could buy, Daniel Hanbury found these alien to his character. By choice his habits were simple and inexpensive. He shunned self-indulgence and ostentation. Even his diet was spare—vegetables with a little meat. He always arose early and did a large amount of writing before breakfast. At all pharmacy meetings Hanbury was always the silent member. Not married, he lived with his parents, to whom he was most kind. Never robust, Hanbury nevertheless was never ill. THus it was a shock when he was confined to bed with typhoid fever and died after eighteen days March 24, 1875, at the age of fifty.

Today the memory of this most remarkable pharmacists is perpetuated by the Hanbury memorial medal that is awarded approximately every two years for original research in pharmacy; the Hanbury Collection of ancient and modern Drugs; the Personal Library of Daniel Hanbury now housed in that of the Pharmaceutical Society; his collected publications; and of course the classic "Pharmacographia—A history of the Principal Drugs of Vegetable Origin." Pharmacy gained very much by its contacts with Daniel Hanbury and his family. The firm of Allen and Hanbury is still strong and is still well known throughout the world.

F. A. Flückiger

Friedrich August Flückiger was another of the 19th century pharmacists who developed and established pharmacognosy as a discipline of its own. He was born in Langenthal, Switzerland on May 15, 1828, as the son of a commercial entrepreneur, and was sent to Berlin to attend a commercial school.

However, he transferred himself out and changed over to courses in chemistry. He continued with chemistry in Bern in 1847, but that same year he started to study pharmacy, first in Solothurn, Switzerland, then in Heidelberg, and finally in Paris. In 1853, he sought citizenship in Burgdorf and was accepted. In 1860, Flückiger was put in charge of the Staatsapotheke in Bern. By 1861, he had become a member of the staff in the University of Bern. In 1870, he was appointed associate Professor, and that same year was made President of the Swiss Pharmaceutical. By 1873, Friedrich Flückiger was appointed a full Professor and Director of the Pharmacy Institute in Strasbourg. He worked intensively until he was retired in 1892 and returned to Bern. After a lengthy sickness, he died there in 1894.

Because pharmacognosy as a subject was not yet stabilized in the 19th century, Flückiger attempted to put it on a scientific base, with many publications designed to serve as guides to teaching. One of these guides was "Pharmazeutische Chemie" or "Pharmaceutical Chemistry" of 1879 and 1892. Another was "Reaktionen," or "Reactions," of 1892. One of Flückiger's classic works is "Pharmakognosie des Pflanzenreichs" or "Pharmacognosy of the Plant Kingdom," printed in Berlin in 1867 and reprinted in 1883 and 1891. Based on this work was "Grundriss der Pharmakognosie," or "Textbook of "Pharmacognosy," printed in 1884 and 1894. The most important book, and one now a classic work, was the one he co-authored with Daniel Hanbury ane published in London, "the Pharmacographia—A History of the Principal Drugs of Vegetable Origin," by F. A. Flückiger and Daniel Hanbury. This book was also translated into FRench. Still another publication was the 1873 "Grundlage der Pharmazeutischen Warenkunde" or "Fundamentals of Pharmaceutical Substances," which he wrote Alexander Tschirch. In addition to all these, Flückiger published several more historical works, such as "Beiträge zur älteren Geschichte der Pharmazie in Bern," or "Contributions to the Older History of Pharmacy in Bern," in 1862 and the "Frankfurter Liste," Frankfort Lists "(of registered drugs, taxable items and so on), of 1873, and in 1876 "Dokumente zur Geschichte der Pharmazie."

As for the man himself, Friedrich August Flückiger can best be described by the nickname given him by his students—Papa. Apart from his many publications, "Papa" will retain a plae in the history of pharmacy because of the Flückiger Foundation established by his friends. The Foundation awards the Flückiger medal periodically to worthy researchers upgrading pharmacognosy. Themedal was first impressed in bronze in 1892. Friedrich Flückiger outlived Daniel Hanbury by almost twenty years. Their lives were dedicated to their professions. Their writings formed a great part of their lives. Their medals will let both of them live on in the annuals of pharmacy. Their lives wer always modest, it is fitting that the Foundation of each has acted in accordance with the means available, which explains why the Hanbury medals is of gold and that of "Papa" of bronze.

A.W.O. Tschirch

Alexander Wilhelm Oswald Tschirch was the fourth in the quartet of the founding pharmacognosists. Based on the accomplishments of the others—Pereira, Hanbury and Flückiger—Tschirch could do an immense amount of work to develop pharmacy and pharmacognosy still further. His more than 500 articles of all kinds and his more than dozen books are witness to his achievements.

Although of modest circumstances, Alexander Tschirch was able to study in Berlin, thanks to his mother, who unselfishly aided him. His father had died when Tschirch was 19 years old. He was born in the small Prussian village of Guben on October 17, 1856, and had an uneventful childhood At age 16, he commenced his education in pharmacy, at first in Freiburg and then in Berlin. There he was an intensive student and attended all types of lectures suchas those of August Hofmann, who helped found organic chemistry; Hermann Helmhöltz, who helped develop physics; and Audolf Virchow, who helped found pathology. The big names of the scientific world were gathered in Berlin and Alexander Tschirch was to join them.

It is tho no wonder that by 1880, at the age of 24, Tschirch delivered a lecture titled "Pharmacognosy as a Science and its Importance in the Study of Pharmacy." Tschirch argued that pharmacognosy was not merely a branch of botany to be taught by botanists, and surely not a "museum for dried plants." In a further attack upon the doctrine of signatures, Tschirch emphasized that "the botanical description does not determine the valve of the plant as a drug." Instead, he stressed the constituents of drug plants. As he said, "the chemical constituents determine whether the plant can be so used. Therefore they are the most important." He was eager to put more emphasis on this new biological pharmacy and to put all of pharmacy on a higher scientific plane.

After receiving his doctorate, Tschirch spent some time acquiring experience in technological procedures and food chemistry. He then spent three years as an assistant in the Institute for Plant Physiology where he eventually became a member of the faculty and could concentrate on pharmacognosy. He treated the subject as pharmacochemical and pharmacobotanical and insisted on extensive microscopic botany and later on microbiology. He had great plans for a Pharmaceutical Institute or rather a Pharmaceutical University Institute as well as a Society for Pharmacognosy.

When the City of Berlin refused to sponsor his Institute, it was easy for Tschirch to accept an offer to found such an Institute in Bern, Switzerland. Here Tschirch was given a more or less free hand to carry out his ideas and here he remained for almost 50 years until his death in December 1939. His facilities were at first rather modest. In 1890 the Swiss Pharmaceutical Institute consisted of Friedrich Flückiger's former first floor apartment, almost unchanged. Tschirch's office and library was formerly a child's bedroom and his private laboratory the kitchen. The bedroom became a pharmaceutical chemistry laboratory, the living room his lecture and microscope room. But his immense drive more than made up the deficit.

Tschirch did put pharmacognosy on a high level chemical basis. He himself became a pioneer in the chemistry of plant gums and resins. His book "Die Harze und die Harzbehälter" has become a classic. His "Handbuch der Pharmazie" in seven volumes is still the authority for much of pharmacognosy and pharmacy in general. Pharmacognosy has become a science only because. Alexander Tschirch pulled all the loose ends together to obtain a tightly knit subject on drugs of various origins: plant, animal, synthetic, and microbiological. Tschirch worked his whole life to bring into a system the flood of pharmaceutical preparations and agents. Now the flood is even greater, but at least we can follow the guidelines of Alexander Tschirch.

It would not be fair to him to not mention his private life. After graduating and receiving his doctorate, the new Doctor Tschirch visited his uncle to gather some experience in his relative's food processing factory. There he met his cousin, Elise Zierek. And there he married her. Alexander Tschirch also did some traveling both on the European continent and in India. His travel reports were written in a literary style more like anecdotes and were printed in various journals and compiled in a book, "Indian Drug and Economic Plants," published in 1891. Tschirch was also an excellent photographer and could sketch very well, so much so that his co-authored book, "Anatomic Atlas of Pharmacognosy and Foods, published 1897 in Leipzig, was written around his sketches. The lectures delivered by Alexander Tschirch were well attended because he spiced them up with humorous or sarcastic remarks and anecdotes. Among his friends were internationally famous painters as well as friends from the world of the theatre and literature. Some of these artists gave him lessons in painting and Alexander Tschirch also exhibited his water colors. A cardiac condition curtailed his activities but he retained his fabulous memory and mental possess until he succumbed on December 2, 1939.

Alexander Wilhelm Oswald Tschirch (1856-1939).

Dr. Alexander Fleming (1881-1955).

DEVELOPMENT OF
THE PHARMACEUTICAL
INDUSTRY

In a way it may be said that a pharmacist who has compounded a physician's prescription has manufactured something. He could also manufacture his own formulation for sale to customers of cough medicines, plasters, antispasmodics and other such items. If he were ambitious, the pharmacist would build an annex. If he were very successful he would build a factory. And that factory would be big or small and in private or public hands. Thus began the pharmaceutical profession of today.

Italy, as the cultural center of the world for many centuries, started the development of pharmaceutical and chemical manufacturing. Venice, from the year 1294 onward, was manufacturing cinnabar, corrosive sublimate borax, soap, lead, Venetian talc, Venetian treacle and turpentine.

Moreover, as Edward Kremers and George Urdang have pointed out, there was a lot of industrial activity within monasteries. Monks prepared cosmetics as well as distilled waters, and, of course, alcoholic drinks. Most of these had secret formulas consisting, as in Chartreuse, of many herbs and spices. Another still-favorite drink is Bénédictine, a secret, viscous, aromatic liquor containing various herbs and spices such as cloves, nutmeg, cinnamon, thyme, cardamon, peppermint, arnica, angelica, lemon, and sugar. And only the Monks know what else. The Bénédictine Monks also had other preparations, to combat diarrhea, cramps and loss of appetite as well as many other conditions treated in Folk Medicine.

In the changeover from a pharmacy to a pharmaceutical factory, the Italians contributed artistic representations such as pottery, glassware, vases and jars. In fact the pharmacy itself and even storerooms were art galleries; the establishment itself was one of architectural beauty. In addition, the Italians exerted an impact on the pharmacy of today through their literature of the profession: dictionaries, manuscripts and philosophical treatises and so on. The Italian pharmacists were not so scientific-minded as the Germans, who rushed into print to record every little change in a reaction. The Italians were more inclined to medicine, as attested by Salerno, Bologna, Pavia, Padua, Venice and other great centers.

OTHER COUNTRIES

The impact exerted by other countries was of varying degrees. When Columbus discovered America he dealt a serious blow to the Italian pharmaceutical industry. The reason was that with an all-water route to the East Indies, there was no reason for Venice to send ships to Egypt and the Near East. The Portuguese and the Dutch transported Oriental drugs and spices directly to Europe, and the New World drugs became available through the Spanish and English. Italians were not needed.

The French impact on the pharmaceutical industry was not too great. Camille Poulenc started out by manufacturing mineral salts and doing research on organic therapeutic agents. Later his establishment was fused with Rhône to become part of the giant Rhône-Poulenc of today.

ENGLAND

English influence was not too small but was centered in a few large places. Pharmaceutical industrial centers were in Scotland, Manchester, Leeds and London. John Fletcher Macfarlan of Edinburgh was one of the first to manufacture alkaloids on a large scale, at first in his laboratory and later in his factory. The factory of Allen and Hanbury is another example of a small enterprise over a century old and still keeping up the high level of the English pharmaceutical industry. Another enterprise, certainly not small, is that of Burroughs, Wellcome & Co.

After being graduated from the Philadelphia College of Pharmacy, the two Americans, S. M. Burroughs and Henry Wellcome, settled in England. The factory they established was unusual. All profits were to be turned over to a trust and to be used to fund medical and pharmaceutical research.

GERMANY

It was in Germany of course that the pharmacists and pharmacies provided the nucleus of the giant pharmaceutical industries, aided and abetted by the dyestuffs establishments. At first, pharmacists who liked to manufacture did so in their own laboratories. Then they enlarged their own small factories. Later on they sold, or bought, such factories. In reality, only a few could carry out their activities so far.

One of these was J. D. Riedel of the Schweizer-Apotheke in Berlin in 1814. Another was E. Merck of Darmstadt in 1827 whose Mother Pharmacy was the Engel Apotheke in Darmstadt. The Grüne Apotheke in Berlin was the starting point in 1852 for Schering, and in 1907 the Löwen Apotheke in Dresden became the Mother Pharmacy of Leo-Werk.

Advertising for Pilule Pink, 1899.

1890 env.

DEVELOPMENT OF THE PHARMACEUTICAL INDUSTRY AMERICA

General Remarks

Many events exert an impact on pharmacy as a whole, but especially on the pharmaceutical industry. Thus, in Europe it was mostly the discovery of America and the colonization of other large areas. That affected the industry. In America it was the Revolutionary war and the Civil war that brought changes in pharmaceutical manufacturing. In Europe the changes seemed to be fewer because the profession was more stable. Pharmacists had been in the same families for decades and generations. Pharmacists were better educated and their contacts with university laboratories were closer. Manufacturing was carried on more as a sideline or for self-satisfaction.

Some pharmacists were research minded. Prices were generally controlled and to this day pharmacists cannot form chain shops. They also cannot establish a shop except in controlled areas—usually one shop per two thousand population and not closer than five hundred meters from another pharmacy. In America, conditions were almost the opposite—a neighbor might be five hundred kilometers away.

The educated pharmacists tended to locate in the large cities: New York, Chicago, Philadelphia or New Orleans, and were usually French or German immigrats. The rest were merely shopkeepers; they were self-educated in pharmacy or else apprentices either to a pharmacist or to a physician. Doctors who had the money usually purchased or established a drug store and then sold it to their apprentices clerks. As for others, as they drifted across the plains and prairies, they tended to settle down in a spot that took their fancy or else one that needed a general store. It must not be forgotten that many people became pioneers only because the government gave them plots of land which became theirs free of charge after a few years of development. This explains the geography: very small villages spread far apart from each other and both states and counties having the shape of a square. The names of these squares are usually family or personal names. It was in such hamlets that a druggist was expected to make a living. He could not. Thus he started to sell what the pioneers and settlers needed most.

They homespun their own textiles and thus needed dye tuffs. They also needed paints for the cabins and houses they built, wallpaper, books and miscellaneous domestic medicines. It was not easy, as Edward Kremers and George Urdang pointed out, in some parts of the West. In what sounds like cowboy thriller, they recounted the difficulties encountered by some pharmacists.

Goods could be dispatched to Helena, by boat only three months yearly. For the other nine months, they had to be transported 2400 kilometers overland and were often hijacked along the way.

As the textile business grew and grew, it became independent and had its own chemists, who soon manufactured oils and paints for the building trades, too. Thus, it was only those establishments that already had manufactured pharmaceutical preparations that could expand. The government gave the larger firms a lot of help by manipulation of the alcohol tax. One way was to place a big tax on alcohol. A small firm would buy alcohol and use it to make tinctures or elixirs, for example, and use up its alcohol. A large firm would buy alcohol in very large quantities and use it to extract drugs, and recover the alcohol. Naturally, he was not purchasing it again and could use it to make tinctures or elixirs at a much cheaper price than the pharmacist, since the alcohol component was free.

The Amercian way of doing business was also a factor that had an impact on pharmaceutical manufacturing. This included free samples, special discounts, bonuses, price cuttings, chain stores, cooperative buying and manufacturing and franchise outlets.

Most of these are self-explanatory. Since pharmacists could not combat the price cutters by cooperative buying, they resorted to cooperative manufacturing, at first by trying to meet the wishes of individual pharmacists for their own brand preparations. After trying to organize regional units in 1896 a movement to put cooperative manufacturing on a national basis was started in 1897 by the United States Pharmacal Company of Chicago. A second movement to form a national cooperative manufacturing unit was the United Drug Company of Boston inaugurated by Louis K. Liggett, who was its first general manager. The United Drug Company in 1933 became a subsidiary company of Drug Incorporated which was a giant cooperative and better known as Rexall. Most of the Rexall drug stores are independent units of from one to a hundred employees. They are franchises of Rexall by which after they agree to purchase minimum yearly amounts of merchandise, they profit by lower prices and discounts of all kinds and can participate in advertising campaings and sales campaigns. In short, they manage the smaller pharmacies in its plan. Soon other corporations also attempted to make units along the same plan. Among others can be mentioned American Druggists Syndicate which in 1930 had over twenty thousand retail shops in its membership. Soon other cooperatives were also being formed as mutal buying clubs or mutual manufacturers or mutual wholesalers. Among the more importat were Mutual Drug Wholesalers Company, McKesson and Robbins, NARD + (National Association of Retal Druggists), Boots Ltd., Charles R. Walgreen, national Wholesale Druggists Association, and many others.

It can be said that perhaps all these groups had too much success. But the chaos of pricing and cut-rate discounts led to the introduction of the Fair Trade Laws of 1931 onwards, first by California and then by almost all states. The courts tried to prevent fixed prices and blacklisting of members and again made it possible for the manufacturer to use contracts binding on all in enforcing his prices. At any rate, the question was complex and fraught with controversial problems.

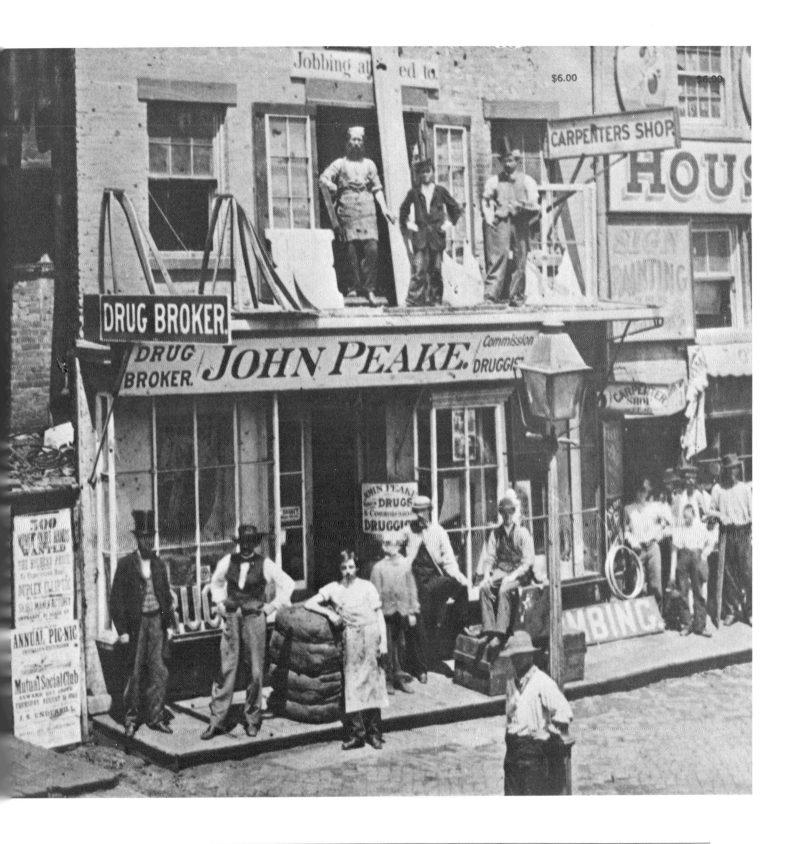

Drug Brocker New York, 1890 (Courtesy New York Historical Society).

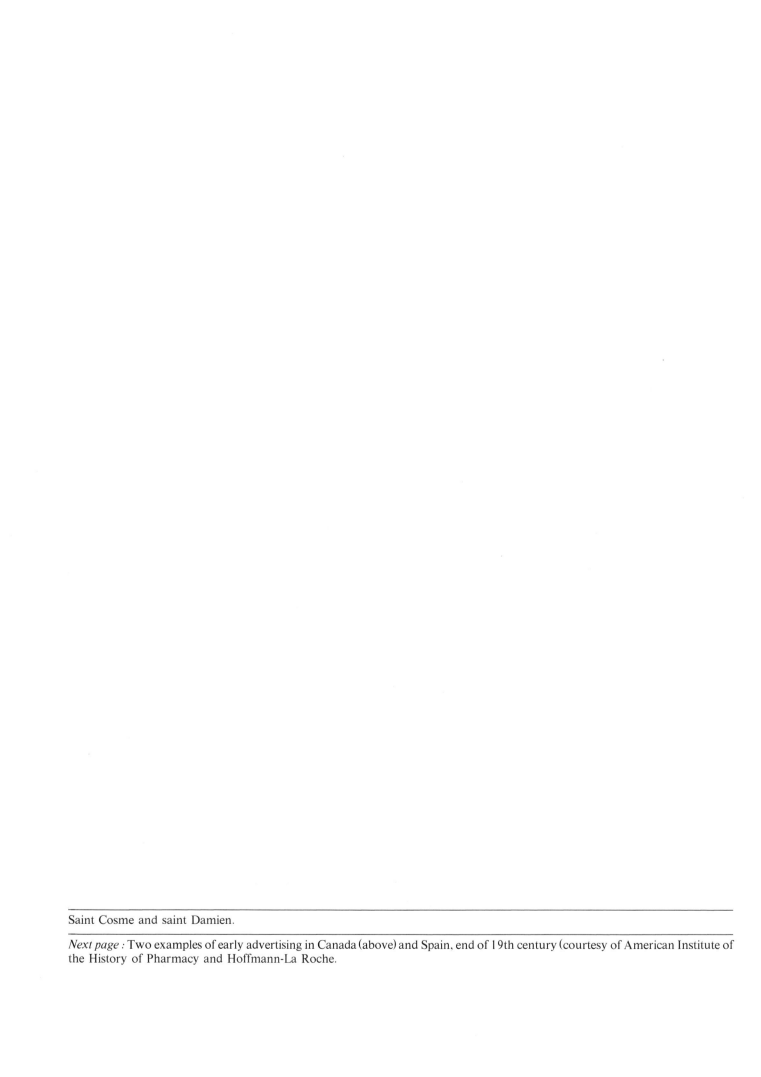

Saint Cosme and saint Damien.

Next page : Two examples of early advertising in Canada (above) and Spain, end of 19th century (courtesy of American Institute of the History of Pharmacy and Hoffmann-La Roche.

THE LITTLE DOCTOR.

SCOTT'S EMULSION

MUSEO DEL LOUVRE
Santa Ana (*Leonardo de Vinci*)

el
Jarabe "ROCHE"
es
el medicamento clásico
de las
Afecciones
bronco pulmonares.
15 años de éxitos
Consultad a vuestro médico.

IV

A FEW GREAT INTERNATIONAL COMPANIES

GREAT PHARMACEUTICAL COMPANIES

EDITOR'S NOTE :

It would have been particulary impossible to describe the history of all the important pharmaccutical companies around the world. This would have necessited a book in itself. The choice we have made has been dictated by the interest of illustrating the three principal ways by which large pharmaceutical companies have reached their present status.

1. Development of a small pharmacy into a giant company as illustrated by Merck, Schering, Abbott.

2. Companies created for the manufacture of pharmaceuticals by businessmen like for example Hoffmann-La Roche or Eli Lilly.

3. Companies growing from chemicals manufacturers ; the best examples being Bayer, Ciba-Geigy.

Besides, we have chosen some very special people because of their particular character like Dr. Abbott or Dr. Squibb.

We apologize to other pharmaceutical companies for having to make this choice.

In case the history has been written for us by the companies themselves, this has been clearly indicated. In other cases, the history has been written by our staff and approuved by the companies themselves.

ABBOTT

In 1871, Wallace Calvin Abbott was a fourteen year old husky muscular Vermont farm boy whose father thought that a farm was more important than a school. The boy was alert and learned quickly—but father Luther Abbott was adamant and all the pleas of mother Wealtha Barrows and her son were of no avail. Thus it was only in 1877 that twenty year old Wallace could continue his education. After attending Normal School, he decided that he would like to become a physician. Then after a year of premedical studies at Dartmouth, he transferred to the University of Michigan where he earned his Doctor of Medicine degree—his coveted M.D.—in 1885. Now he was alone. Unlike the Searle, Upjohn, Lilly, Squibb and other families, Wallace Calvin Abbott had no brothers and no sons. He was alone and penniless. On the other hand he was energetic enough for three or four other people. He slept only five hours per night and often got up at 3 a.m. As for finances—he had none. None except for what he had saved to get married to Clara Ingraham—his childhood sweetheart. Nevertheless he could borrow the one thousand dollars he needed to buy the practice of a family friend in Ravenswood—a village north of Chicago. Wallace Calvin Abbott then married Clara in 1886 and moved from Vermont to Ravenswood. As was usual at that time many physicians had drug stores—managed by hired clerks—where they concocted, advertised and sold household remedies. Dr. Abbott's Tooth Ache Drops. Laxative Lozenges. Blackberry Balsam. And many other such preparations. Dr. Abbott named his establishment People's Drug Store. He and his wife lived in two rooms at the rear of the shop. His life then consisted of making his rounds as a physician either on a bicycle horse or sled. And then manufacturing his formulas for sale in the People's Drug Store. But most important were granules and his writings.

After Sertürner isolated morphine from opium early in the nineteenth century many pharmacists started to make abstracts of drug plants. Meissner in 1819 then gave the name "alkaloids" to all such extracts. Concurrently the German physician Samuel Hahnemann was extolling his theory of homeopathic medicine that "Like should be cured by like" in small doses. In allopathic medicine the opposite is true—drugs with the opposite effect are given in large doses. He believed that minute diluted doses of strong drugs should be administered to patients for their ills. For example, quinine in allopathic doses causes symptoms of malaria—fever chills—in healthy persons and therefore to treat malaria the physician should give quinine in minute doses.

Hahnemann acquired a large worldwide following. In some centers, the Rudolf Steiner movement still today carries on with its "anthroposophic" and "intellectual" medicine which is very similar to homeopathy—at least as far as its dosage dilutions are concerned. At any rate, homeopathic medicine had nothing to do with Meissner's alkaloids nor Dr. Wallace Abbott's granules.

It must be remembered that in the early nineteenth century physicians had at their disosal only the raw dried crude drug or liquid preparations of them. Syrups. Elixirs. Fluid extracts. As for solids, only pills were available. And Tablets—also called compressed pills—were getting ever more popular. With the tablets came the coatings—gold, silver and sugar were the most employed. In fact, Dr. Abbott contributed a lot to the improvement and use of sugar coating in his granules.

As pharmacists and chemists isolated the initial alkaloids from plant after plant, they could give physicians preparations which were less bulky and therefore more potent. Much less had to be given. However they were not homeopathic. They were simply allopathic but in the form of pellets—small and round and coated with sugar. Dosages were standardized as much as could be at the time. But they varied from half milligram to five milligrams. Thus the doctor could dose the preparation individually. This came to be known as Dosimetric Medicine. Akaloidal Therapy. Dosimetry. Alkalometry. And other such terms. Dr. Abbott had a lot of success with his granules. So much so that he spent almost all his time making them and advertising them in the Medical World. He also considered himself as the advocate for the Middle West of the new therapy—from France mostly—and contributed many articles on it to the medical journals. He also wrote his own advertisements and labels. Today it is amusing to read some of the texts at the turn of the century. For example:

Abbott staff, 1913. D.G. Abbott. ▼

"Making money is good. Pleasing patients is better. But a combination of the two by using Dr. Abbott's sugar coated Alkaloidal Granules (Dosimetric) of the active priciples is best."

By that time Wallace Abbott had incorporated as The Abbott Alkaloidal Co., Ravenswood Post Office, Chicago. Branches in New York and San Francisco.

Later he added Seattle and London England. In an advertisement for Iodized Calcium for croup we find: "Doctor, you should have it on hand, for when you need it the need is urgent. No time to send then, the time to send is now. Brown in color, true to act and right in price." Above and below a photograph of the factory we find: "The Home of the Abbott Alkaloidal Company and Clinical Medicine and Headquarters for Exact Therapeutic Ideas, Means and Methods." Dr. Abbott was never at a loss for words.

Another practice which he advocated was to encourage self-dispensing. In fact, he designed an étui—a sheath or case—holding nine different vials of granules and sold them as a pocket pharmacy from which to dispense to patients. He defended self-dispensing on the grounds that most druggists were not trained well enough to manufacture—nor to prescribe them. Nor to promote them. Dr. Abbott was a genius as a copy writer and publisher.

Besides acting as contributor to The Medical World, Dr. Wallace Abbott became a charter subscriber to the Dosimetric Medical Review. He published The Alkaloidal Clinic. American Alkalometry. The Wallace Abbott Text Book of Alkaloidal Therapeutics—actually a collection of texts used in other pamphlets such as Abbotts Therapeutic Digest. Helpful Hints for the Busy Doctor. And then The Alkaloidal Clinic became The American Journal of Clinical Medicine. The fiirm built a complete printing plant with all machines necessary. Printing presses. Monotypes. Linotypes. Book binding. Composing room. Editorial offices. But not everything was tranquil. Competitors were at work—the most powerful being the AMA or American Medical Association.

For years, Dr. Abbott had been under attack because the American Medical Association, APHA, and the Journal of the American Medical Association, JAMA, claimed that The Alkaloidal Clinic was only a house organ. Thus it was not entitled to the lower postal rates it enjoyed. The dispute between the Editor of JAMA and Dr. Abbott soon grew very heated. There were just as many vehement in agreement as in disagreement. Not satisfied with mere letters, Dr. Abbott and his associates prepared a forty-eight page pamphlet to answer all accusations and attacks. He mailed it nationwide to the profession. The storm raged on for many years. Most likely it was only the onset of World War I which gave everyone other things to worry about instead of an acrimonious dispute drawn on and on. But as time went on, even Dr. Wallace Calvin Abbott supported Dr. George H. Simmons—editor of the Journal of the American Medical Association—especially at the time the Pure Food and Drug Act was being promulgated. It finally passed on June 30, 1906 and came into effect on January 1, 1907. As part of his support for AMA and JAMA, Dr. Abbott published still another magazine named "How To Live". It was typically Abbott in fighting the nostrums on the market and defending Dr. Simmons and his Journal of the American Medical Association.

As the year 1914 approached the whole pharmaceutical field was in a state of flux. War clouds over Europe made drugs and chemicals difficult to obtain. Internal structures had to be changed. Pharmacy was no longer a re-formulation of well established drugs. Thus the first thing was to change the name to Abbott Laboratories. The Abbott Alkaloidal Co. had run its course. Another change which the firm did was to hire a brilliant staff and to give it a lot of autonomy.

Abbott Laboratories was ready to expand and to respond to changes in the medical and pharmaceutical worlds.

Thus Dr. Alfred S. Burdick saw the need for a field antiseptic which was being developed by Dr. Henry H. Dakin and Dr. Alexis Carrel and which they had named Chloramine. Abbott Laboratories could obtain the rights to manufacture and distribute Chloramine under the name Chlorazene—it had to be changed due to similar names for previous products. Thanks to its chemical staff, Abbott was in a position to obtain the same rights for other chemically related disinfectants such as Halazone. Synthetic derivatives of other drugs were to follow.

In 1917 Congress passed the Trading with the Enemy Act. This allowed American companies to synthesize their own versions of well-known but scarce German brands. To protect the German products the Americans had to produce drugs of high quality under a different name and able to pass tests designed by the American Medical Association—besides paying five per cent royalties to the Alien Property Custodian and honoring the original patent. The Abbott Laboratories had a staff or brilliant organic chemists and soon had synthesized and marketed Veronal as Barbital. Novocaine as Procaine. Atophan as Cinchophen. Anesthesin as a preparation similar to Procaine. Salvarsan as Arsphenamine. Later Abbott Laboratories could add Butyn and Butesin Picrate to its list of self-made synthetic drugs. The company believed in research. This led to Metaphen—an organic mercury germicide. To Ephedrine—closely related to epinephrine. And to Nembutal—the short-acting barbiturate. Soon even larger triumphs were to come—such as capentothal sodium for intravenous anesthesia.

All credit is due to Dr. Wallace Calvin Abbott and his staff for entering the nutritional field at an early date. This new field was complex. Investigators were looking for unseen foods. They knew that milk contained one—as did lime juice and rice husks. But they had no name. Then Casimir Funk in 1913 came on the scene. This Polish chemist finally isolated what he thought was chemically an amine and that it was a life-giving amine. Thus he named his substance "Vitamine". It later was shown to be nicotinic acid. Further work led to the isolation of Vitamin A in 1918. Quickly the search was on for Vitamin A in all different kinds of foods. And of course for vitamins which were not Vitamin A. Surely if there were an A there must be Vitamin B and C and D, and so forth. Abbott Laboratories supported a lot of such work.

Synthetic vitamin D was first prepared by irradiating ergosterol with ultraviolet light. Abbott Laboratories was one of five pharmaceutical firms allowed to produce commercial quantities of irradiated ergosterol—which it marketed as Viosterol. By the mid-1930's, Abbott Laboratories had many types of vitamins available—including Vitamins A and D from halibut livers. Abbott found that halibut liver oil had one hundred times more Vitamin D than cod liver oil.

Abbott Alkaloidal Co. 1901.

Another plunge into another new area was Abbott's entrance into the bulk intravenous solutions field. Then came World War II. As Abbott boasted—they were ready for anything. They were.

Abbott could supply the U.S. Government with large supplies of dried blood plasma. They had the staff and equipment and devised ways to dry-freeze plasma. Abbott also supplied various sulfonamides and Steriolopes—containing sterilized drug—for use in the war zones. Abbott was allowed to manufacture quinacrine—in effect a copy of the German antimalarial Atabrine. Just as important was the Joint venture with four other companies to produce penicillin on a large scale. This led to other antibiotics.

The chief one of these is erythromycin—one of the safest of all.

After the war Tridione for the treatment of petit mal epilepsy was introduced in 1945. Abbott was the first pharmaceutical firm to deal in radioactive isotopes. It made these available for diagnosis treatment and research. Radioactive agents—gold iodine phosphorous thiovrea—were prepared on the spot for conversion to finished pharmaceuticals ready for the physician.

One product which Abbott had on the market, but lost it due to unusual circumstances—to say the least—was its table top sugar substitute Sucaryl Sodium. This product started with a cigarette. In 1937 a graduate student busy making derivatives of sulfamic acid in the University of Illinois laboratories took a short break to smoke a cigarette. Between puffs, he laid it on his work bench. When he resumed smoking he noticed that it had a peculiar sweet taste. To find the source of the sweetness he tested and tasted all the compounds on the desk. He found the sweet agent to be the derivative sodium cyclohexylsulfamate. For several years, extensive pharmacological and clinical investigations were carried out. Then researchers also showed that—like saccharin—Sucaryl was safe for use in foods. Its use quickly spread. Alas—in September 1970 the U.S. government banned domestic sales of cyclamate, because of controversial safety studies. Legal processes concerning proofs of safety and results of long term studies will probably continue for years to come.

Meanwhile Abbott is proceeding along, hoping to continue to the making of medical history. It has developed a newer faster test for detection of immunity for rubella or German Measles. A new type therapy Abbokinase for pulmonary embolism. Abbokinase is urokinase—a blood clot dissolving agent. A new electronic instrument MS-2 which shows which antibiotics will combat specific infections most effectively. Mental Health products. And new cardiovascular agents. Abbott has also intensified its efforts in basic research. It is working on fundamental recombinant studies with DNA or deoxyribonucleic acid and with NMR or Nuclear Magnetic Resonance plus other complex and expensive apparatus.

It has been a long journey for Abbott Laboratories from a flamboyant genius with one-man rule via a small but loyal, brilliant staff to its modern in every respect establishment. Its 31-500 employees are responsible for over two milliard dollars in sales annually from health-care products in about 130 countries. Abbott is truly international.

EXAMPLE OF THE EVOLUTION OF MEDICAMENTS' PRESENTATION
FROM 1900 TILL NOW

1904

1900

1919

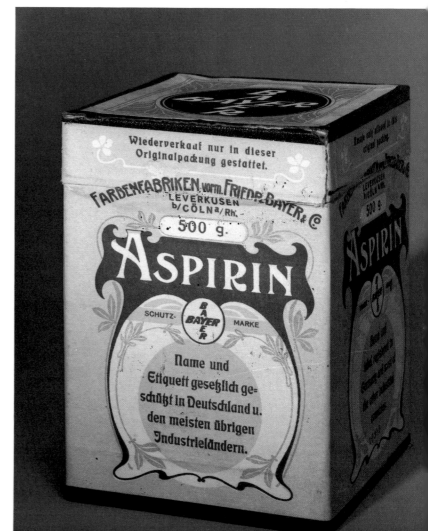

1930-1940

1930-1940

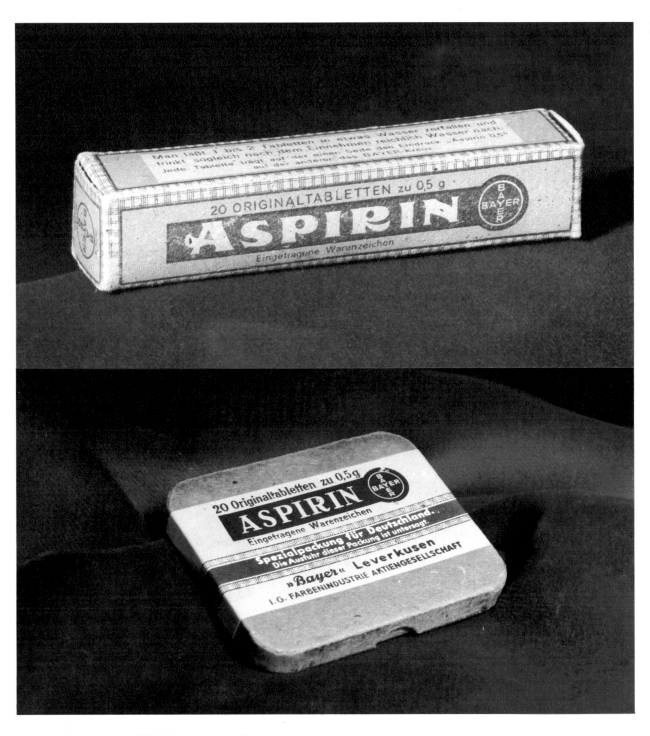

1950

Récents

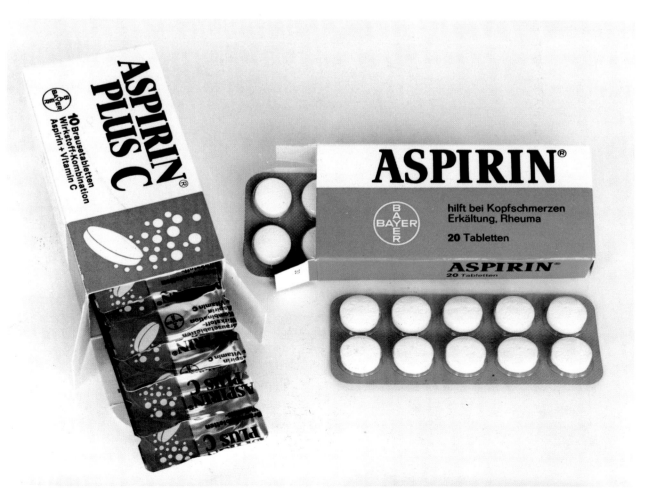

(Courtesy BAYER A.G. Leverkusen)

BAYER A.G. LEVERKUSEN (GERMANY)

Introduction/Summary

The pharmaceutical division of the chemical company Bayer AG, Leverkusen (Germany), ranks among the world's biggest drug manufacturers. Traditionally R&D oriented, Bayer AG laboratories turned out firsts like Aspirin (1899) and Prontosil (1935), the sulfonamide that was later regarded as the forerunner of antibiotics.

Among the new contributions to therapy are clotrimazole, azlocillin and mezlocillin in the anti-infectives field, nifedipine as an outstanding cardiovascular drug, acarbose as a new approach to dealing with metabolic diseases and praziquantel, the one-dose cure for schistosomiasis.

THE COMPANY THAT INTRODUCED
NOT ONLY ASPIRIN

The Start

In the wake of the rapid development of the tar dye industry in the 1860's following the discovery of aniline dyes, dye-merchant Friedrich Bayer and master-dyer Friedrich Wescott founded the firm Friedrich Bayer et comp. in Barmen, Germany. Starting with a single workman in 1863, they soon extended their business. Four years later, they employed 50 people. Subsidiaries arose in many countries, one of the first in the USA in 1865. These were the beginnings of a chemical enterprise that would later operate on a worldwide scale.

The advance into the virgin territory of synthetic drugs was made by the development of phenacetin from a by-product of dye manufacture in 1888. N 1890 the company set up its own pharmacological laboratory. By 1910 Bayer had received several international awards for pharmaceutical products from its research such as on of the world's best known tablets: Aspirin®.

Aspirin®

Who was the first man to succeed in synthesising acetylsalicylic acid (ASA) in a chemically pure and stable form? It was Felix Hoffmann, brilliant pharmacist and chemist, who joined Bayer in 1894 at the age of 26. To ease the pain of his arthritic father, he searched among various salicylate compounds and came upon one synthesised four decades earlier, 1853, by Charles Frederick von Gerhardt, an Alsatian chemist. It was acetylsalicylic acid. Hoffmann got interested in the compound, tested it and developed a commercial method of producing it. Upon his request, Heinrich Dreser, the company's director of pharmacological research, considered the drug and became sufficiently convinced of its efficacy to consign samples to various physicians. It was an outstanding success.

Important Note : Bayer and the Bayer Cross—the corporate name and the company's symbol—are well-protected trademarks of Bayer AG, Germany. Only in the U.S. and Canada are certain rights to the Bayer and the Bayer Cross trademark registered by Sterling Drug, Inc., USA. Sterling Drug uses these marks for their Bayer Aspirin. In most other countries of the world, Aspirin is registered in favour of Bayer AG, Leverkusen, Germany.
Bayer AG, Leverkusen, is not connected with the Bayer Company, Glenbrook Laboratories, division of Sterling Drug, New York, markers of Bayer Aspirin in the USA, to which in 1918 the US assets of the German company have been transferred.

217

HISTORY OF PHARMACY

The substance, launched in 1899 under the trademark Aspirin®, was to circle the globe (vide: Bayer and Bayer Cross). Today, after more than 80 years, Aspirin is still the most frequently used drug and a trump of pharmaceutical research. It shows new interesting aspects regarding efficacy, mode of action and interaction with endogenous substances.

The development of a great number of other drugs can be attributed to Aspirin. It has given decisive impetus to the research into rheumatic diseases and been discovered as a new therapeutic principle for thrombo-embolic diseases. Renowned scientists regard a microencapsulated formulation, the ASA preparation Colfarit®, as tomorrow's prophylaxis of myocardial infarction. Immense possibilites in drug treatment are predicted in view of the new biochemical findings regarding the mode of action of ASA.

Early Milestones

However, there are other examples of early Bayer research which may be considered even more important. Milestones from the Bayer labs are doubtlessly the first remedies for tropical diseases and Gerhard Domagk's discovery of the chemotherapeutic effect of the sulfonamides. The decisive investment in this direction was made by Bayer already in 1910 when the first chemotherapeutic laboratory ever of a pharmaceutical company was established in Elberfeld.

Tropical Diseases

Sleeping sickness, until that time a scourge of the population of tropical areas which had been tolerated fatalistically, was cured with suramin sodium, introduced as Germanin® (Bayer 205) in 1923. The drug was tested successfully during a two-year expedition in Africa, headed by Prof. F. K. Kleine, a student of Robert Koch.

Malaria was another target of Bayer scientists. For a 100 years quinine was the only agent known as a therapy. In 1924 pamaquine (Plasmochin®) was developed, followed in 1932 by primaquine (Atebrin®) and in 1934 by chloroquine (Resochin®) which remained the most widely used antimalarial.

Besides the individual treatment of the malaria patient, an interruption of the cycle of transmission of malaria by the Anopheles-mosquitoes is necessary. Baygon®, an effective insecticide, was developed for this purpose. It is also used to control a reduviid bug which transmits the dangerous Chagas' disease in South America. The chemotherapeutic nifurtimox (1970) (Lampit®), was, after many years of research and experiment, introduced as a further advance in the treatment of this disease.

In a similar way, Bayer scientists tackled schistosomiasis, an infection with flukes of the genus schistosoma which is transmitted in infested water, the invertebrate host being small water snails. Drugs for the treatment of this disease, affecting 7% of the world population, were marketed by Bayer already in 1929 and in 1953. The latest contribution to schistosomiasis therapy is praziquantel (Biltricide®), a joint development of E. Merck, Darmstadt (Germany) and Bayer AG with the particular advantage of a single-dose treatment, launched in 1980. To interrupt the cycle of infection Bayer introduced already in 1963 the molluscocide clomitralide (Bayluscid®).

Sulfonamides

In 1939 Gerhard Domagk, head of the laboratory of experimental pathology and of the bacteriological laboratory, was awarded the Nobel Prize in medicine for his discovery of the chemotherapeutic effect of the sulfonamides. His scientific work paved the way for modern antibiotic treatment.

The sulfonamides were the beginning of a specific treatment of bacterial infections. Besides, the class of sulfonamides was to be the origin of antidiuretics and antidiabetics later. The first chemotherapeutic effective against tuberculosis is also a product of Domagk's sulfonamide research: thiosemicarbazone (Conteben®), discovered in 1946, at the same time as PAS. The breakthrough in antituberculotic treatment gave rise to the development of Neoteben (INH) by Bayer and other research laboratories in 1952.

Dr Felix Hoffmann (1868-1946). Discovered Aspirin 1899.

Domagk's work contributed decisively to make the name of Bayer and the Bayer Cross a symbol of reliable drugs and successful research.

R & D today

What was a small pharmaceutical laboratory with only few employees in 1888 has developed into an international pharmaceutical enterprise with 600 pharmaceutical, dental and veterinary preparations and more than 31 000 employees all over the world including the affiliates abroad. Bayer reached the top of drug manufacturers in the late 70's when Miles and Cutter, two major companies in the USA, were acquired.

Today, the main points of Bayer pharmaceutical research are : cardiovascular diseases, thrombo-embolic diseases, metabolic diseases, bacterial infections (antibiotics, semisynthetic penicillins) fungal diseases, tropical diseases and cancer. Dental and veterinary medicine are becoming increasingly important, ecto-and endoparasiticides and feed additives being the major veterinary products.

The discovery of antibacterial chemotherapy has often been likened to the invention of the first flying apparatus, for in those cases works on the projects, modifications, improvements and innovations have continued ever since. A review of the major results of research obtained during the past few years underlines this observation which, in fact, can be applied to the entire spectrum of pharmaceutical developments. Especially the permanent threat of bacterial resistance will challenge chemotherapists again and again to develop new *antibiotics*.

In 1959 a biological procedure was found at the Bayer laboratories which was to be of decisive importance for the largescale technical production of semi-synthetic penicillins, i.e. modified penicillins with superior spectrum of action. To name but a few: propicillin potassium (Baycillin®), ampicillin trihydrate (Binotal®) and carbenicillin disodium (Microcillin®) which have become indispensable medical tools. The most recent developments in the field of broadspectrum penicillins are mezlocillin (Baypen® ; Mezlin® in the USA) and azlocillin (Securopen® ; Azlin® in USA). With the discovery of these "acylureido penicillins" Bayer continues on the road charted by Paul Ehrlich at the beginning of our century.

Owing to the success of anti-infectives research, the population of the industrial countries is now much less affected by the once dreaded infectious diseases. Threatening our health today are most of all hypertension and heart diseases. Bayer scientists reached a temporary climax of *cardiovascular research* in 1975 with the coronary drug nifedipine (Adalat®). This trailblazing preparation, meanwhile available in nearly all countries, was awarded the French "Prix Galien" in recognition of its merits as a new therapeutic principle.

In the field of *metabolic diseases,* Bayer research succeeded in working out a new compound (acarbose) for the controlled inhibition of intestinal enzymes to delay carbohydrate digestion. This new principle is expected to be beneficial in the treatment of metabolic diseases such as diabetes mellitus and its ensuing complications.

When in the early 1960's the incidence of *fungal infections* increased more and more due to various environmental factors, Bayer set up a medical-mycological laboratory. As the first result of this large-scale research clotrimazole (Canesten®, in USA Mycelex® or Empecid®) was introduced in 1973 for the treatment of a broad spectrum of fungal diseases. The group of chemotherapeutic substances of the imidazole group from Bayer Research has become established all over the world. In the future, too, Bayer hope to contribute to drug therapy by further intensive research and development, thus continuing in a tradition which has resulted in a great number of therapeutical milestones already.

The high scientific standard and orientation of its members can, i.a., be related to the fact that 30 of them are also associate professors or lecturers at German universities. This lively interchange between industrial research and academia has proved to be a fruitful one in the past and will certainly remain an indispensable factor in the interest of successful research also in the future.

Prof. Gerhard Domagk born on 30/10/1895 in Lagow (Germany), died on 24/4/1964 in Burgberg. Nobel Prize for Medicine for the finding of Sulfonamide.

Fig. 4,

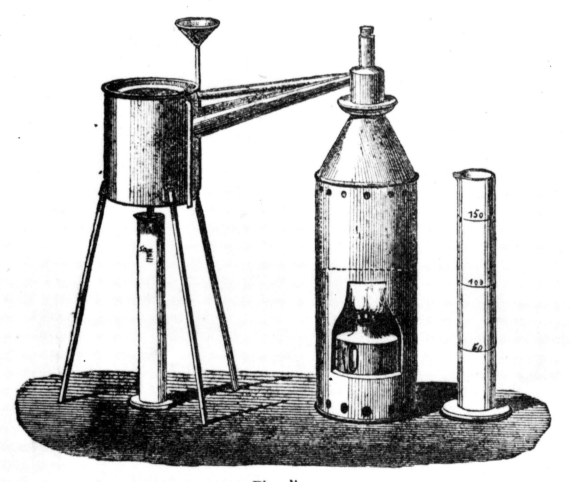

Fig. 5.

Alambic de Gay-Lussac pour **apprécier** la richesse alcoolique des vins et des liqueurs spiritueuses (fig. 5). 50 »

Alambic Salleron pʳ l'essai des vins, des liqueurs alcooliques sucrées, etc., avec l'instruction (fig. 6) .... 25 »

Alambic Salleron, plus grand modèle. 35 »

Alambic Salleron, très-grand modèle, opérant sur 1/2 litre de vin.......... 150 »

Albuminimètre de Becquerel pʳ doser l'albumine contenue dans le sang. 150 »

Alcoomètre centésimal de Gay-Lussac, de 0 à 40°, pour les alcools faibles....................... 2 50

Le même, à larges divisions..... 4 »

— de 40 à 100°........ 2 50

— de 40 à 100°, à larges divisions .... 4 »

Instruction et **Tables** de Gay-Lussac, à l'usage de l'alcoomètre centésimal............. » »

Alcoomètre étalon, portant de 0 à 35° divisé ....

BOEHRINGER INGELHEIM

In the summer of 1885 Albert Boehringer bought a small chemical factory in Ingelheim on the Rhine where cream of tartar and so-called Rochelle salt were manufactured. These products were marketed mainly to pharmacies and, amongst other places, also to dye works. The business was registered under the name "Albert Boehringer, Factory of Chemical Products, Nieder-Ingelheim" on 31st July, 1885. Albert Boehringer was the second son of Christoph Heinrich Boehringer of Mannheim, owner of the local firm "C. H. Boehringer and Sons." He therefore renamed this own firm after his father in 1892, calling it "C. H. Boehringer Son, Nieder-Ingelheim." In the year of its foundation the firm had a staff of 28.

In 1886, only a year after the acquisition of the factory, the production of tartaric acid for the food industry was begun in addition to that of cream of tartar and Rochelle salt. With the rise to popularity of baking powder and effervescent soft drinks during these years, tartaric acid had become a widely desired commodity. The commercial success achieved with this product encouraged Albert Boehringer to search for new and financially viable production methods for yet another organic acid. In the first half of the 1890's the manufacture of lactic acid was initiated. By the turn of the century the young firm had already become one of the largest lactic acid producers in Europe. This rapid progress was made possible mainly because Albert Boehringer opened up new markets for the use of lactic acid as, for example, the leather industry, dye works and, at a later date, the food industry.

The successes which the owner of "C. H. Boehringer Son" had with the organic acids in the first twenty years of the firm's existence were a contributing factor to the decision to turn to a differend field, that of the alkaloids, specific plant substances. In 1905 a special production plant was set up in which morphine and codeine were produced initially and, a few years later, atropine and theobromine also. These were sold to pharmacies and the pharmaceutical industry which was at that time only just beginning. A separate unit for the extraction of alkaloids from raw drugs was added in 1909. In 1910, the year in which the firm celebrated its 25th anniversary, there were 150 employees. The work-force had therefore multiplied more than five-fold since the firm's foundation. Around this time Albert Boehringer was honoured with the title of *Kommerzienrat*.

The alkaloids gave the incentive to become involved in yet another field, that of medicines. In 1912 the first pharmaceutical product, a painkiller under the name of Laudanon, was brought onto the market. The work in this field continued intensively throughout the following years, in spite of the First World War. Based on research carried out by Prof. Dr. Heinrich Wieland, a later Nobel prize laureate and a relative of the firm's founder, the production of bile acid was begun in 1916. This formed the foundation for the development of, among other things, two heart preparations, Cadechol and Perichol, introduced at the beginning of the 1920's. A further preparation resulting from the work of Heinrich Wieland was the respiratory analeptic Lobelin Ingelheim introduced in 1921.

As early as 1918 a separate scientific department staffed by several chemists was established for the improvement of existing products and the development of new ones. In 1919 a division "pharmaceutical specialities" responsible for the manufacture and sale of the medicines was set up. With this, "C. H. Boehringer Son" followed the general trend of the times of commercially producing medicines in prepacked and easily dispensible forms. The preparation of medicines in pharmacies alone, which had been usual until then, was no longer sufficient to cover the increasing demand.

The years following the First World War were not easy ones for the business. The inflation which set in at the beginning of the 1920's and its negative influence on all spheres of life in Germany caused Albert Boehringer to issue his own emergency currency in 1923 to enable him to pay salaries and wages. As it was backed by a well-known and established firm, this money was accepted without any problems.

Difficulties with the French occupational forces in the Rhineland culminated in the expulsion of Albert

Old phamaceutical laboratory material.

Boehringer from Ingelheim in the spring of 1923. He went to Hamburg, not to give up, but resolutely intent on building up a branch factory there. He gained valuable support from the banking establishment Donner and so a new alkaloid works could already begin production in the summer of 1925.

In the meantine work continued unabatedly in Ingelheim. The division for pharmaceutical specialities brought the gallbladder medicine Bilival onto the market in 1923. At the end of the 1920's two cough medicines—Codyl-Syrup and Acedicon—were introduced. The latter was based on the substance Thebain, a by-product of morphine manufacture. The circulatory medecine Sympatol, a derivative of adrenaline, was to become particularly successful and with it Boehringer Ingelheim launched a series of sympathicomimetic drugs. Codyl, Acedicon and Sympatol are still available today.

The expansion of alkaloid production in Ingelheim was not neglected either. Theobromine and theophylline were added to the existing range. The enterprise had grown considerably in the meantine. At the beginning of the 1930's it employed 760 people. The work-force had therefore again multiplied five times in the 20 years since 1910. Albert Boehringer, who returned to Ingelheim from Hamburg at the start of the 1930's looked around for new fields of activity. To the production of tartaric and lactic acids was added that of citric acid. This was at first manufactured from imported calcium citrate and later, towards the end of the 1930's, from molasses by means of a fermentation process. Based mainly on citric acid, the development of products for bakeries was begun in 1930. They required substances to prevent dough from becoming 'ropy' and to inhibit formation of mould on the finished product. Also, the manufacture of leaven bread could be considerably accelerated by the addition of fermentation acids. A separate division for baking and foodstuffs, which was responsible for the marketing and methods of application of these products, was established.

Albert Boehringer's life was soon to come to an end. In the spring of 1939, after 54 years of successful activities in Ingelheim and Hamburg, the firm's highly honoured founder died at the age of 78. The direction of the firm was taken oven by his two sons, Albert and Dr. Ernst Boehringer, and his son-in-law, Julius Liebrecht, all of whom had already entered the management in the 1920's.

The years of the approaching Second World War were difficult ones for the firm as they were everywhere in Germany and the world over. During this time pharmaceuticals mainly Sympatol, Lobelin and Codein, were delivered to the health authorities of the Wehrmacht and organic acids were supplied chiefly to the food industry. Initially, research and development activities continued. As a result of this, a further medicament, the first asthma preparation—Aludrin, could be introduced into the market in 1951. The start of large-scale production of synthetic caffeine in Ingelheim in 1942 was of particular significance. Its production on a laboratory scale had already been successful as early as 1928.

After the end of the war and the occupation of Ingeltheim by American and later French troops, the factory began to operate again in late May 1945 following a two month's closure. By the end of July production had recommenced in all fields—acids, pharmaceutical chemicals, baking and foodstuffs as well as pharmaceutical specialities. The workforce had, however, shrunk to barely 600.

The owners of the fifm "C. H. Boehringer Son » in Ingelheim and its branch firm in Hamburg also possessed the chemical factory "Dr. Karl Thomae Ltd." in Winnenden/Württemberg which Albert Boehringer had already bought in 1928. It had been transferred to Biberach on the Riss at the end of the war and was intended to serve as an alternative location in case production could no longer be maintained in Ingelheim. The owners then decided to extend their pharmaceutical activities and to produce and market medicines in Biberach as well as Ingelheim. The first preparations of the firm "Thomae" included Perxanthin (a heart medicine), the analgesic Thomapyrin and the 'flu medicamen Thomasco. The taking over of the marketing of medicines of the Swiss firm J. P. Geigy, Basel in 1949 sparked off a very successful development of "Thomae" which employed 200 people at that time.

Activity also continued in Ingelheim in the first years after the war. Mainly as a result of the damage caused in agriculture by the Colorado beetle, the "CELA Agricultural Chemicals Co. Ltd." for research, development and marketing of plant pesticides was founded in 1946. Its products were initially manufactured in Ingelheim and later at the works in Hamburg.

Interior of a pharmacy, painting by M. Borgeaud, 1919, Lausanne, Museum of Fine Arts.

"C. H. Boehringer Son » continued to be successful in the field of pharmaceuticals. In 1949 Effortil, yet another preparation to stabilise the circulation, was introduced as was Vasculat, a product for the treatment of peripheral circulatory disorders. Two years later the spasmolytic Buscopan could be put on the market. Effortil and Buscopan still occupy a prominent position in the product range of the company. In 1950 the total work-force in Ingelheim, Hamburg and Biberach numbered nearly 2,400 and had once again increased almost five-fold since 1945.

At the start of the 1950's a systematic expansion of the pharmaceutical business was begun abroad. Initially, the sales were mainly carried out through agencies in foreign companies. There followed the establishment of separate companies for scientific information and advertising which later also took over duties of selling. The next step was the founding of pharmaceutical manufacturing establishments which eventually grew up in many countries.

At the end of the 1950's and in the 1960's further pharmaceutical products were put on the market. The heart medicament Persantin which was introduced by "Thomae" and which was to become the most successful product of "Boehringer Ingelheim" in the present day should be mentioned first. Of importance amongst those which followed were the asthma medicine Alupent and the blood pressure depressant Catapresan in Ingelheim as well as the laxative Dulcolas, the secretolytic Bisolvon and the tranquilizer Adumbran at "Thomae". The emphasis of the company's production moved more and more in the direction of pharmaceutical specialities. This development also continued in the 1970's. "C. H. Boehringer Son" and "Thomae" added to the pharmaceutical market with Berotec and Atrovent (developed from the asthma preparation Alupent), Partusisten (a labour inhibitor), Glurenorm (an antidiabetic), Gastrozepin (a preparation against stomach ailments), Mucosolvan (a successor of Bisolvon) and finally, at the start of the 1980's, Mexitil (a preparation against heart rhythm irregularities).

At home and abroad several new daughter firms had been founded since the beginning of the 1960's. In 1976 the corporation "Boehringer Ingelheim" consisted of 145 companies active not only in the field of pharmaceuticals but also in veterinary medicine, laboratory diagnosis, chemicals, bakery products and plant pesticides. This rapid and still continuing growth made it necessary to reorganise the structure of the "Boehringer Ingelheim" corporation. This was done at the beginning of 1981. The original firm "C. H. Boehringer Son" became the holding company for the national firms whilst "Boehringer Ingelheim International Co. Ltd." became the holding company for the firms abroad. The gross turnover of "Boehringer Ingelheim" amounted to 3 36 billion DM in 1981, 74% of which was effected abroad. A considerable proportion of the total expenditure, namely 376 million DM or 11% of the gross turnover was invested in pharmaceutical research and development in 1981. In addition to the two large research centres in Ingelheim and Biberach, there are further research establishments in the USA, Japan, Austria, Italy and France. In 1981 a total of about 22,000 people was employed by the corporation, more than 10 % of them working in research and development. Since 1950 the total work-force had therefore increased by more than nine times.

Kommerzienrat = commercial counsellor (honorary title formerly conferred on distinguished financiers, industrialists etc. in Germany.)

Cycladic idol showing two flowers of opium on her head (2000 B.C.).

La Pommade du Lion n'est autre chose que la graisse des Lions d'Afrique nourris au jasmin et aux plantes aromatiques. Elle est souveraine pour la pousse des cheveux, la destruction des punaises, la purification de l'haleine et la guérison des maladies ophtalmiques, épidémiques, épileptiques, organiques et politiques. Elle a guéri des rois, des princes, des militaires et même des commissaires de police. Le Constitutionnel, le Gratis, et une foule d'autres ouvrages scientifiques en ont rendu un compte très flatteur! &c.ª &c.ª

Drug seller on market place.
(France 1840. Drawing by J. Platier).

CIBA-GEIGY

The pathway leading from a Geigy village store to a Geigy multinationakl was a maze of family relationships and inter-relationships. Their long history would or should provide sociologists with a lot of material concerning life and customs for decade after decade in Basel.

In 1758 Basel even at that time was an important commercial center Geographically it was settled astride the Rhine River. Thus all the trade routes coming north from Italy and passages through the Alps converged in Basel. Here goods of all types were transferred for transportation—by waterways usually—to northern and eastern Europe. Moreover because of religious persecution and the Reformation many persons from Holland and from France also fled to neutral Switzerland and Basel. Many were skilled in various professions. One of these was called "materialism". Merchants who dealt in the import and sale of materials—or goods as we say today—were called materialists. Such goods—or materials—were grouped under other terms such as "Spezerei" meaning groceries and spices. Or "Drogen" meaning "healing herbs" and "dyestuffs herbs". As more and more of all these "materials" were used, further groupings were made. Thus—drug merchants. Spice merchants. Pharmacy suppliers. Plant dyes. And other grouppings. One reason for these groupings were the guilds—they controlled not only membership but also the number of employees and prices and salaries and all other union-guild-affairs.

In Basel in 1606 the first materialist was a certain Jacob Miville of Colmar and Geneva. He was followed by other materialists, including the Roschet family of Savoy. Peter in 1616. Nicholas in 1631. Peter Jr. in 1646. More famous were Caspar Battier Bauhin and Jacob Bernoulli. And of course Johann Rudolf Geigy who in April 1758 opened up his own establishment as a "materialist" dealing in drugs. Had he so wanted he could' have had more leeway in choosing a guild by being a wholesaler only and dealing in bulk packages. But since he preferred to have a retail shop and dealing in spices groceries dyes nonpharmaceutical drugs and other items, he had to agree to join the establishment guild. This then was the beginning of Geigy as we know it today.

Johann Rudolf-Geigy-Gemuseus was sole owner for two decades and could boast that he had the fourth largest shop in Basel. At the beginning of the year 1780 he decided to incorporate as Geigy & Bernoulli with Nicholas de Johannes Bernoulli (1754-1841) as his partner. Since Nicholas de Johannes Bernoulli had studied pharmacy at Strasbourg and Basel, he was valuable to the firm because he was allowed to compound prescriptions. This was very important because under the guild laws a pharmacist had certain privileges. Thus prescriptions were written by physicians and compounded by a pharmacist who was then allowed to sell them at his price to the patients. Therefore shops run by "materialists" without a pharmacist were at a disadvantage.

Johann Rudolf Geigy died in April 793. He left his widow with three daughters and two sons. The older son Hiero nymus was twenty-two years old whereas the younger son Thomas was a small boy. Management of the firm was left to Hieronymus and his mother Anna Elisabeth Geigy-Gemusus. The first act they did was to dissolve Geigy & Bernoulli in 1794 and rename it Joh. Rudolf Geigy. Mr. Bernoulli established his own business. Mrs. Geigy retired in 1809—leaving everything to her son. She died in 1818.

The business flourished. The emphasis was on dyestuffs—especially indigo. But also woods of all types from which dyes were extracted. Wines and vinegars and spirits were also traded—the special domain of thomas Geigy who was a younger brother of Hieronymus. Hieronymus Geigy had married the seventeen years old Charlotte Sarasin. They had nine children. Her father, Jacob Sarasin, was one of the most distinguished men in europe at that time. Besides being wealthy—he had a silk ribbon factory and built luxurious buildings such as the one for his daugther Charlotte which is still a Basel landmark-Jacob Sarasin was known more as a religious man and philosopher. Together with Isaac Iselin they promulgated the Physiocratic Movement—with the belief in broad outline that only farmers and agricultural goods were productive whereas the arts and sciences were sterile.

Whereas Thomas Geigy could not get along with his brother Hieronymus and left the firm to start his own wine import and export business, it was otherwise with his brother Carl Geigy (1798-1861). As the eldest son and destined to take over the business, he was well prepared. Carl Geigy was alert and participated in all events of the times. THus as the Basel textile industry grew and grew, Carl Geigy responded by concentrating on the dyestuffs field. He no longer merely bought and sold dyes but he starded to extract his own dyes from various woods. The wooden mill powered by running water was exchanged for a steam operated mill used in the extraction of dyestuffs from wood. This meant the de-emphasis of a commercial import-export wholesale-retail business. It meant too the beginning of an industry. The first small factory had been built by Carl Geigy. He seems to have been born at the right time in history. Let us see.

Carl Geigy was born in Basel in June 1798. He had the usual schooling-including attendance at the Bernoulli Institute—and served an apprenticeship in his father's establishment. He then went for further training in a commercial enterprise in Marseille in 1817 and 1818 but had to return somewhat earlier because of his father's poor health. In 1824 Hieronymus Geigy made his son Carl part owner of the firm. Then in August of that year, Carl Geigy married Sophie Preiswerk. She too was the daughter of a silk ribbon manufacturer. Unlike his father, Carl Geigy-Preiswerk was active in public affairs. Thus together with Johann Jacob Speiser he founded a bank in 1843. In 1845 he was put on the board of an issuing bank. In 1848 he became associated with the Basel Credit Bank. Before that in 1847 the Mayor of Basel and the City Councillor were forced by the liberal wing to resign because they were thought to be too conservative. Carl Geigy—although he was listed as a conservative—was asked to join the government because of his vast experience in economics and finance. He controlled finances and was put in charge of the local duty office. Another discussion at the time xwas whether or not the railroad system of Alsace should be extended to Basel. Carl Geigy was one of the few who favored this. When in June 1844 the railroad system became operative, it was the first and only railway system in Switzerland. The next goal was to extend the railroad system into central Switzerland. The Swiss government appointed Carl Geigy to make a commercial study of a complete railraod system of all Switzerland. In general his plans were heeded and he became head of several commissions to carry these through. Since some lines were private, the envy and internal scheming and sabotage can be imagined. At any rate all this work took its toll. Carl Geigy died in January 1861 at the age of sixty-two years.

After the decease of Carl Geigy his brothers all took over in various capacities. Brother Wilhelm Geigy established his own firm. Brother Eduard preferred to travel and to visit his clients. Both, however, at some time or other returned to their original establishments. Meanwhile other companies were formed—for example a second Geigy-Bernoulli firm. The firm of Carl Geigy. The firm of Geigy and Heusler. Of course the Geigy brothers were active in other enterprises too. And were too members of the local government. Wilhelm Geigy was interested in water transportation and strived to establish a steamboat service between Basel and Kehl near Strasbourgh.

Then another strong personality entered the scene. He was Johann Rudolf Geigy—the son of Carl Geigy and Sophie Preiswerk. He was born in March 1830. He enjoyed a thorough education at home and abroad and spent some time in Marseille and Bordeaux as well as in Le Havre and London. He even went to India to learn what there was to learn about Indigo. And he then returned to Basel by way of Egypt and Constantinopel—now Istanbul. In 1854 he entered the firm his great-grandfather had pioneered and his father had brought to flourishment. And the next year Johann Rudolf Geigy married Marie Merian. Johann Rudolf Geigy-Merian was ready to settle down at last.

One of his problems was to modernize his extraction methods for dyestuffs from woods. Another aim was to incearse his sales markets to encompass the whole world. And most important of all was to increase as much as possible the manufacture of synthetic dyestuffs. The demands for these increased tremendously—especially since American cotton was being brought to Europe in massive quantities. Moreover chemical dyestuffs manufacture involved industrial chemistry—sulfuric acid. Lead chambers. Soda.

Since William Perkin in England could manufacture aniline in large quantities, the race was on. England, of course, was leading. But Germany was catching up by setting up its research laboratories and manufacturing establishments in Germany. America had hardly a chemical industry despite its cotton. Switzerland was not yet involved to any great extent. Each country seemed to wait to find itself because of the coming problems. August Kekulé's structure and benzol theories. Patents. Social studies. Cooperation with

---

P. Muller, born 1899 in Switzerland. Nobel Prize winner in 1948 for his discovery of DDT.

Professors of Chemistry at the universities. In Basel Professor Christian Friedrich Schönbein as teacher and consultant was of great help to the fledgeling chemical industry. When he died in 1868 his place was taken by Professor Jules Piccard—a member of the famous stratospheric Piccard family. Meanwhile too Johann Rudolf Geigy-Merian (1830-1917) died and his place in the firm was taken by Johann Rudolf Geigy-Schlumberger (1862-1943).

By concentrating on the synthetic dyestuff preparations the Geigy scientists did not neglect the other branches of chemistry. Thus in September 1931 the first synthetic moth prevention agent was subjected to biological testing. Results were good. Then, within the next few years hundreds of derivatives were made of Mitin—the name of these insecticides—and several dozen were patented. In March 1938 Mittin FF—the most important of all Mitins—was made.

Another new product obtained in September 1939 was Dichlor-Diphenyl-Trichlor ethane. It is better known as DDT. This agent was a popular pesticide and was widely used. During World War II DDT was dusted on refugees either freed by allied soldiers or fleeing to safety. Un malaria zones whole forests were sprayed to control mosquitos. Practically the whole population of Naples was dusted by DDT in a successful attempt to abort an epidemic. For these reasons the discover er of DDT—Dr. Paul Müller of Geigy in Basel—was awarded the Nobel Prize for Physiology and Medicine in 1948.

With such successes it was easy for the Geigy Management to decide on a full scale Geigy Pharmaceutical Department replete with Research sections and Production facilities.

To have a pharmaceutical department must be a pleasure. To have a successful one is expensive. Surely. Very expensive in fact. In its choice of research themes Geigy decided to carry out strictly chemical syntheses of organic chemistry compounds. Not the isolation of biological agents. Nor the syntheses of well-known natural substances. Geigy started by transfering some of its experienced dyestuffs chemists to the new laboratories. They were requested to synthesize chemical derivatives of use in several fields of medicine—antihistamines. Anticoagulants. Antiseptics. Disinfectants. Chemotherapeutics. Antirheumatics. When we think of products such as Butazolidin. Desogen. Tofranil. Irgamid. Hygroton. Synopen. Tromexan. And many others, than we can see that the scientific staff has chosen well. J.R. Geigy S.A. will have many other new products to add to its long list. And many other new Geigy personal personnel to manage them all.

Its fusion with CIBA in october 1970 changed the name to CIBA-GEIGY. But—what's in a name ? The products are the same. And there have been fusions in the past such as Geigy-Bernoulli and Geigy-Heusler. The future lies in the results of future research workers—be they chemical physical or biological—and in the manner in which they shall be utilized. Because—as we have seen—neither facilities alone nor money alone nor brains alone can result in a new product—be it against cancer or against the common cold.

CIBA The Chemical Industry of Basel. CIBA had an interesting beginning on its way to the development of a pharmaceutical industry. Unlike the large Geigy family it may be said that CIBA—now CIBA-GEIGY—started off with one immigrant. One man from Lyon France. Alexander Clavel. He was born in Lyon in 1805. In 1838 he was still an immigrant but could be employed as manager of the Oswald dyes factory whose owner was Karl Theodor Oswald-Linder who had died several months before. Alexander Clavel was a good friend of the family—and two years later, in 1840, married the widowed Louise Henriette who then bore the name Louise Henriette Clavel-Linder. As owner of the factory, A. Clavel brought it to fruition and expanded it quite steadily. It seems that he was popular because in 1849 he requested citizenship and was sponsored by many well-known personalities in Basel. Meanwhile his stepdaughter Rosine Henriette Oswald in 1854 married Joseph Renard who owned part of the Renard Frères & Franc silk dyeworks in Lyon.

Thus, when the French staff chemist Emanuel Verguin in 1859 discovered the bluish-red silk dye named magenta or fuchsine after the fuchsia plant, there was a great clamor for this beautiful synthetic color. Under protection of the French patent laws Renard Frères enjoyed a monopoly in the manufacture of fuchsine. With his son-in-law holding the French monopoly, it is easy to see that Alexander Clavel would be the first in Basel to manufacture fuchsine for Switzerland. In 1859 he obtained for 100'000 francs the license to manufacture fuchsine and its violet green and blue derivatives for five full years. Only French chemists were employed.

The Clavel factory grew and grew. So much so that the populace complained about the smells and dust and noise. And firetrap. Sure enough in april 1864 there was a fire which caused severe damage. Thus

Alexander Clavel purchased land outside the city walls—Basel still had them but knocked them down soon after—and built a new larger safer factory on the site where CIBA-GEIGY now stands. One of the chemists employed as chief chemist was Louis Durand who later founded Durand & Huguenin which eventually was fused in parts with various enterprises—those of Dolfus Huguenin Couleru Mueller Busch Bindschedler Gerber CIBA-GEIGY Sandoz and many others. Some were completely assimilated.

Due to failing health and business difficulties as well, Alexander Clavel decided to dispose of his business—especially since his son Alexander Clavel-Merian (1847-1910) was not interested. He preferred to manage the silk dyeing section only. Thus the firm of Alexander Clavel passed over to Bindschedler & Busch on St.Valentine's Day 1873. Eight days later Alexander Clavel died. Some ten years later his firm was re-named Society of Chemical Industry in Basel or CIBA. All because an immigrant from Lyon decided to stay in Basel.

CIBA entered the pharmaceutical field gradually and naturally. It seems that one thing led to another and soon there was a chemical compound which could be employed therapeutically. After all the practice of medicine itself was at the beginning of a revolution—as was the science of medicine. Thus in 1841 the French physician Joseph-François Malgaigne published the first medical statistics. After amputations sixty per cent of patients died. Childbirth deaths were very high. In 1842 Justus von Liebig published his classic work on life processes—Organic Chemistry in its Application to Physiology and Pathology. In 1847 Ignaz Philipp Semmelweis in the obstetrical clinic of Vienna ordered that all the personnel who dealt with patients had to wash their hands with calcium chloride solution before each examination. Mortality quickly went down. Rudolf Buchheim in 1849 established the first pharmacology laboratories—studies of substances on animal organs and whole intact animals—in Dorpat in Estonia. Dorpat wa also known as Tartu and as Jurjew—all according to the vicissitudes of politics and wars. The University of Dorpat was very famous and its library had 250'000 volumes even then.

The greatest impact of all was due, however, to Louis Pasteur. His work opened the doors to antisepsis and sterility. To bacteriology. To safer surgery with antiseptics such as phenol which brought down the death rate after amputations to eleven and one-half per cent. Phenol was a coal tar ingredient and was propagated by Joseph Lister in England. Another giant intellect of the time was Robert Koch who in 1882 identified the bacillus causing tuberculosis. He grew many bacilli by growing them in vitro—in glass—on various culture media such as agar or gelatin. He could then separate the various species and identify them by various methods—staining them. Changing the culture medium. And making pure cultures. In short—creating the subject of bacteriology.

Chemistry now entered upon the scene. For exemple, the undesired phenol left over after coal tar was exhausted could be used as an antiseptic. The aim of chemists would be to make a better phenol—derivaties which would be more antiseptic. Or less irritating to the skin. Or cheaper to make. And so on. In this case it was found that chlorophenol was more strongly antiseptic. When esterified with salicylic acid, phenol formed salol which did not damage tissues. In fact salol could be employed as an enteric coating for tablets and could be administered orally as an intestinal antiseptic. Somewhat later it was shown that quinoline derivatives—especially those which contained in their molecules both phenol and iodine—were even more effective. One example was Vioform—first made in 1899 by Bindschedler and reverted to CIBA after the merger in 1908. In 1934 a small amount of a detergent was added to make Entero-Vioform—and thus to create a most useful intestinal antiseptic. In 1957 CIBA launched Entobex-phenanthrolinquinone—as an intestinal antiseptic so strong as to combat amoebic dysentary. Other antiseptic derivatives found to be useful were Desogen Geigy and Bradosol CIBA as well as Zephirol Bayer.

An interesting example is provided by Prontosil. In 1935 Gerhard Domagk—director of the I.G. Farben experimental pathology and bacteriology laboratories—announced that the reddish brown azo dye Prontosil had a good chemotherapeutic effect—especially against the cocci bacteria such as pneumococcus and meningococcus. Apart from making the urine reddish this dye-drug or drug-dye had controllable side effects—such as having to drink much water during therapy. On the other hand it was very effective. Soon a pharmacological research group at the Pasteur Institute in Paris could show in 1935 that the colour of Prontosil played no rôle in its activity. In fact they found that Prontosil was broken down in the body to sulfanilamide—a colorless compound. The French group—Fourneau, Tréfouël, Mme Tréfouël, Nitti, and Bovet—could show that a cleavage product exerted the chemotherapeutic effect. The product of cleavage was

231

p-Amino-benzene-sulfonamide. Thus Prontosil was the first sulfonamide to be used in medicine. But how did the sulfonamides act? Woods and Fildes showed in 1940 that sulfonamides interfere with the normal metabolism of bacteria by blocking metabolites, such as p-Amino-benzoic acid, which are necessary for life or growth of bacteria. In short sulfonamides are anti-metabolites. Naturally the race was on to find an active but relatively harmless sulfonamide. CIBA won. In 1937 May & Baker in England had brought out Sulfapyridine as Dagenan. But the very next year CIBA chemist Max Hartmann—after choosing from numerous compounds—selected 2-Sulfanilamidothiazole as being even better. It was marketed as Cibazol and helped entrench CIBA as a pharmaceutical firm. The sulfonamides are still today an object of research.

Incidentally the Dr. Hartmann who found Cibazol is the same researcher who away back in 1918 had created the first synthetic cardiovascular drug—now known throughtout the world as Coramine. Between Coramine and Cibazol a tremendous amount of research took place. Merely listing a few names whill show why the Pharmaceutical Department of CIBA—now CIBA-GEIGY—is such a giant among giants in the pharmaceutical industry. Who does not know such old stand-bys as—Nupercaine. Dial. Doriden. Priscol. Privine. Serpasil. Apresoline. Estrone. Progesterone. Testosterone. Cortisone. Desoxycorticosterone. Aldosterone.

Most of these caused happy sensations when they were introduced. Proof that they were—and are—so valuable to physicians is the fact that Professor Tadeus Reichstein of Basel—who collaborated with CIBA researchers—was awarded the 1950 Nobel Prize for his syntheses of the complicated steroid compounds. It was Professor Reichstein too who in 1933 had synthesized vitamin C—which then was manufactured by Hoffmann-LaRoche on a massive scale.

Eli Lilly (1885-1977)
(Courtesy of Eli Lilly and Co).

ELI LILLY and Co.

By Gene E Mc Cormick

Another company which had its origins in the Midwest is Eli Lilly and Company. Founded in Indianapolis, Indiana, in 1876 by Colonel Eli Lilly, with a capital of $1,400 and four employees, including his fourteen-year-old son, it has operated continuously from its headquarters there since that time. Today, with net sales nearing the three-billion-dollar mark, Lilly emplys 29,000 people in the research, manufacture, and marketing of products in the fields of human medicine, agriculture, medical instrument systems, and cosmetics. It has more than thirty manufacturing facilities in the United States and abroad and distributes its products in 130 countries. Members of the Lilly family were active in the management of the firm during its first one hundred years of operation.

Born near Baltimore, Maryland, in 1838 of an ancestry that extended several centuries back to France and Sweden, Colonel Eli Lilly learned the art and practice of pharmacy at Lafayette, Indiana, a few years after his parents had moved to Greencastle, Indiana, in 1852. By the time he opened the doors to his own business two decades later, he had undergone the rigors of the Civil War, in which he served as an officer in various units of the Union Army, and experienced the trials of enterprise in the drug trade and pharmaceutical manufacturing. When he started his venture in the flamboyant years of patent remedies and raucous advertising, the Colonel chose to compound his medicines according to officially recognized scientific standards of the day and promote his products only to the medical and pharmacy professions. He also was active in organizing professional pharmacy in the state of Indiana. Moreover, as a businessman, he took at the time the unusual measure of offering without contract a uniform discount pricing schedule to drug wholesalers and retailers and later, in 1894, adopted the polcy of distributing his products exclusively to wholesale druggists. Thus, to establish his company as an equitable, and therefore reliable, house, Colonel Lilly laid down the fundamental principle of distributing quality products by fair trade practices.

When he became president of the company upon his father's death in 1898, Josiah Kirby Lilly (1861-1948) enlarged upon that principle both in merchandising practices and research commitment. With respect ot the former, he expanded the sales force, introduced sales training, and Widened wholesaler geographical representation to improve distribution efficiency and product availability. By 1911 only wholsaler accounts wcrc supporting the company's sales. That same year the company constructed its first building devoted exclusively to scientific research. It symbolized Mr. Lilly's determination since the 1880s to align the company's research with the advances in medical science, to place Lilly investigations on a rational basis for fruitful exploration. And to foster the parallel objectives of distribution and research, J.K. Lilly instituted policies to maintain sound financial reserves, management incentives, and liberal administration.

When his sons joined the company shortly after the turn of the century—Eli (1885-1977) and J.K., Jr. (1893-1966)—the three of them launched a program of some thirty-years' duration to develop an organization continually responsive to demand by means of internal self-regulation. THis involved developing each company function on a systematic basis and in that process of rationalization integrating them into a cohesive whole. They turned their attention first to the human factor of employment by determining equitable standards in the administration of hiring, job training and performance, work incentives, and benefit programs. With new personnel practices in place, production was newt investigated following World War I, and, as a result, uniform flow of work and steady annual employment were realized by comprehensive production planning and adoption of straight-line manufacturing technology and economical lot-size determination, both innovations in the pharmaceutical industry. These improvements afforded significant cost reductions and more effective use of capital investment.

The separate but complementary ways the Lilly brothers had worked on internal development continued throughout the 1920s. Convinced that market potential had to be evaluated in order to align production with demand, J.K., Jr., undertook a massive sales research program which ranged from defining productive territorial size to intensive professional training of salesmen. For his part, given charge of research administration, Eli instituted university research affiliation through a formal program of royalty followships, a program resulting from the company's collaboration with the University of Toronto in the development of Insulin. The company was the first to introduce commercially the life-saving hormone in the United States—in 1923. Mr. Lilly also established in 1926 a clinical research facility in an Indianapolis municipal hospital, a unique arrangement for a pharmaceutical house at the time and one which still is in operation.

What emerged from the efforts at progressive development by father and sons was a method of planning on a corporate scale, a control by which all activities—from raw materials purchasing to product introduction and sales promotion—could be integrated by scheduled procedure.

The 1920s at Lilly withnessed a number of important product additions. Besides Insulin, there were barbiturates, liver extracts for pernicious anemia, antiallergenics, and various biological preparations. With these additions to the physician's armamentarium and the significant economies arising from the internal improvement program, the company achieved a profitability that allowed it during the Great Depression of the 1930s to retain all employees at full pay; provide credit to wholesalers; make major capital commitments; and, as effort to help increase consumer purchasing power in the harsh times, reduce prices on a wide range of products. By the outbreak of World War II, the Lillys had transformed a family enterprise into an organization of industrial magnitude; they had laid the foundations of the present corporation.

Upon the ideal of strong unit growth Eli Lilly and Company has prospered well and enhanced the nation's well-being. During World War II it supplied more than one million liters of blood plasma for the armed forces on a cost basis; did significant work on human albumin fractionation; and under arrangement with the United States Government participated with other pharmaceutical firms in the production of penicillin. It also engaged in the production of Japanase B encephalitis vaccine and provided enough thyphus vaccine to immunize six million military personnel. Antitoxin for gas gangrene was another agent it produced. Elemental needs also were met; the company supplied antisunburn kits, antisea-sickness tablets, and compounds for treating malaria.

The productivity of Lilly continued to grow under the supervision of others who succeeded the family in managing the business. In the 1950s and 1960s important advances were made in medical care-Salk polio vaccine, of which the company was the nation's major supplier; long-acting penicillins and broad-spectrum antibiotics; a new analgesic; and a number of anticancer agents. Contributing to corporate momentum was entry into the agricultural market with the formation of the Elanco Division in 1960 and the construction of several manufacturing facilities in europe and the Far East. Diversification into research-oriented fields continued into the 1970s with the acquisition of Elizabeth Arden, Inc., and firms in the medical instrumentation market—IVAC Corporation; Cardiac Pacemakers, Inc.; and Physio-Control Corporation. And during these years Lilly broadened its explorations in pharmaceutical research, from which have come therapeutic agents for controlling cardiovascular diseases and arthritis. Its long-term interest in infectious diseases has also resulted in the discovery of new families of wide-spectrum antibiotics and their introduction into the marketplace. The fermentation technology providing this advanced therapy in the fields of human and animal health also is being utilized for recombinant DNA production of biosynthetic human insulin, the first practical use of gene splicing and a potential source of other specific means to combat disease. This application brings to full circle the company's involvement with diabetes management which began sixty years ago.

Responsiveness to the human condition of interdependence remains central to corporate goals. "No business worthwhile", said Colonel Eli Lilly, "can be built upon anything but the best in everything."

Col. Eli Lilly. 1838-1898. (Courtesy of Eli Lilly and Co).

Replica of Lilly's Laboratory.
(Courtesy of Eli Lilly and Co).

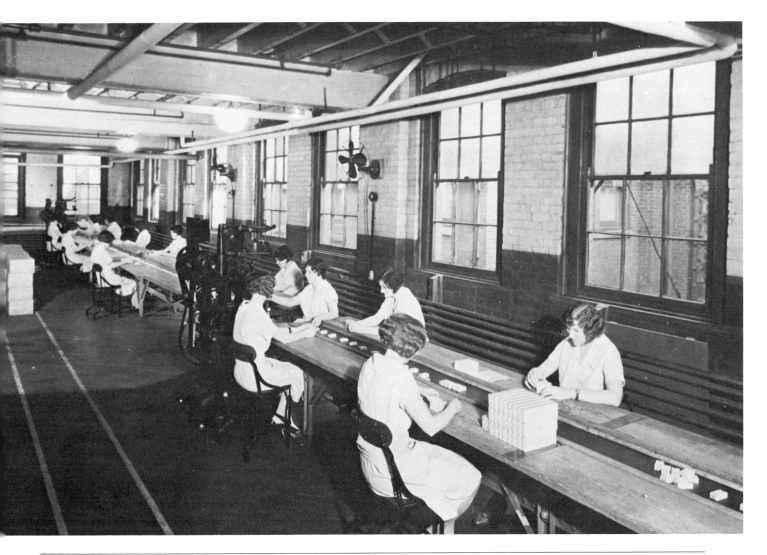

Iletin (Insulin Lilly) c. 1923.
Finishing Line. (Courtesy of Eli Lilly).

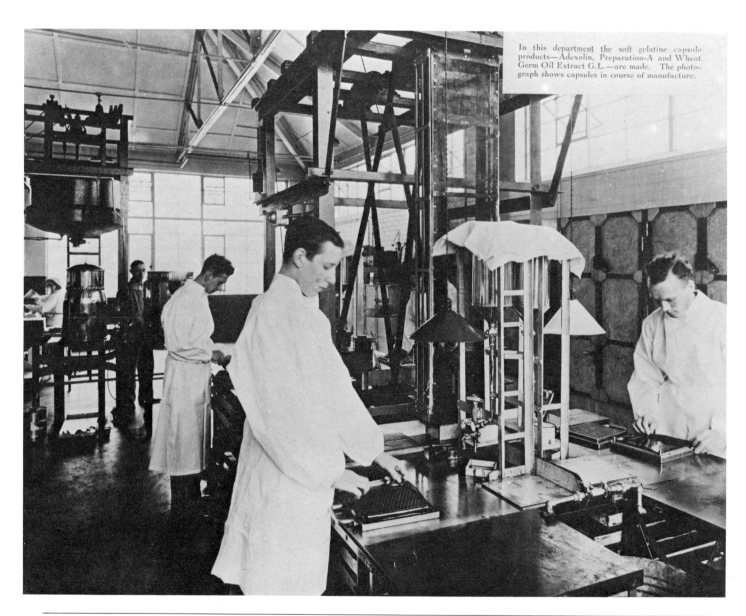

In this department the soft gelatine capsule products—Adexolin, Preparation-A and Wheat Germ Oil Extract G.L.—are made. The photograph shows capsules in course of manufacture.

Pharmaceutical manufacture at Glaxo Laboratories Ltd, Greenford, near London, c. 1937.

GLAXO

The growth of the Glaxo Group into the UK's leading pharmaceutical company is largely due to the efforts of a number of pioneers. The man who founded the company which was to become Glaxo, Joseph Nathan (1835-1912), was the son of a London tailor, who emigrated first to Australia and then on to New Zealand in the mid-19th century. After a period in business with his brother-in-law, he established his own company, Joseph Nathan & Co. Ltd., in Wellington, New Zealand, in 1873.

Nathan's import-export business dealt in general merchandise—wool, stationery, groceries, ironmongery and wines and spirits. But already Nathan was selling patent medicines with exotic names like Dew of the Alps and Lediard's Knickerbocker Schnapps. Nathan was the father of a large family, and six sons joined him in his expanding business. As the export of New Zealand dairy products to the UK became an increasingly important part of the company's business, so its operaional base gradually began to shift to London. Joseph Nathan & Co. were essentially merchants, selling wool, flax and, increasingly, dairy produce.

It was in London that the Nathans first saw powdered skimmed milk. They negotiated successfully for the patent for the process to produce dried milk, and 1904 bought and installed four drying machines in a new factory at Bunnythorpe, New Zealand. Infant feeding trials were arranged with a London hospital, and the trade name Glaxo was registered in 106. A prolonged period of hot weather in the summer of 1911 led to an epidemic of gastroenteritis among the babies in British cities. The conditions stimulated the use of dried mil for infant feeding, and Glaxo rapidly became a household word.

Infant milks remained the Nathans' principal interest until 1923« when a company chemist learned of an American scientist who claimed to have devised a process for extracting vitamin D from fish-liver oil. The Nathan company secured a licence for the process, with the original intention of using vitamin D to fortify Glaxo milk. Instead in 1924 they began making and marketing the extract in phials for drop dosage. Ostelin, as the product was called, was the company's first medical product, and marked the beginning of the modern Glaxo Group.

As major advances in the research, development and manufacture of pharmaceutical products began to change dramatically the face of medical practice, Glaxo Laboratories, which eventually absorbed Joseph Nathan & Co., began to grow. Glaxo entered the antibiotics field in 1943 as one of the first manufacturers charged with the task of pioneering the mass production of penicillin. At that time, penicillin could only be made by the surface culture process, a tedious method which became obsolete in 1945 when Glaxo opened at Barnard Castle, North-east England, the first factory in the UK for the production of penicillin by deep culture fermentation.

Glaxo's success with the biotechnology of penicillin production was followed in 1948 by deep fermentation of streptomycin, an antibiotic for the treatment of tuberculosis, and in 1959 by griseofulvin, an oral antibiotic used for treating fungal diseases of the skin. An eight-year programme of investigation with Britain's National Research Development Corporation into the cephalosporins led in 1964 to the launch of cephaloridine, a broad-spectrum injectable antibiotic effective against a wide range of infections. Research into the cephalosporins continues to produce an increasing range of effective drugs.

The isolation of the anti-pernicious anaemia factor, vitamin B_{12}, in 1948 was a major Glaxo achievement which led to the production of the vitamin by deep fermentation. Research in organic chemistry was rewarded at the same time by the first commercial synthesis of thyroxine, and in 1952 bu the manufacture of liothyronine, the active form of the thyroid hormone. A remarkable multi-stage synthesis of cortisone, developed in 1954, paved the way in 1961 for the manufacture of betamethasone, the basis for a successful range of anti-inflammatory corticosteroids.

Salbutamol, which revolutionised the treatment of asthma, was discovered by Glaxo Group scientists in 1964, while a second major asthma treatment, an aerosol preparation of the steroid beclomethasone dipropionate, was launched in 1972. Fazadinium bromide, an intravenous neuromuscular blocking agent, became available in 1976, and labetalol, the first anti-hypertensive agent to combine both alpha- and beta-blocking properties in one molecule, in 1977. Ranitidine, a unique treatment for ulcers, and another original product of Glaxo research, was made available to doctors from 1981.

Progress was made on other fronts, too. In 1948 Glaxo was marketing over 60 food and pharmaceutical products in the UK and through a growing number of overseas subsidiaries. A decade later began an expansion programme which was to give an even broader base to operations.

Allen & Hanburys Ltd., which was acquired by Glaxo in 1958, is believed to be Britain's oldest surviving pharmaceutical company. SIlvanus Bevan, then aged 24, had opened an apothecary's shop in Old Plough Court, City of London, in 1715. William Allen (1770-1843) joined the business in 1792, marrying Charlotte Hanbury in 1806 and inextricably linking the names of their two families.

The company pioneered in the UK the manufacture and marketing of cod-liver oil, patented a method for manufacturing medicated pastilles, and produced their own infant foods. A thriving surgical instruments business was established, and, early this century, the manufacture of operation tables began. Allen & Hanburys also developed methods of presenting drugs as tablets and as hypodermic injections, and were among the first firms involved in the commercial manufacture of insulin.

When the Glaxo Group acquired Edingurgh Pharmaceutical Industries Ltd. in 1963, it took over three more historic British companies. The pharmacy which was eventually to become J.F. Macfarlan & Co. Ltd. was opened in Edinburgh in 1780. John Fletcher Macfarlan (1790-1861) took over the business early in the 19th century and developed a process for manufacturing morphine salts on a commercial scale—in addition to laudanum and some of the older compounded medicines of the day. In the same city, the brothers Drs. Thomas and Henry Smith established their pharmacy in 1827, developing in much the same way until the two companies merged in 1960.

In 1961 they were joined by a third Edingurgh company, Duncan, Flockhart & Co. Ltd. John Duncan (1780-1871) opened a pharmacy close to that of J.F. Macfarlan in 1825, and it was his lifelong interest in the relief o pain which led to the development of chloroform as an anaesthetic. William Flockhart (1808-1871), one of his first apprentices, joined him as a partner in 1832.

These, and other companies, each with its own network of overseas subsidiaries and distributors, were brought under the Glaxo umbrella during the 1950s and 1960s, creating the UK's and one of the world's largest pharmaceutical organisations. By the 1980s Glaxo had subsidiary companies in almost 50 countries, employing nearly 30,000 people and with worldwide sales of more than £710 million annually.

Pavot plantation (above) and harvest.

HOFFMAN-LA ROCHE Co. Ltd.

Extracts from on article by H. Fehr

Most pharmaceutical enterprises of the present day have developed from chemical factories with different production interest in the course of diversification. Roche, in contrast, is a "spontaneous foundation," the outcome of an "idée maîtresse," an entrepreneurial concept. In this light the founder, Fritz Hoffmann-La Roche, appears as the representative of a type of entrepreneur common in the latter half of the nineteenth century, a type whom Joseph Schumpeter in his now classic essay in his "Dictionary of Political Science" has called "forger of new combinations." The history of the foundation of the firm is thus largely the life history of its founder.

Fritz Hoffmann was born on 24th October 1868 as the son of a well-to-do Basle trader, Friedrich Hoffman-Merian. He was a scion of an old extablished family through both his father's and his mother's line. His father was active in the textile trade, first in the silk ribbon industry, an important branch for the Basle region, then in the wholesale trading of raw silk.

Fritz Hoffmann's parents wanted him to take up a scientific career, but his scholastic record was undistinguished. After attempts at a grammar school, an institute in the Württemberg Kornthal and the Basle Pädagogium, his parents' academic hopes were relinquished, and Fritz Hoffman served a successful apprenticeship with the banking house of A. Piguet & Cie in Yverdon. A futher apprenticeship led the young man straight to the branch which was henceforth to be his live: in 1889, aged 21, he entered the house of Bohny, Holliger & Cie, druggists and grocers, in Basle. His apprenticeship there lasted only two years. He subsequently moved to London, where he worked with a firm trading in technical chemicals, Ferd. Krohn & Co. But the death of the proprietor prompted Fritz Hoffman to leave London after only a few months and to take up another training position with the druggist G. Lipman & Geffcken in hamburg.

In 1893 Fritz Hoffmann's father acquired an interest in Bohny, Holliger & Cie, his earlier employers, with a share of Fr. 200,000, and enabled his son to return to the firm in a senior position. In the following year he married Adèle La Roche, the daughter of an important Basle family, whose predecessors, like his own, had been engaged in the silk and ribbon industry.

Bohny, Holliger & Cie was a trading firm with a rich tradition. In 1889, however, the firm took over a small chemical laboratory on the Grenzacherstrasse, the present site of the Roche head office, where extracts, tinctures, various galenic preparations and linseed oil varnish and floor waxes were produced. This small factory was managed for Bohny, Holliger & Cie by a Munich chemist, Max Carl Traub, and also for a time under his own name. The firm's proprietors seem always to have thought of this manufacturing activity as a side-line, and to have treated it in consequence. But Fritz Hoffmann turned his whole attention to it, and it was a logical development to separate the factory from the trading firm.n 3rd March 1894, Fritz Hoffmann and Max Carl Traub joined to form a sleeping partnership, to which Hoffmann senior transferred his shares. On 1st April, they took over the factory on Grenzacherstrasse from Bohny, Holliger & Cie and renamed it Hoffmann, Traub & Co.

The new owners clearly had a penchant for the pharmaceutical field. The manufacture of linseed oil varnish and floor wax gave way to that of the familiar pharmaceutical preparations of the time, such as antifebrin, phenacetin, guaiacol carbonate, creosote carbonate and salicylic acid. Fritz Hoffmann looked around for a chemist, and fournd him in the person of Dr Lüdy of Burgdorf. Lüdy devised a combination of besmuth and iodine as a wound-healing powder that was taken up in the firm's programme and sold under the trade name of "Airol." Lüdy left the firm after a few months. The gap left by the departure of the chemist Lüdy remained until 1st February 1896, when it was filled by Emil Christoph Barell, who shortly before had obtained his doctor's degree in Berne and had been working as a teacher at the Rütti Agricultural School nearby.

The German patent laws granted protection to fereign products for only three years, after which time they had to be manufactured in the Reich. As the deadline for "Airol" drew near, Fritz Hoffmann resolved to

Study on model of a mollecule.

start production in Germany. Thus the history of the most important Roche factory in Europe can also be yraced back to the time before the firm as we now know it was founded.

The young Hoffman was here, there and everywhere in his early years as a businessman. Max Carl Traub could not keep pace with him. Thus it was quite in character that Traub should offer to resign from the company on 1st october 1896.

Thus the Roche story in the narrow sense began on 1st October 1896, when with the departure of Traub Fritz Hoffmann took the fates and fortunes of the pharmaceutical factory into his own hands.

It is important to place Fritz Hoffmann's enterprising idea against the background of the period.

Medicines were still normally prescribed for the individual patient and made up at the pharmacy by hand. The elixirs, pills and extracts produced were naturally not uniform in their active-substance content or their quality. In France, on the other hand, a move was already being made towards the development of branded pharmaceutical specialties. But the links between the scientific world and the industry were few, and the idea of interdisciplinary collaboration between the sciences was still in its infancy.

The lucid mind of Fritz Hoffman saw the potential in this situation. Industrially produced drugs, of constant quality and content, bearing the stamp of a knownmanufacturer, represented a definite advance. If it were possible to create the plant needed to produce such products and to sell them on an international scale, success was guaranteed. He remained firm in this conviction through a multitude of trials. To others, however, his ideas seemed audacious and even utopian. The target Fritz Hoffman had set himself seemed far too high for a firm without a well-established apparatus and a firmly anchored business to lean back upon. Max Carl Traub and others lost heart and turned away. But not Emil Christoph Barell and Eduard Hentz.

Barell brought with him a sound knowledge of chemistry, an alert intelligence, an inborn talent for organization and above all iron self-discipline and rigour. This was the character that was to determine Barell's progress from ray wyoung chemist to chief executive. He played a crucial part in the translation of Hoffmann's ideas into an efficient instrument. With his specialized knowledge he was quick to realize that manufacturing techniques were the key to the implementation of Hoffmann's idea. And it was he who put the young firm on the highest technical footing.

Eduard Hentz is overshadowed by the two strong personalities of Hoffmann and Barell, but it would be a mistake to underrate the part he played. He was a loyal worker at home and at the front. Unerringly persuaded of his duty, he remained loyal to Fritz Hoffmann through all crises, took care of the details, and was the solid pillar of the firm in troubled times.

Thus was the constellation of the ideas and personalities abroad when on 1st October 1896 F. Hoffmann-La Roche began its activity.

Otto Lanz was associated with Carl Schaerges, and they attempted to isolate the active components of the thyroid gland in chemically pure form as basis of an effective and safe thyroid preparation.

Their isolation process was patented in the name of F. Hoffman-La Roche & Co. In 1896« and doubtless constitutes the first Roche patent. The thyroid preparation thus produced was sold under the name "Aiodin."

In 1887 the Bernese clinician Prof. Hermann Sahli recommended guaiacol for the therapy of tuberculosis. Dr Barell chose pur synthetic guaiacol as starting material. The result of these studies was ortho-guaiacol-sulfonic acid, the potassium salt of which Roche introduced into therapy in 1898 under the name "Thiocol."

Carl Schaerges as an experienced pharmacist persisted in his search for a pleasant form of administration for "Thiocol." Schaerges commissioned the "Golden Pharmacy" in Basle to elaborate an orange syrup, and this, in combination with "Thiocol," produced the first success of Hoffmann-La Roche, "Sirolin."

These strenuous efforts were being made under extremely difficult conditions for the production programme was still anything but economically sound.

Crisis loomed when from one day to the next the Basler Handelsbank withdrew Fritz Hoffmann's credit.

Succour came with the entry of Carl Meerwein into the company. Meerwein had been dealing in pharmaceuticals in London, but had wound up his business and returned to Basle, where he was looking around for a new field of activity. He was introduced to Fritz Hoffmann through the Basle banking house La

Thiocol (1898).

Reprint from the
Aerztlichen Central-Anzeiger, Wien, No. 26, 1896.

AIROL
a new antiseptic for wounds.

FROM MEDICAL PRACTICE.
Occasional articles and therapeutic suggestions.

BY

Dr HANS DEGLE
KINDBERG.

A few brief reports, published by medical men, had drawn my attention to a new antiseptic for wounds, called Airol. The statement of its being odourless was a special inducement for me to give it a trial and so I wrote to the manufacturers for a sample which very kindly they sent to me at once. And I am happy to say that thus I obtained a remedy which proved to be very serviceable indeed. It so happened that just then I had to attend to a series of severe and light injuries, enabling me to extensively try the remedy. Strange to say the first patients in this respect were 2 children whose hands had been caught by the wheels of chaff-cutting engines, extensive contused and lacerated wounds with fractures of a few phalanges being inflicted. The next case was a boy with a gash of the right hand index-finger, the two extreme phanlanges being nearly severed, a narrow bridge of skin only uniting them to the stump. The patient, next in order, was a woodworker with a very neglected incised wound that showed a diphtheritic coating, on the right thigh; then followed a young working man with an extensive lacerated wound in the little finger of the right hand, and, ultimately, a man with a contused wound

1

No 45. 1. 04. 6500.

Technical paper on Airol.

Roche & Co. Meerwein agreed to become an active partner in the business once it had been put on a sound basis.

In the meantime Friedrich Hoffmann had died. Fritz wrote off almost Fr 422,000 from his and his father's assets and personally assumed the commitments to suppliers. Thus the old debts were cleared and the way opened to establishing the new company.

The company was founded on 31st May 1898 and was composed of Fritz Hoffman-La Roche and Carl Meerwein, each with an investment of Fr. 200,000, a share of Fr. 100,000 from Fritz Hoffmann's mother and a new share of Fr. 300,000 from his father-in-law, Alfred La Roche-Passavant. On the strength of this reorganization the banks were once again prepared to grand credit.

A noteworthy detail of the contract drawn up for the company and partnership was its provision that 10 % be earmarked for bonuses to employees. Thus in these early years the basis of the social welfare of the employees was established.

At the turn of the century "Thiocol" and "Sirolin" were the mainstays of the entire Roche activity. Through the profits from these products rapide progress was possible on the sceintific and technical fronts.

In 1904 Max Cloëtta succeeded in producing a pur preparation that cntained an acceptably uniform mixture of the active principles of digitalis. The new preparation was named "Digalen," and in 1904 Roche took up its production and distribution. It received an enthusiastic welcome from the medical profession, and remained in production until 1964.

The development begun with "Digalen" continued in 1909 with "Pantopon." The therapeutic hopes placed in the preparation were fulfilled, and "Pantopon" is the only speciality from that period still in use today.

In fact, the years before the Great War contain the germ of almost all the main branches of Roche's activity. A broad and solid foundation had been laid. Above all, however, Roche had won the recognition of the medical profession.

In 1905 the Hoffmann-La Roche Chemical Works Inc. was founded in downtown Manhattan with a capital of $25,000. Branches followed in Vienna in 1907 and in London in 1909. The year 1910 was a milestone when after several trips to Russia, Fritz Hoffmann and Carl Meerwein founded a Roche company in St. Petersburg, for the Russian market had become one of the main outlets for "Sirolin" and "Thiocol."

With the outbreak of the Russian Revolution the entire Russian market, which before the war had accounted for up to a fifth of the sales volume, was lost at a stroke. This and the losses sustained in the other countries affected by the war brought F. Hoffmann-La Roche & Co. to the brink of bankruptcy. Without an influx of fresh capital the firm was doomed.

The situation was saved by transforming the sleeping partnership into a joint-stock company in April 1919. Of the equity capital of Fr. 4 m. Fritz Hoffmann received 3 m. for his initial share, while the remaining million was made up by Hoffmann's brother-in-law, Rudolf Albert Koechlin-Hoffmann, president of the Basler Handelbank, Barell, and two further close colleagues of Hoffmann's. In addition Alfred Wieland-Zahn, Hoffmann's legal adviser, also became a member of the board. This was the team that set itself the task of reconstruction. The management was now taken over by Barell, for Fritz Hoffmann's health had been greatly undermined by the strains of the war and business crises. SInce spring 1919 he had been suffering from a serious kidney ailment, from which he was to die on 18 April 1920, never to see how his enterprise rose once again out of the slough.

With the passage of time the memory of Fritz Hoffmann has tended to pale against that of Emil Barell, who remained active for three decades after the early death of the founder. Unjustly so, however, for the fundamental ideas underlying the growth of the firm were without a doubt the intellectual property of Fritz Hoffman. As industrialists, Barell was the pupil, Hoffmann the master.

After World War I

The first endeavours in the vitamin field were not crowned with success, but the ground had been well prepared when in 1933 Professor Tadäus Reichstein achieved the total synthesis of vitamin C. Thus began the vitamin era at Roche; it was to last for several decades, and is still very much alive today. The highpoint in the history of the vitamins at Roche, however, is without doubt the elegant synthesis of vitamin A by Otto Isler in 1946.

244

The founder of the company, Fritz Hoffmann-La Roche (seated) together with Dr. Emil C. Barell who was later to become President of the Board. (Photo Roche).

The importance of active substances by free chemical synthesis grew continuously between the wars.

The creation of the well-known analgesic "Saridon," which was introduced in 1933, was the result of a very attractive concept. None of the analgesics in use at that time was fully satisfactory. Either they were handicapped by side effects, or their action was inadequate, or they were too expensive. The Roche laboratories thus received from Dr. Barell the commission to develop a preparation on the basis of a formula which, although commonplace today, had at that time not yet been clearly put into words: efficacy, safety, price. The result was a good combination of active substances that included isopropylantipyrine, developed by Hans Stenzl, and that met all the demands formulated by Barell.

At research institutes and in the industrial laboratories all possible substances were being feverishly tested for an antituberculotic action. In the Roche laboratories this activity culminated in the discovery by Robert Schnitzer, at Nutley in 1951, of the antituberculotic action of isoniazid. The substance was immediately sent out for clinical testing, but on New year's Eve it transpired that the American firm of E.R. Squibb had been testing the same substance. Later it became known that Bayer of Leverkusen were also testing isoniazid. Roche and Squibb carried out their clinical investigations simultaneously and without undue publicity, so as not to arouse hopes which might prove illusory. However, they had failed to reckon with the "power of the press," for early in the new year the "New York Post" carried banner headlines: Wonder Drug Fights TB.

In treating tuberculous patients with "Rimifon" and its successor "Marsilid" clinicians noted that their patients tended to become much more cheerful in outlook, a psychological change which could not be wholly explained in terms of the improvement in their general physical condition. This finding awakened interest in psychotropic substances. In Basle and Nutley extensive research was begun. The era of monoamine oxidase inhibition began with "Marsilid" and ledto the development of "Marplan" (1960). The antidepressant "Laroxyl" developed by Hans Spiegelberg followed in 1962. This substance is also important as a component of combinations ("Limbitrol").

In Nutley progress was slow until 1960, when the chemist Leo Sternbach achieved an important breakthrough. A newcomer to the psychotropic field, he remembered a group of substances that he had studied in another connexion decades earlier, and there stumbled on the benzodiazepines. One of the fist compounds he synthesized proved active against anxiety and tension, thereby relieving their organic sequelae, but without affecting alertness. The active substance was introduced under the trade mark "Librium" and proved a world-wide success. Further research devoted to the benzodiazepines resulted in a broad range of specific drugs—"Librax" (1961), "Valium" Roche (1963), "Mogadon" (1965) and "Nobrium" (1968).

A new milestone in the history of Roche specialities was the introduction of "Larodopa" in 1970. THis preparation, based on a natural amino acid, can be claimed to be the first drug effective against Parkinson's disease. The active substance was first elucidated in 1913 by the then director of research Markus Guggenheim, but it was not till 1970 that the preparation was ripe for commercial introduction. Thus fifty-seven years elapsed from elucidation of the structure to the finished preparation.

Quite another story attaches to "Prostigmin," introduced in 1931. Its history dates back to 1864, after some children in Liverpool docks had eaten Calabar beans, the poisonous fruit of an African papilionaceous plant, with mass intoxication as result. This tragedy prompted the English researchers Stedman and Barger to investigate the structure of the active substance of the Calabar bean, physostgmin. ROche laboratories took up work on the substance in 925 in an attempt to find an intestinal stimulant with a physostigmin-like action that would reverse the intestinal paralysis caused by anethesia for surgery. Since the natural physostigmin affects the blood pressure, a search was made for an effective analogue without this side effect. In 1930 Dr. John Aeschliman found the agent Roche was seeking. It was introduced as "Prostigmin." It is today one of the few remaining "classic" drugs.

Special efforts were also directed at the problem of blood coagulation. In 1938 the anticoagulant factor of the blood, heparin, was produced in pure form, and the compound was then introduced as "Liquemin." It was followed shortly after the war by the coagulation enzyme thrombin, marketed as "Topostasin," used in emergencies to staunch otherwise intractable bleeding.

The period dealth with in this chapter was characterized by a great expansion of experimental medicine. Thus research increasingly came within the scope of the industrial undertaking, as important aspects of the work no longer depended on direct contact with the patient.

As early as the nineteen twenties, Roche had followed this trend by constructing pharmacological as well as chemical laboratories. As time went on she began to specialize on an ever increasing number of fronts.

In Welwyn Garden City, on the outskirts of London, a department for chemical research was instituted in 1939.

Before the outbreak of the Second World the firm's existing network of branches in Milan, New York, Paris, Rio de Janeiro, Montevideo, Barcelona, Vienna and London was reinforced by the establishment of Roche companies in Brussels (1920), Bucharest (1922), Warsaw and Tokyo (1924), Shanghai (1925), Bombay (1928), Buenos Aires (1930), Montreal ang Riga (1931), and Stockholm (1939).

A fex words may be devoted to the history of what is today by far the most important of the Roche companies abroad, namely the USA concern. Hoffmann-La Roche Chemical Works Inc. was formed in New York in 1905. At first it chiefly impoted chemicals, to which "Thiocol" and "Sirolin" were added in 1906 after the liquidation of the unsuccessful "Sirolin" company. Until shortly before the First World War the American company continually ran at a loss. In 1910 a scientific division was formed, headed by Dr. Alexander White, and a year later there entered the firm's employ a young clerk who was destined to enjoy a remarkable career: Elmer Bobst. A typical go-getting American salesman, but of exceptional calibre, Bobst pushed up sales to unprecedented heights. He was appointed a director in 1920, and subsequently became the Company's president. Incidentally, his initial engagement was based on what is perhaps best described as a "misunderstanding." He was given the job because of the favourable impression created by the handwriting of his letter of application, which was, however, written by his wife!

During the Frist World War the American Roche Company succeeded in wiping out the losses of the pre-war years, but found itself in renewed difficulties at the end of the war owing to the collapse in prices of its raw material stocks. One of the first tasks of the public company which had recently been formed in Basle was to send its merchandising director to New York to reorganise the American subsidiary's accounting system. With growing prosperity in the twenties the Company was able to buy a large industrial site at Nutley in the following year, when the Company assumed its present name of Hoffmann-La Roche Inc.

The great depression did not leave Roche Nutley unaffected, but in contrast to most of American industry dismissals took place only on a small scale.

During the first years of the Second World War Nutley rapidly became an important manufacturing and research centre, in spite of numerous wartime restrictions. The first research laboratories had to be set up in a bare warehouse.

The war years were a period of power and ascendancy not only for the United States, but also for the American Roche Company. Under Elmer Bobst powerful forces were at work to obtain maximum independence of the parent undertaking for the American subsidiary. Besides the task of extending the Roche organization in the USA and the free world, Emil Barell was faced with far-reaching decisions of a political nature and travelled to the United States. Although he knew the country, he was in an essentially alien environment, nearing seventy, and alone, except for the advisers who crowded in from all sides. It was the time of Pearl harbour. In the general uncertainty it was not always easy to distinguish between real and imaginary dangers. The road ahead was not clear. It was suggested that the firm should seek American protection, "fly the Stars and Stripes." A number of agencies and markets in the free world were in fact allocated to the American company, and this may well have strengthened the position of the Roche concern in these countries. When, however, it was suggested that at least part of the capital of the American concern should be in American hands, Barell scented danger.

Tough bargaining set in, but it terminated in maintenance of the status quo. This decision was of immense importance for the future of the company, for the question of who was to be boss in the USA was settled once and for all. It was not to Elmer Bobst's liking, however, and in 1944 he left Roche to take over the management of Warner Lambert.

SAPAC comprises essentially the American, British, Far Eastern and Pacific parts of the organization. It is not, however, a daughter company of Roche, but rather—to retain the family analogy—a ser company. Roche does not own the SAPAC shares; the position is that Roche shareholders are also SAPAC shareholders, because every Roche share is inseparably linked with a SAPAC share.

The fundamental idea governing the relationship between Roche and SAPAC emanated from Dr. Alfred Wieland-Zahn, an outstandingly able and far-seeing lawyer who had given Fritz Hoffman the benefit of his counsel and who had been appointed to the board of the new public company in Hoffmann's lifetime. He played a large aprt in the rise of the firm, and later guided its destinies as President. THe system he evolved has been frequently imitated. Particularly in the Second World War it proved its worth up to the hilt.

Today Roche is one of the three most important drug manufacturers in the world.

Dr. Emil Christoph Barell was a martinet who insisted on the strictest staff discipline. He kept a vigilant eye on the timekeeping and the work of every employee, from departmental director to factory worker. Hierarchical distinctions were strictly observed; he did not approve of fraternization between different grades and categories of staff. Stenzl remembers: "There were separate entrances for laboratory and office staff. Once Professor Fromherz, head of the pharmacological department, was engrossed in conversation with an "office" colleague and inadvertently entered the precinct through the office gate. The same day a staff circular noted Dr. Barell's "surprise" at this distressing incident! On the other hand, Barell knew nearly every worker by name, and took an almost sentimental interest in his personal welfare. Many a worker had cause to be grateful for the "Governor's" help. Hence Barell's militaristic, monastic regime never bred the resentment that might have been expected, and friction between management and workers hardly ever arose. At the same time, there was never any room for an executive who failed at any time to toe the line marked by the Chief.

Many anecdotes still circulate about the Barellian regime. There is one which is characteristic. Dr. Barell had appointed a chief storeman who he thought had far too much embonpoint. He therefore accepted him on condition that he lost weight. The unfortunate employee had to report every week to the managing director with weight card duly stamped, so that his slimming progress could be checked. Those were the days!

Today the Roche organization consists of two independent groups of companies which are combined in F. Hoffmann-La Roche & Co., Limited Company, Basle, and SAPAC Corporation, new Brunswick, Canada.

Heinrich Emanuel Merck (1795-1859).

MERCK (Darmstadt)

One of the oldest German pharmacies in continuous activity belongs to the Merck family. A very early clue we have of a Merck is the mention of Johann Merck (1573-1642) as bailiff of Schweinfurt, Germany. One of his elder sons was Georg Merck (1611-1683) who was a pharmacist as was the younger son Friedrich Jacob Merck (1621-1678) who became the owner of the *Engel Apotheke* in Darmstadt, Germany, and started the series of father to son ownership of that pharmacy for the next few centuries. To be very correct it must be pointed out that *Friedrich Jacob Merck* and his wife had no children so that a nephew *Georg Friedrich Merck* (1647-1715), son of Georg Merck, became the owner and thus the true founding father of all the father to son relationships. The Engel Apotheke itself was established in 1654 by a pharmacist named Samuel Boeckler of Darmstadt. This makes it three and a half centuries old. After Georg Friedrich Merck the pharmacy passed on to his son Johann Franz (1687-1741) and then to his son Johann Justus (1727-1758) and his son Johann Anton (1756-1805) and finally to his son Heinrich Emanuel Merck (1794-1855) who established a factory on the premises of the Engel Apotheke. It is to him and through him that the Merck firm of today is what it is—a modern well organized establishment with the spirit of a family pharmacy where father and son and mother too all participated in keeping up the ethics of the profession.

Heinrich Emanuel Merck was born in Darmstadt in September 1794. His father was Johann Anton Merck and his mother was also a Merck—Adelheid Merck whose father was Johann Heinrich Merck and who became famous as the friend of a young man named Johann Wolfgang von Goethe. Emanuel—he did not use the name Heinrich—Merck was destined as a child to inherit the Engel Apotheke. Therefore, he could start preparations at an early age and with the best of apprenticeships. After the usual school education in Darmstadt and Geneva, Emanuel Merck was sent to Erfurt, Germany, in 1810 to spend two years with Professor Johann Bartholmä Trommsdorff at his famous Institute. This was followed by assistantships in 1812-1814 in Eisenach and Frankfurt and Strasbourg. In 1815 Emanuel Merck started studies at the University of Berlin. He attended private lessons as well. He would have liked to study further in Vienna but had to return to Darmstadt to take charge of the family pharmacy. Thus, at the age of twenty-two years, Emanuel Merck took his licencing examinations and, a few years later, he started to create a pharmaceutical industry. His way. His reputation was such that Professor Trommsdorff sent his son to Darmstadt as did Justus Liebig with his son in order that they could apprentice with Emanuel Merck.

As a pharmacist Emanuel Merck liked phytochemistry best. He worked a lot with opium and its constituents—his son Georg Franz also, for the discovered papaverine—and published very frequently. Emanuel Merck developed the manufacture of *Santonin* to introduce this *anthelmintic* into medicine. He also worked on other plant drugs in his Engel Apotheke—such as Sabadilla. Since 1827 he offered small collections of alkaloids to interested scientists and, at the same time, announced the fact that he had begun to produce them "in bulk" in his pharmacy. Soon he had to move his laboratories to more spacious ones. His business now consisted of preparing alkaloids and other preparations by the hundreds of pounds. Emanuel Merck and his products were well known. In 1853 the Merck family won a citation at the New York World's Fair for its alkaloids. Previous to this Merck was awarded a gold medal in 1830 by the Société de Pharmacie in Paris for proposing better methods of recognizing alkaloids in forensic medicine. Meanwhile the firm just grew and grew and the list of items it carried now numbered in the thousands. Most, of course, were the usual pharmacopeial preparations. But specialities now entered the picture—Dionin. Luminal. Veronal. Ergotin-Merck. Phanodorm. Doryl. And many others. Probably most important were the vitamins. As one of the very first firms working with vitamins, Merck acquired a lot of experience with Vitamin C. In fact, in 1934 Merck had isolated larger quantities of Vitamin C. Cebion. Merck soon had available Vitamin D_2. Vitamin B_1 or Betabion. Vitamin B_2 or Lactoflavin. D_3. B_6. B_{12}. And Synthetic Vitamin A. Among the other groupings of drugs Merck has done very much with the steroid hormones—especially cortisone.

Of course, Merck is preoccupied with modern medicine—Psychopharmaca. Neuro-activators. Hormones. Cardiovascular drugs. Antibiotics. Chemotherapeutics. Dietetics. And many others in addition to Veterinay drugs and Cosmetic and Ermatological drugs. Merck has endeared itself to scientists the world over for their authorative publications, such as The Merck Index and E. Merck's Annual Report and others.

SANDOZ

Two middle aged men—a chemist and a businessman—in 1886 established a dyestuffs factory in Basel with nary a thought of dealing in pharmaceuticals. Or perhaps they did after all—there is evidence that they did manufacture several pharmaceutical preparations. The chemist was Dr. Jakob Alfred Kern of Bülach near Zurich. He was simply fascinated by chemistry. And he enjoyed a thorough training in the subject. Only eighteen years old he was one of the first students to be graduated from the famous ETH or Federal Institue of Technology which was founded on October 15 in 1855. Even before graduation, young Kern was besieged with offers of employment—for example in Offenbach am Main in Germany in the factory of Karl Oehler Jr. Alfred Kern accepted this offer. In 1874 two more important events occurred. He received his "Doctor" title—his Ph. D. in chemistry from the University of Giessen. And he married Johanna Katharina Emma Anselm. Her father was active in the commercial circles of Offenbach. The city was bombed and burned during World War II so that many documents and photos were destroyed—thus many details concerning the activities of Alfred Kern cannot be made available. We do know that he left Offenbach am Main for Basel in October 1878.

In Basel Alfred Kern in January 1879 accepted a four-year contract with Bindschedler and Busch—the firm which had purchased the business interests of Alexander Clavel five years previously. He was to regret this move later on. Almost immediately, Dr. Kern started to synthesize important compounds. Even more important—Kern started to develop his method of using Phosgene to obtain whole new series of derivatives for dyestuffs cosmetics pharmaceuticals pesticides and foam substances such as foam rubber or foam sponges. Probably Alfred Kern would be amazed today to see his invention used in automobiles boats and furniture. At any rate he was synthesizing and creating some of the most important compounds of his life. Too bad. For all the patents were going to Bind-schedler and Busch as agreed upon in the contract. Alfred Kern got along well with Mr. Busch but his relations with Bindschedler were rather strained. Thus, when Busch left the firm, Bindschedler was left alone as director. His first act was to rescind Kern's contract as of December 1884. The ugly moods and deep depressions of Alfred Kern can easily be imagined.

Now that he was free, Dr. Kern received many offers. From BASF—Badische Anilin— & Soda-Fabrik AG. From Collineau et Cie. From Durand and Huguenin. From Edouard Sandoz. As concerned Durand and Huguenin—they sent as their delegate to see Dr. Kern one of their senior commercial directors—a certain Edouard Sandoz. The plan was to build a factory for Alfred Kern which would be a separate entity under the aegis of Mr. Sandoz on behalf of Durand and Huguenin. To have his own factory would be a dream come true for Alfred Kern. Therefore he held out for complete independence. And obtained it. Mr. Sandoz resigned his position to join Dr. Kern on a personal basis. The final arrangement was that Dr. Kern would put up 100'000 francs and Mr. Sandoz twice that amount to form a joint enterprise named Kern & Sandoz Bâle Suisse. Or in (Swiss) German, as registered in Basel on July 1 in 1886—Chemische Fabrik Kern & Sandoz. The new firm was located on the rhine River adjacent to the French border and just opposite to the factory of Ciba in Lesser Basel, adjacent to the German border. This is the famous Three Countries Corner where France Germany and Switzerland have a common border—in the middle of the rhine River.

Dr. Alfred Kern—the technical and production director now thirty-six years old—was all ready to create new synthetic colors. But who was Edouard Sandoz, the thirty-three year old commercial financial and marketing director? His background was just the opposite of his partner. Whereas the Kern family tree could be traced back to many generations of village mayors and other local positions in the Swiss German regions of Zurich, the Sandoz family originated in the Swiss French regions of Switzerland. Neuchâtel mostly. And in France. The story here is that the father of Edouard—Charles-Auguste Sandoz—wasborn in 1809 in La chaux-de-Fonds in Switzerland. As an adult he became a dealer in the cloth and drapery trade. Then, in 1835 he married Marie-Louise Luya whose father was a Captain in the French Army. The Luya family originated in the Dauphine, but after King Louis XIV declared the Edict of Nantes null and void the Luya family fled to Geneva and became citizens there. They were not of modest circumstances. However Charles-Auguste Sandoz-Luya decided to try his luck in other places. He spent some time in Vienna and later in Basel where he dealt in cloth and wool. He must have been quite successful because he retired at an early age. Mr. Sandoz-Luya was very active in church affairs and thus became the laughing stock to be mocked at by a pun made on his name. Mr. Sandoz-Luya was usually greeted as Mr. Sandoz-Alléluya. But he had the last laugh since he could retire without working. And could support a large family as well.

Edouard Sandoz was born in Basel as the youngest of nine children in October 1853. He had the usual schooling offered in Basel until he could attend the University of Lausanne. He spent two semesters there and then went back to Basel to apprentice in the firm of a silk dealer. After that he worked in a Paris establishment which sent him as far afield as America where aniline dyestuffs were not yet well known. This then was the person who would share with Alfred Kern the destiny of a small factory. Edouard Sandoz believed in the future. That is why he meanwhile had married, in June 1880, the beautiful and artistic Olympe David of Lausanne. Madame Sandoz-David was an accomplished painter. She liked music and dance and poetry. They lived in Basel of course and were active in cultural affairs—Edouard Sandoz possessed a good tenor voice and was a member of Basel's famous Liedertafel—an elite glee club. Edouard Sandoz travelled to China India and America and created some excitement in that he offered credit terms in those places. ALl in all, everything was all right. Until March 2, 1893. The day Dr. Alfred Kern died of a heart attack. He long had had a cardiac condition.

Thus, after only seven years the young flourishing establishment was in serious difficulties. Edouard Sandoz changed the firm from a collective enterprise to a special limited partnership renamed Sandoz & Cie. He carried on alone. Successfully. However, Edouard Sandoz too was suffering from a rheumatic condition which kept on getting worse and worse. And when he too suffered a heart attack in 1894, he decided to retire from the business. Thus he changed the corporate structure from a collective enterprise to a joint stock company with a starting capital of two million francs. He restructured the company and placed the most important employees in their proper places—technical or administration and so on. And then—always original—Edouard Sandoz gifted some of the shares to the employees to keep them within the company. It's name was Chemische Fabrik, vormals Sandoz. Finally in 1939 the name was changed to Sandoz S.A. Edouard Sandoz could rest now.

He moved to Lausanne. Near Lausanne. Actually in Ouchy. There the piece of land he had purchased was in reality a park of over 66'000 square meters which eventually was gifted to the public. Meanwhile he and his family could enjoy the house they lived in set in among the trees. Mrs. Olympe Sandoz-David made it a home. She was a talented cultured woman who taught her three sons how to enjoy the muses. Edouard Marcel Sandoz-Passavant sculpted and painted. Aurèle became a banker. Maurice-Yves became a globetrotter and author as well as a musician. They and their father dabbled somewhat in Sandoz, the firm. All four are now deceased—but all had the satisfaction of seeing that their firm had an important pharmaceutical department.

Professor Arthur Stoll was, at least for awhile, the Pharmaceutical Department of Sandoz. An an assistant of the Nobel Prize winner Richard Willstätter, Arthur Stoll had had many years of experience in isolating from plants their active substances. Thus when the Sandoz management decided to add on a pharmaceutical department to their firm, they had the right man in the right place and at the right time.

Arthur Stoll was born in 1887 in relatively nearby Schinznach in Aargau Switzerland. After the usual education there, he studied in the Federal Institute of Technology at Zurich—the ETH. Stoll could start his studies in 1909 in the private laboratories of Professeur Willstätter. In 1917 both transferred to the newly built Kaiser-Wilhelm-Institut für Chemie in Berlin-Dahlem where Arthur Stoll was Chief Assistant. In 1913 their now classis publication 'Untersuchungen über Chlorophyll" was published. In 1915 R. Willstätter was awarded the Nobel Prize. In 1916 this research pair had transferred to the Bayerische Akademie der Wissenschaft where in 1917 they published their second book "Untersuchungen über die Assimilation der Kohlensäure". And finally in 1917 they published their investigations on enzymes—"Ueber Peroxydase". It was in 1917 too—on October 1—that Arthur Stoll accepted the challenge to establish a pharmaceutical department for Sandoz in Basel. And still in 1917, he was awarded an honorary Professorship—the title of Königl. Bayrischer Professor or Royal Bavarian Professor.

The Stoll method was essentially the binding of the active principles to the plant cells which are then separated from the inactive substances and then isolating them. At any rate Professor Stoll was to revolutionize medicine and pharmacy. The first drug plant he investigated was ergot. Here, after several

Sandoz Plant-Basel 1886.

hundred years of unsuccessful research by many chemists, Professor Stoll succeeded in isolating ergotamine—they main alkaloid in ergot—by March 1918. Physicians the world over now had a reliable ergot preparation. It was gravimettric. Constant in its effects. The spectre of postpartum hemorrage was practically banished. Ergotamine was ergot. Ergot was ergotamine. And hemorrage in childbirth was no longer to be feared. But ergot was to reveal itself as being full of surprises. Pleasant surprises. In 1926 it was reported that ergotamine—Gynergen Sandoz—was specific against migraine headaches. ALl that was needed was one injection—and this most excruciating of all headaches would be aborted. By adding caffeine to ergotamine, absorption is enhanced—thus such tablets replace injections. Later it was to be shown that the ergot alkaloids could be hydrogenated and thus their pharmacological properties could be changed. In the case of ergotamine it was shown that hydrogenation to dihydroergotamine caused hardly any change in parenteral use—by injection it was just as effective in acute migraine. It was not effective in childbirth. It was effective in migraine prophylaxis when administered by mouth.

Hydrogenation of the ergotoxine complex to form dihydroergotoxine mesylate—better known as Hydergine—gives a drug which normalizes and restores metabolic founctions of the ganglionic cells. It is a most valuable drug in geriatrics. Hydergine is used in cerebrovascular insufficiency and arteriosclerosis. Representative manifestations of aging are symptoms such as confusion. Mood-depression. Impaired self-care functions. Unsociability and dizziness—all of which have been approved by the U.S. Food and Drug Administration as indications for Hydergine.

Still another ergot derivative with a promising future is Bromergocryptine—whose full name is 2-Br-alpha-Ergocryptine, Methane Sulphonate or CB 154.

The effect of this compound is that it has a specific inhibitory action on prolactin release. That is—it suppresses lactation. SInce the action of Bromergocryptine is specific, it makes therapy possible without the use of concommitant hormones—therefore there are no fears of thrombo-embolic complications.

Also very exciting are the newest reports that Bromergocryptine may make surgery of brain tumors unncessary. There seems to be an association between the increased secretion of prolactin and the production of tumors. THus suppression of prolactin should lead to non-formation of tumors. Actually it does not entirely do so. Small tumors may disappear altogether and large tumors may get smaller so that they can be operated upon. Furthermore all other proclactin dependent body functions such as loss of libido and lack of ovulation will revert to normal. Besides these effects upon tumors—especially pituitary types—it seems that Bromergocryptine exerts a beneficial effect on the Parkinson Syndrome too.

Of course there were other many, many achievements by Professor Arthur Stoll with and without his staff of co-researchers. In the ergot field he isolated a water soluble alkaloid which proved to be ergometrine. Later he and Dr. Albert Hofman synthesized ergometrine and Lysergide which, unfortunately as LSD, was taken up in the drug scene—but now seems to have left it to a great extent. The Sandoz staff made hundreds of achievements such as the total synthesis of ergotamine. And when we add the non-ergot compounds, it has made thousands of achievements. One of these was the preparation of the first painless injectable calcium salt. Another was the clarification of the chemistry of digitalis. Now, instead of plant alkaloids, Sandoz had to research plant glycosides. Along with digitalis, Sandoz studied the other cardiac plants such as squill and strophanthus. Professor Sandoz and his staff showed the chemical differences between Digitalis purpurea and Digitalis lanata and their interrelationships.

Witt all the research carried out by Professor Arthur Stoll and his small staff as a base, Sandoz could well expand into all fields of chemistry—plant drugs. Cyclosporins Peptides. Synthetics of all kinds. Immunosupressives. Psychotropics. Beta blocking agents. And any other field which may show promise for the future. Sandoz will be ready.

Sandoz made important discoveries about natural products in the course of research on the active substances contained in ergot and digitalis (the foxglove plant). Ergot, a fungus that attacks rye, had been used as a drug in midwifery of many centuries, but it was in the Sandoz laboratories that the first successful attemps was made to identify the main active principles of ergot, to isolate them and prepare them in a pure state (e.g. ergotamine, the active principle of *Gynergen*). Among these were substances which, in amounts of less than one-thousandth of a gram, were capable of arresting haemorrhage durint childbirth. The preparation of the active principles of ergot in a pure state made it possible to elucidate their chemical structure.

Chemical modification of these natural substances opened up the way to the synthesis of new drugs

254

Edouard Sandoz (1853-1928).

Dr. Alfred Kern (1850-1893).

with different properties. Other such derivatives alone or in combination are used by the physician for the relief and prevention of migraine headaches *(Cafergot, Deseril),* for treating nervous disorders *Bellergal),* for controling a variety of symptoms of old age caused by reduced cerebral circulation *(Hydergine),* for treating hypotensive cardiovascular disorders *(Dihydergot),* for venous disorders of the legs *(Sandovene),* and for the prevention of thromboembolic complications following surgical operations *(Heparin-Dihydergot).* Recently a further semisynthetic ergot derivative was made available in the form of *Parlodel,* a drug which inhibits the secretion of prolactin by the pituitary gland. This property makes Parlodel an effective causal treatment for unwanted lactation following childbirth and the only known treatment for certain forms of sterility. In addition it is the first effective drug in acromegaly, a rare but serious endocrine disorder.

The treatment of human heart diseases, which demands very exact dosages of the drugs used, has long been a special field of research at Sandoz and valuable results have been obtained. Isolation of the active principles of the foxglove *(Digitalis lanata) and other plants containing cardiac glycosides (Scilla, Strophanthus)* led to the development of a variety of preparations which today play an important part in the fight against cardiac disease *(Cedilanid, Digoxin).*

Besides the substances derived from natural materials, there is the vast field of synthetic drugs and here, too, Sandoz research workers have been instrumental, through their pioneering efforts, in achieving real progress in therapeutics; for example, the development of *Calcium Sandoz,* an injectable dosage form which laid the foundation of modern calcium therapy. Research into synthetic drugs has led to the discovery of preparations which are a boon to the physician in treating a wide variety of disorders. Among the synthetic drugs discovered and developed in the Sandoz laboratories, *Melleril,* a major tranquillizer employed in psychiatry, has won wide acclaim throughout the world. It is supplemented by a new type of drug developed in the Wander laboratories for the treatment of severe depression *(Noveril).* Furhtermore, Sandoz has contributed to therapeutic progress by developing drugs for treatment of nausea and vomiting *(Torecan),* allergic diseases *(Tavegyl),* to promote diuresis *(Brinaldix)* and for treatment of high blood pressure *(Brinerdin, Visken).* Latterly the company's range of synthetic drugs has been extended to include drugs for the prevention of anginal attacks and for the treatment of caridiac arrhythmias *(Visken)* as well as drugs for the interval (prophylactic) treatment of migraine *Sandomigran).* Biarison, an antirtheumatic agent, with an unconventional chemical structure, occupieds a special place among antiinflammatory agents, its principal features being its wide activity spectrum and its above-average tolerability. The novel mechanism of action and oral dosage form of *Zaditen* give it an important position in the prevention of ashtma.

Sandoz also achieved the first industrial synthesis of posterior nituitary hormones, notably oxytocin *(Syntocinon)* which finds wide use in obstetrics, and related substances which do not occur in nature *(POR 8 Sandoz, Calcitonin Sandoz, Sandopart).*

SANDOZ is also involved in the fight against infectious diseases. One of tis subsidaries, the Austrian company Biochemie, was the first to develop an effective oral form of penicillin *(Ospen).* Work on combatting infections now goes on at the Group's Research institute in Vienna, where the influenza vaccine Sandovac was developed. *Sandovac* countains only those parts of the influenza virus which are necessary of the develoment of immunity, and it is thus very well tolerated as well as being highly effective.

The wide range of research carried out by Sandoz illustrates the benefits which can accrue to science in general from work done in a firm's own laboratories; in turn, the work of the pure scientist can make an indispensable contribution to progress in applied research. Without this stimulating two-way relationship modern drug research would be inconceivable, and it is highly gratifying to know that Sandoz plays an important role between university scientists and industrial research workers.

Activities in the hospital supply field, which take the form of a joint venture (Sopamed Ltd.) with the French pharmaceutical company RHONE-POULENC, represent a diversification of interest in health. Sopamed in primarily involved in the kidney machine and artificial respiration fields.

Advertising for a french medicament (1910).

Si vous toussez

PRENEZ DES

PASTILLES GÉRAUDEL

SCHERING A.G.

Courtesy Schering A.G.

Like many other chemical and pharmaceutical enterprises, the Schering joint stock company evolved from a pharmacy. The firm's founder, Ernst Schering, opened his "Grüne Apotheke" ("Green" Pharmacy) in North Berlin in 1851. In 1864 an E. Schering factory was built near the shop. This soon became so large that it was transformed into a joint stock company in 1871 in order to widen it's financial basis. 1871 is therefore regarded as the official foundation date of the Schering joint stock compagny.

2. Chemische Fabrik auf Actien (vorm. E. Schering)

Ersnt Schering was active on the board of directors and in the management of the "Chemische Fabrik auf Actien (vorm E. Schering)", until his death in 1889. The company initially dealt with all types of chemicals, mainly iodine and bromide compounds for medicinal and photographic purposes. Since 1864 these have been produced in a factory in Berlin Wedding which has developed into the present Wedding works.

By 1927 the "Chemische Fabrik auf Actien (vorm E. Schering)" had acquired various factories in Charlottenburg and Eberswalde which enabled them to considerably expand their production programme.

As a result of the merger between the "Chemische Fabrik auf Actien (vorm. E. Schering)" and the "C. A. F. Kahlbaum Chemische Fabrik GmbH" the "Schering-Kahlbaum Ag" was formed in 1927.

3. Schering Aktiengesellscaft

The Schering joint stock company resulted from the merger of the "Oberschlesische Kokswerke und Chemische Fabriken AG", founded in 1890, with the "Schering Kahlbaum AG" in 1937. Before 1937 the two joint stock companies had seperate management and spheres of operation. After the First World War the "Oberschlesische Kokswerke und Chemische Fabriken AG", whose field of activity originally covered the running of coke works and plants for the recovery of by products, had developed more and more into a pure holding enterprise. The industrial establishments it possessed were let out on lease to firms in which the company had interests. In contrast to this the "Schering-Kahlbaum AG" was a concern which was mainly active in the industrial field. The emphasis of industrial production since the foundation of the business was on the manufacture of chemicals and pharmaceutical specialities.

3.1. Schering – KahlbaumAG

The firm "Kahlbaum" was set up in 1818 as a spirit purification works and in 1870 was expanded to produce chemically pure reagents and laboratory preparations. By 1912 the firm consisted of three divisions: a chemical factory, a spirit factory and a liquor factory.

In 1922 the chemical factory of the "Oberschlesische Kolswerke und Chemische Fabriken AG" was acquired. This factory continued to produce chemicals for industrial and laboratory purposes as well as pharmaceutical specialities under the trade name "C. A. F. Kahlbaum Chemische Fabrik GmbH." These became established as quality products not only in Germany, but also abroad. In the same year, the "Oberschlesische Kokswerke und Chemische Fabriken AG" obtained a substantial proportion of the shares of the "Chemische Fabrik auf Actien (vorm E. Schering)." The cooperation between "C. A. F. Kahlbaum Chemische Fabrik GmbH" and "Chemische Fabrik auf Actien (vorm E. Schering)" which had begun in 1924 led to the merger of the two enterprises in 1927. The firm was renamed "Schering – Kahlbaum AG."

By 1936 "Schering – Kahlbaum AG" had built up a world wide export business which was backed by numerous subsidiary companies abroad. Amongst the pharaceutical specialities introduced in those years,

---

Vitamin B crystal (above), vitamin A crystal (courtesy of Hoffmann-La Roche).

the first hormone preparation, "Progynon" (1928), the first X-ray contrast agent "Uroselectan" (1930), and the first gestagen preparation "Proluton" (1933) are worth mentioning. In addition to this, the building of the first electro platings factory were begun in 1936.

3.2. Kokswerke und Chemische Fabriken AG

The "Oberschlesische Kokswerke und Chemische Fabriken AG", founded in 1890, maintained several coke works and plants for the prtjsocessing of useful coke oven by-products as well as a stell mill. After the First World War the industrial foundation was expanded by the acquisition of coal pits and the purchase of shares in the chemical industry.

A Considerable expansion of their own chemical branch took place in 1922 through the acquisition of the controlling interest in the "Chemische Fabrik auf Actien (vorm. E. Schering)" and all the shares of "C. A. F. Kahlbaum AG" which therefore was now legally a subsidiary company of the "Kokswerke und Chemische Fabriken AG."

In 1937 "Lokswerke und Chemische Fabriken AG" took over the assets of "Schering-Kahlbaum AG" and renamed the firm "Schering Aktiengesellscaft" in view of the world famous Schering name.

Chemical laboratory Schering end of the nineteenth century.

Ernst Schering (-1889).

4. Chronological development of the "Schering Aktiengesellschaft"

1937   The "Schering Aktiengesellschaft" becomes the legal successor of "Kokswerke und Chemische Fabriken AG"

1938   In the last year of peace six factories in Germany and more than 30 subsidiary and holding companies abroad belong to the "Schering Aktiengesellschaft"

1945   After World War II dismantling of all production sites and loss of all patents and trademarks as well as factories and subsidiary firms abroad

1946   Expropriation of the firm's possessions in East Berlin and the rest of East Germany

1947   Exportation of pharmaceuticals recommences

1949   Acquisition of a factory in Wolfenbüttel and consequent extension for the production of plant pesticides and galvanochemicals

1951   Initiation of building galvano technical plants in Feucht near Nürnberg

1959   Acquisition of all shares of the "Chemische Werke Bergkamen AG"
        The factories of the former "Chemische Werke Bergkamen AG" and those which the firm already possessed in Bergkamen continued to operate within the framework of the concern as a branch enterprise under the firm name "Schering Aktiengesellschaft, Zweigniederlassung Bergkamen". In this works the production of industrial chemicals and synthetics was begun.

1963   The capital stock of "Duco AG", a holding company dealing with the production of nitrocellulose varnishes until 1949 and that of synthetic resin lacquers later, and whose headquarters were transferred from Berlin to Bergkamen in 1961, was increased by 11,3 million DM to 16,3 million DM in return for contributions in kind. The "Schering Aktiengesellschaft" took over the new shares by realising almost all its foreign interests

1963   Purchase of the company "Productos Quimicos Naturales Proquina S. S. Orizaba, Mexico"

1965   Acquisition of a 25% share in the "C. F. Asche and Co. AG, Hamburg", (increase of the share in 1969 to about 94%, in 1970 to 99,6% and in 1972 to 100%)

1967   Establishment of a second headquarters in Bergkamen (Westphalia) and closure of the Bergkamen branch office

1968   Acquisition of the "Isar-Chemie GmbH, München" which produces and markets adhesives for various fields of application

1969   Acquisition of the "Peschken und Stewner GmbH, Busethude" and the "Rakoll-Werke Peschken und Stewner GmbH & Co., Nienburg", now "Isar-Rakoll Chemie, Nienburg"

1969   Founding of "NOR-AM Agricultural Products Inc." in Chicago in conjunction with "Morton-Norwich Products Inc.", (50% participation)

1970   Acquisition of 74% of "Inertol Holding GmbH, Stuttgart", amongst whose most important holding companies are "Lechler Chemie GmbH, Stuttgart", "Lechler Bautenschutz Chemie KG, Stuttgart" and "Lechler Chemie GmbH, Gelsenkirchen"

1971   Merger of the subsidiary companies active in the field of adhesives—"Isar-Chemie GmbH, München" and "Rakoll-Werke Peschken und Stewner GmbH & Co., Nienburg"— to form the "Isar-Rakoll GmbH" with its headquarters in Münich

1972   Inauguration of a new production plant for liquid chemicals in Berlin Charlottenburg

1974   Occupation of a new administrative centre in Berlin

1975   100% takeover of "Lechler Chemie GmbH, Stuttgart"

1976   100% takeover "NOR-AM Agricultural Products Inc., Chicago"

1976   Acquisition of the "«Nepera Chemical Company Inc., Harriman, New York"

1976   Surrender of the shares in "Concordia-Chemie AG" and take-over of all shares of the former Concordia subsidiary companies: "Fritz Hamm GmbH, Düsseldorf", "Chemiewerk Curtius GmbH, Duisburg", "Chemische Werke Rombach GmbH, Oberhausen" and "Agricultura GmbH, Düsseldorf"

1977   Acquisition of the German plant pesticide and special fertilizer business of "Philips Duphar GmbH, Düsseldorf"

1978   Acquisition of the controlling interest (8 million DM capital − 52% holding) of "Diamalt AG, München"

1978/
79   Acquisition to 100% of the "Sherex Chemical Company Inc., Columbus/Ohio, USA"

1979   Enlargement of the shares in "Diamalt AG, München" to 71%

1979   Acquisition of the "BERLEX Laboratories Inc., Cedar Knolls/New Yersey, USA" to 100%

1980   100% acquisition of "Chemcut Corp. Inc., State College/Pennsylvania"

1980   100% acquisition of the "REWO-Gruppe, Steinau/Hessen"

The grüne apotheke (1855).

Grüne Apotheke: Green Pharmacy
Aktiengesellschaft, AG: joint stock company
GmbH: exempt private limited company—a type of closed corporation under German law
Chemische Fabrik auf Actien (vorm E. Schering): Shareholders chemical factory (Formerly E. Schering)

SEARLE

In the early days, the Searle company was known as small in amount of sales but prominent and reliable. Today G. D. Searle & Co. is still known as prominent and reliable but can be classified as a medium size company. It's 1981 sales from continuing operations were $942.3 million and it spent a little over $82 million in research and development in 1981. It has about 1500 persons in R&D. In 1980 Searle acquired the Cosmos product line for Venezuela. This made Searle the second largest pharmaceutical firm in that country. In the ninth largest pharmaceutical market—Brazil—Searle acquired Laboratil. And in the twelfth largest—South Korea—a fifty percent interest in Keun Wha Pharmaceuticals. Searle in Australia acquired Commonwealth Ammonia in 1980 and in Illinois a plant to manufacture intravenous drug forms. Searle also acquired the product line of Swedish Astra for the French market. And various products for various countries—verapamil from German Knoll for the U.S.A. as well as the whole Knoll product line for Belgium and Spain. Searle's Metamucil became the number one bulk laxative throughout the world in 1980.

Searle has an active licensing and acquisition program and is increasing its investment in R&D. With all this and more it becomes very tempting to say—Oh, if only this company were mine! It is a far cry from the plains of Indiana in 1868—from which there has been an unbroken line of Searle companies managed by four generations of Searle family members. It all started with the Civil War.

In 1864 Gideon Daniel Searle was only eighteen years old but already had had an eventful live. As a member of the 135th Regiment of Indiana Foot Volunteers, he had participated in several campaigns of the War between the States—the Civil War. He had spent some time in an Army Hospital for treatment of infection and fever. It was during confinement there that he read and studied all medical books and papers within reach. These plus his indelible impressions of the battlefield wounded and all the suffering he had witnessed only increased the interest of Gideon Searle in things medical and pharmaceutical. He continued to buy and read books on these subjects.

After returning home from his army service, young Gideon helped his father Herman Searle run the local hotel in Kokomo, Indiana. As the oldest child in a family of eight, there was plenty of work to do in the hotel. Thus when Corporal Gideon Daniel Searle of Company D of the 135th Regiment of Indiana Food Volunteers was discharged—honorably, of course—from "the services of the United States this twenty-first day of September 1864 by reason of expiration of term of service", he had little choice except to return to Kokomo. However, when the Civil War ended in 1865, his family thought it best to send Gideon to Chicago to attend business college. Upon his return he took a job as a "traveling agent" for "a man from Anderson" Indiana who was in "the medicine business". Soon afterward he spent more time in the office and less in traveling—although he did have to call on drug stores. Each such visit only enhanced his ambition to own his own shop. How he did acquire his own drug store is best told in an excerpt from his father's diary.

Herman Searle wrote about his son Gideon: "Gid had given some attention to the study of medical books to qualify himself for keeping a drug store as he had taken some notion in that direction. In looking around for a business, he ran across a small drug store that could be bought in Fortville, Indiana : The store (called O.K. Drug Store) proved a profitable investment." The father went on to say that Gideon Searle sold his first drug store in Fortville to buy out a partner in an Anderson, Indiana Drug Store which was renamed Henderson & Searle.

It seems that Gideon Searle bought out other drug stores and sometimes operated several at once.

For this reason he had been called the prototype of a chain-store pharmacy for having acted as a retailer, wholesaler and manufacturer—albeit on a small scale. He has also been called a prototype of a detailman because he used to take extensive trips with his horse and buggy to call on physicians and pharmacists and remind them of his preparations.

After moving to Omaha, Nebraska for two years—during which time he built a pharmaceutical manufacturing unit—business was so prosperous that G.D. Searle & Co. decided to move to Chicago. Omaha was just too small. Chicago was made distribution center for the whole Middle West.

Searle published its first catalog in 1889 and offered standard products including over four hundred standard fluid extracts; medicine preparations of 150 elixirs; 100 medicinal syrups; 30 medicinal wines; 75 powdered extracts; some 25 tinctures; and about 150 standard botanical drugs. In 1891 Searle offered one of the first lines of compressed tablets to become available to the American physician. In its 1892 catalog, Searle added other tablets—compressed triturated hypodermic—and compressed lozenges. These brought the preparations he could offer to over one thousand. Impressive—but what a difference from today.

Gideon Daniel Searle in 1909 could no longer carry on alone due to failing health which led to his death in 1917. His only son was Claude Howard Searle—physician with two active practices in Chicago and Milwaukee.

Dr. Searle gradually gave up his medical activities to manage his father's pharmaceutical factory. This he did until 1936 but kept on as Chairman of the Board until his death in 1944. In 1936 it was his son John G. Searle who took over from his father.

As a matter of fact, John G. Searle entered the company in 1923, shortly after he had obtained his B.S. degree in pharmacy from the University of Michigan. The result was that John Searle could lend new emphasis on various phases of the G.D. Searle & Co. activities.

The more than one thousand general preparations were reduced and replaced by only thirty Searle specialities. John G. Searle attached great importance to research activities. During the time of his leadership, over forty percent of the personnel at world headquarters in Skokie, Illinois were engaged in research. Moreover, about fifty percent of the technical personnel had Doctor of Philosophy or Doctor of Medicine degrees. With such a team it is no wonder that G.D. Searle & Co. could develop such world known preparations. John G. Searle could bask in the sunshine of his results.

Searle became truly international in 1960 when it introduced Enovid[R]—the first contraceptive. Other well known Searle products include Banthine[R]; Dramamine[R]; Flagyl[R] and Flagyl I.V.; Lomotil[R] for adjunctive therapy in the treatment of diarrhea has been carried by astronauts on every space flight; Metamucil, the world's most widely used bulk laxative; NutraSweet, Searle's brand name for aspartame, a new low-calorie sweetener now approved by the Food and Drug Administration; and Calan, a calcium antagonist. It is no wonder that a thousand listings in the Searle catalog could be replaced by a handful of specialties. And still—G.D. Searle & Co. can even yet be called a prominent and reliable firm.

S.G.750

ÆTHER.
MANUFACTURED BY
EDWARD R. SQUIBB, M.D.
NEW YORK.

Ether as it evaporates from bibulous paper, should give but little foreign odor, and that of light oil of Wine only, as the last portion passes off from the paper; and should leave the paper moist for a short time, but with the odor of alcohol only.

When shaken in a test tube with an equal volume of water, it should lose twenty two percent of its volume. In a test tube half filled and grasped in the hand for a short time, it should commence to boil very slowly on the addition of small fragments of broken glass.

CHLOROFORMIUM
MANUFACTURED BY
EDWARD R. SQUIBB, M.D.
NEW YORK.

When equal volumes of Chloroform and colorless concentrated Sulphuric Acid are shaken together in a glass stoppered Vial, there should be no color imparted to either liquid, or but a faint tinge of color imparted to the acid, after twelve hours standing; neither should there be any sensible heat developed at the time of mixing.

Chloroform as it evaporates from bibulous paper, should give but little foreign odor, and that only as the last portion is passing off from the paper, and the paper should be left odorless.

Chloroform should not be used without having been subjected to these tests. See Amer. Journal of Pharm. Vol XXIV page 427.

SQUIBB

By Dr. J. Sheehan

Undoubtedly it was his deep faith and extraordinary self-discipline that gave Edward Robinson Squibb the strength to overcome difficulties and carry on in spite of adversity.

He was born in Wilmington County, Pennsylvania in 1819, of simple Quaker parents. His mother and three sisters died the year he was eleven, leaving yound Edward to be raised by understanding relatives. After his marriage, his wife developed epilepsy and without any treatment available at that time, he could only stand by and try to keep her from harm during her seizures. With his wife he suffered the loss of one of his four children, who died at the age of six months.

During Christmastime in 1858, with his pharmaceutical business barely started, an assistant tipped over a bottle of ether near an open flame. When Dr. Squibb tried to save his files from the fire that broke out, his face and hands were burned severely. His eyelids were seared and his left hand later on had to be amputated. For the rest of his life he had to wear dark glasses by day to avoid the sunlight and eye pads by night in order to sleep.

Aside from instances of adversity, what other events shaped this man, one of the pioneers of the modern pharmaceutical industry? From boyhood his ambition was to become a doctor of medicine. Since neither he nor his guardians had the money to pay for such an education he apprenticed himself to an apothecary in Philadelphia. He was eighteen years old. He remained in this position for five years, meanwhile saving his meager wages and at the same time learning thoroughly the work of pharmacy. In 1842 Edward Squibb was finally able to start his medical studies at Jefferson Medical College. He was graduated three years later with high honors and was offered the post of demonstrator in anatomy.

Following the outbreak of war with Mexico in 1848. Dr. Squibb overcame the pacifist philosophy of his Quaker upbringing and became an Assistant Surgeon in the United States Navy, where he served for the next ten years. He was assigned to the vessels Perry, Erie and Cumberland. The brig Perry took him to Mexican and South American waters for two years while the storeship Erie brought him to Mediterranean waters.

Shipboard life was of much less interest to him than the problems that arose from the drugs used on the ship's men. Stated simply—these drugs were unreliable. One reason for this was that the Navy bought drugs as it did beans or machines—from the lowest bidder without any reference as to quality. As a result the crude drugs—especially those obtained from foreign countries—contained dirt, twigs, leaves, grass and other impurities. In addition, some drugs derived from varied species of plants had lost their potency with age. Consequently it was not possible to know the strength of any given preparation.

Most distressing of all to the surgeon, the ether available to him was so variable in quality that patients naturally responded erratically to it. For the most part the ether was below standard. With persistent regularity Dr. Squibb, a mere Assistant Surgeon of the United States Navy, wrote to Naval Headquarters report upon report pointing out the evil effects of not having production, product and assay standards for the drugs they bought. At length his voice was heard and his advice taken. Dr. Squibb was transferred to shore duty and assigned to the Brooklyn Navy yard. There, with limited funds appropriated in 1852 by Congress for the Navy to establish a laboratory for drug research, in a small room above the morgue in the Naval Hospital, he went to work.

He started on ether—for that was the most urgent need of the naval surgeons—and indeed of all surgeons. The chief problem was that the ether available lacked uniformity. It contained variable amounts of toxic impurities. Moreover, its manufacture was carried out under hazardous conditions in open vessels, heated over an open fire. The surgeon Edward Robinson Squibb changed that. He found that steam heat from ordinary boilers could be used for the etherification of alcohol. This process produced an anesthetic ether consistently of a high uniform quality, and safer, easier and more economical than any then in use. So that all could profit from his new process, Dr. Squibb published a full account with drawings in the *American Journal of Pharmacy* in September 1856. The Squibb process has been changed in detail but the company he founded manufactured ether by virtually the same process he invented in 1852 until it discontinued its manufacture in 1974 because of the advent of superior methods of anesthesia.

Dr. Squibb also provided for its efficient use by devising a suitable face mask to use during operations when ether is the anesthetic. He also worked on other anesthetic agents at this time and developed a chloroform of high quality as well as a stabilized cocaine solution.

Despite the improvement and advances made by Dr. Squibb in his efforts to develop reliable drugs and medicines of standard quality and tested potency, Congress refused to vote more than niggardly appropriations for the Naval Research Laboratory. Work was hampered and expansion was impossible. Besides, reserach was only one of a number of duties required of Dr. Squibb. He also served as a physician and surgeon in the hospital. In this situation the gentle, religious Quaker grew frustrated and discouraged and he began to look for an opportune moment to resign from the Navy.

In 1857 the chief medical purveyor of the U.S. Army made an encouraging proposal. The army had been trying to create a reliable source of supply for drugs and anesthetics but had not succeeded in getting an appropriation. If Squibb would establish his own laboratories, the chief medical purveyor assured him, the army would buy the bulk of his output and there would be a ready market for the remainder among hospitals and civilian doctors. Of added urgency was the belief that a war between the States was inevitable and imminent and that would require the army to stockpile quantities of drugs and anesthetics from a reliable source. With this encouragement Dr. Squibb offered his resignation to the Navy and on December 4th it was accepted.

There was no difficulty in raising capital, mostly among professional friends in Brooklyn, and late in the summer of 1858 the laboratories of "Edward R. Squibb, M.D." in a small brick building near his home, were furnished. By December they were in operation and ready to meet many of the needs of the army. In his laboratories, it was Dr. Squibb's practice to work all day, go home to dinner and then walk back to work for a few more hours. Holidays were no exception—that is, until the tragic fire that Christmastime, the fire that maimed him for life. But phoenix-like he rose from the ashes of this tragedy. Even as he was recuperating at home, a group of doctors and surgeons of the New York and Brooklyn areas banded together and subscribed over two thousand dollars to help reestablish his laboratory. The testimonial letter accompanying the check read: "You have brought to the work a sanc consideration of practical chemical sciences, pharmaceutical skill and professional attainment such as we had hardly dared to hope for. We look upon your cause as our cause, your enterprise as the inauguration of a new era, and yourself as the exponent of the great principles of Truth and Humanity in array against dishonest cupidity." Neddless to say Dr. Squibb subsequently repaid this entire sum of money.

With his laboratories restored and his business expanding Dr. Squibb retourned to what was his lifetime passion: uniformity and purity in drugs, a crusade that was to embrace all pharmacy. Though usually rebuffed repeatedly on the national scene he made headway on the state and local levels as more and more people came to understand his purpose. But let us pause to see for ourselves what he was advocating and why he thought this work more important than practicing medicine and why it became for him both an obsession and a crusade. Let us see why he spent his time writing model laws for legislative bodies, petitioning for the enforcement of present laws and working on many committees to frame new ones.

A pharmacopeia is a descriptive listing of approved medical preparations and drugs and the tests used for their identification. It contains also tests for the strength and purity of these substances as well as a listing of the synonyms by which a preparation is known. The first official pharmacopeia in the United States was that of 1820—the United States Pharmacopeia. It had the provision that it be revised every ten years. This first edition listed only a few drugs—hardly enough to have impact. It was fortunate therefore for Dr. Squibb to receive an appointment to the Committee of Revision of the U.S.P. in 1860. Committee meetings were held in Philadelphia and this required that Dr. Squibb make the journey often from New York, travelling by horse and carriage, by boat and then train. Nevertheless, he now had a forum to bring forth his ideas. He could indicate to committee members what formulas could be accepted, improved—or dropped altogether. In short, he could do all those things which we characterize today under the term "Quality Control". Moreover, with his background he could, in 1862, justify his criticism of the American Pharmaceutical Society for its continued failure to insist upon the enforcement of the Act of 1848, prohibiting the import of adulterated drugs.

Dr. Edward R. Squibb, 1819-1900, founder of the laboratories bearing his name. His papers on the standardization and purification of medicinal products materially aided in the establishment of standards for early revisions of the U.S. Pharmacopoeia.

In 1879 Dr. Squibb presented a report to the New York State Medical Society entitled "Rough Draft of a Proposed Law to Prevent the Adulteration of Food and Medicine and to Create a State Board of Health." This proposal—the Squibb Bill—became law in New York the following year and in New Jersey shortly thereafter. It was the first such law in the United States and it served as a guide not only for other states and for the federal government but also for other countries as well. It even served as the foundation stone for Dr. Harvey W. Wiley to bring into being the Federal Pure Food and Drug Act of 1906. By then Dr. Edward Robinson Squibb had died and so he was denied the satisfaction of seeing the passage of this landmark legislation.

During the closing years of his life the management of the company fell largely to the two sons of Dr. Squibb, Charles F. (1857-1942) and Dr. Edward H. (1853-1929). In fact the company was renamed for them; in 1892, it became known as "E. R. Squibb & Sons." These sons had been well trained and managed the company for nearly a decade but only maintained the status quo—admittedly no one could take Dr. Squibb's place. In 1905 the Squibb family, realizing that both new capital and new management were needed, passed the reins to different hands.

Lowell M. Palmer and Theodore Weicker, who purchased E. R. Squibb & Sons, were responsible for its transition from a one-man enterprise to a big business. Both were thoroughly familiar with Dr. Squibb's principles and methods, and were determined to maintain them. They supported new laws—including enactment of the revised Federal Food, Drug and Cosmetic Act of 1938. They represented the firm before Congressional hearings—both in the House and Senate—and supported all laws which promised to impose uniform standards of purity and potency on pharmaceutical preparations. Therein lies the explanation of how the House of Squibb grew to its present stature without losing any of the unique characteristics of the old regime.

E.R. Squibb & Sond, Inc., has flourished and has become a giant in the pharmaceutical industry following mergers, acquisitions and other corporate changes throughout the world. It is a major manufacturer of pharmaceuticals, health care products, hospital instruments and patient monitoring systems. Its World Headquarters is now located in Princeton, New Jersey, U.S.A. E. R. Squibb & Sons is the major subsidiary of Squibb Corporation of New York City, whose worldwide operations have been directe sinced 1968 by Mr. Richard M. Furlaud.

It is self-evident that such a reserach oriented company with its strong determination to achieve the ultimate in quality, purity and potency, would have a long list of "firsts" among its scientific accomplishments. Some of these are:

Ether. Dr. E. R. Squibb himself invented a continuous steam distillation process for the manufacture of pure uniform quality ether for surgical anesthesia plus an improved face mask for its administration.

Fluphenazine decanoate. An injectable antipsychotic agent for the treatment of shizophrenia. Its duration of action lasts for atleast four weeks.

Isonicotinic acid hydrazide. Coincidently with the Roche laboratory the tuberculostatic property of this compound was discovered.

Penicillin. To supply the rare new drug, penicillin to meet the need during World War II, Squibb was a member of three American manufacturers who first produced this antibiotic via deep culture fermentation in 15,000 gallon capacity reactors. Production reached a level of two tons daily of bulk penicillin. A "Squibb Strain" for penicillin cultivation was developed; and Squibb was the first to make crystalline penicillin as well as a depot penicillin for injection that provided long acting therapy. Among other antibiotics discovered, introduced or produced were one of the related cephalosporin type, an antifungal agent and lately a new class of beta lactamase inhibitors known as monobactams.

Capoten, the world's first orally-active ACE inhibitor. With the introduction of captopril, an angiotensin converting enzyme inhibitor in 1981, a significant new approach for the treatment of hypertension and congestive heart failure has been inaugurated.

Monobactams. Also in 1981, scientists at The Squibb Institute for Medical Research announced the discovery and development of the first monocyclic beta lactam antibiotics, a new family of anti-infective agents. The first synthetic monobactam, called azthreonam, is proving highly effective against serious hospital acquired infections.

Besides being the first to market a therapeutic vitamin dosage and pioneering in the development of

Norld headquarter. E.R.S. Squibb Corp. Princeton, N.Y.

curare products—marketing the first pure curare alkaloid—Squibb has also developed a new beta blocker, fluorinated steroid antiinflammatory agents and many different radioisotopic preparations of wide diagnostic value. All of these are but a small part of the diverse and extensive number of products Squibb has marketed in becoming a giant among giants in the pharmaceutical industry.

All of this could not have been accomplished if The Squibb Institute for Medical Research had not been established in 1938. The Institute is considered the first laboratory founded in the United States by a pharmaceutical firm dedicated to basic research in medical science. It has attracted to its staff scientists from all parts of the world. From among its staff past and present are those who have been honored for their work by such awards as the Albert Lasker Medical Research Award for its work in the field of tuberculosis therapy, the Nichols Medal, the Benedetti-Pichler Award, the Morley Medal and the Alfred Burger Award in Medicinal Chemistry, for the development of captopril.

Some also have been honored by election to membership in the National Academy of Science, while one of its directors ultimately became the head of the United States National Institutes of Health. As it approaches its mid-century birthday in 1988, the Institute continues to reflect the ideals of Dr. Squibb and holds fast to his goal to ever work for the "Health and Well-Being of all Humankind."

In summary, the name of Dr. Edward Robinson Squibb has been memorialized in many ways aside from the great firm that bears his name. Following his graduation as a doctor of medicine and while he served in the United States Navy he established at the Brooklyn Naval Hospital a research laboratory dedicated to the improvement of drug standards, forerunner of the modern complex Naval Research Laboratoires. As late as November 1944, the Navy recognized its debt to him by launching the Liberty Ship S. S. Edward R. Squibb.

"We Salute Thee Sir! Bon Voyage!"
Dr J. SHEEHAN

UPJOHN

In 1884 Dr. W.E. Upjohn was a young general practitioner in Hastings, Michigan. He must have been a good pharmacist too because he invented the friable pill. At that time doctors usually prescribed pills—and pills they got. These were blobs of medicine plus adhesives and gums. They usually were coated—with shellac or other coatings including gold or silver. The pills were hard of course. And many times they did not disintegrate at all. Dr. Upjohn was vexed. He studied the problem thoroughly in his own home laboratory and within the year had made pills which were reduced to a powder under the thumb and yet stable enough to reach the gastro-intestinal system where they could be absorbed. This was important because compressed tablets were new and not readily available. Thus a good soft but not too soft—a friable pill—was of great advantage. Dr. W.E. Upjohn patented his friable pill process in 1885.

In 1886 Dr. W.E. and Dr. Henry U. Upjohn founded a pill company. The Upjohn Pill and Granule Company in Kalamazoo, Michigan. Their first catalog listed 186 pill formulas made from 56 different drugs. As the pills vied with compressed tablets, the Upjohn brothers added standard preparations to their catalog—powders, ointments, compressed tablets, syrups, elixirs. They even shortened their name to The Upjohn Company in 1903. At first the brothers were too busy to expand their product line of outstanding but nevertheless standard drugs—Phenolthalein in pink candy-type compressed tablets or Citrocarbonate or Cheracol or even Digitora which was the first major development of Upjohn research in 1919.

Back in 1913 the Upjohn Company had hired Dr. Frederick W. Heyl as its first Ph. D. chemist. His task was to control production and to develop newer methods of assaying drugs. By 1914 he had set up a bacteriological laboratory for bioassays. He soon was made Director of Research and as a chemist quickly put Upjohn into the mainstream of chemical syntheses to yield organic chemicals and their derivatives—not all in the pharmaceutical field.

As early as 1927, The Upjohn Company established a nutritional research laboratory to develop nutritional supplements such as various vitamin combinations and multivitamins such as Unicap in 1940.

During World War II Upjohn earned an impressive record. It succeeded in finding a way to sterilize sulfanilamide powder in 1942. Small packets of sterilized powder were carried by all combat troops and were known as Wound Packets. Upjohn developed in 1943 a program to produce serum albumin—so necessary for battlefield transfusions. The company could also introduce Heparin as the first highly effective anticoagulant.

Another great Upjohn achievement was its erection of a pilot plant in 1943 for the mass production of penicillin. This experience was most helpful in the post war competition for antibiotics. It led to Cycloheximide—which has a selective antifungal activity in plants.

To Neomycin—useful in treating mastitis in cows. To Albamycin—a broad spectrum antibiotic—which was found in a soil sample in Queens, New York. To Lincocin—another broad spectrum antibiotic and its derivative Cleocin. And lastly Trobicin as a one injection therapy for gonorrhea.

Research has been called the heart of Upjohn—which does not scatter its talents. Thus the company concentrates on six different fields and with separate research teams for each field. These are hypersensitivity, fertility, infections, diabetes, cardiovascular, central nervous system.

It is with such type programs that The Upjohn Company could introduce into medicine preparations like Orinase as an antidiabetic. Gelfoam as an hemostatic in surgery. And Provera as a steroid hormone. It was Upjohn which found a microbiological method of attaching an oxygen atom to carbon 11 of progesterone. This made possible the preparation of steroid hormones, such as cortisone and progesterone from one ton a year to one ton a month. And a steep drop in price.

Upjohn was one of the first groups in the field of prostaglandins. These hormone-like substances serve as biological regulators.

In 1973 it introduced Prostin F_2 Alpha for the interruption of pregnancy when required. Foreseen for the near future are antitumor agents and products for peptic ulcer and thrombosis. Most important are agents in development for treatment of acute leukemia in children and adults.

An innovation in the pharmaceutical industry is the sale of health services—not tablets—to the population and laboratory services to physicians. The Upjohn Health Care Services or UHCS engages paramedical personnel for care of the aged or sick and convalescent patients. Home personal health care is expanding more and more due to the pressures of economic and social factors. Upjohn has about three hundred offices with a staff of sixty thousand full or part-time employees. It is meant to augment the staffs of nursing homes and hospitals. Upjohn also has a Chemical Division and Agricultural/Veterinary Division with manufacturing *facilities* worldivide.

WYETH

This pharmaceutical firm was another of the establishments founded by brothers. This time it was John Wyeth and his younger brother Frank of Philadelphia. Their greatuncle NOAH Wyeth was one of the group which participated in the now famous Boston Tea Party. Thus it can be seen that the Wyeth family were from the city—one were Father and Grandfather Wyeth were newspapermen.

Joh Wyeth—born in 1834—enrolled in the Philadelphia College of Pharmacy for their two year course. This in 1852, at a time when others had only an apprenticeship in a pharmacy—if that. Upon graduation in 1854 he worked in a leading Philadelphian pharmacy until 1860. Then in that same year John and Frank Wyeth opened their own drugstore at Walnut Street in Philadelphia. It can be said that they were an immediate success.

Having had a taste of research after writing his thesis on the properties of Gillenia trifoliata, John Wyeth made his aime the improvement of the taste of pharmaceutical products. He became famous for his "Sweetened tinctures" or "elixirs" as they are now known. The prescription business of John Wyeth and Brother grew and grew and occasioned a physician friend to make a suggestion. The friend was Dr. John V. Shoemaker. His suggestion was that—since his patients complained that they had to wait a long time until their prescriptions were compounded—would it not be feasible to prepare prescriptions in advance? It was.

In 1862 John Wyeth and Brother could publish a catalog listing the Wyeth preparations available in labeled bottles for wholesale distribution. During the Civil War the firm supplied the Union Army with many medicines. John Wyeth and Brother specialized in compressed tablets and sugar coated tablets. Glycerine Suppositories produced in the United States were first made by Wyeth—as were soluble gelatin capsules and effervescent salts.

It would be thought—with such a successful enterprise managed by John Wyeth and Frank Wyeth—that other family members would be more than happy to obtain it. But—no. John's son Stuart studied law and was not interested. Frank's son Maxwell did join the management but showed no interest. Thus when the founder, John Wyeth, died in 1907 the interest in the family business was inherited by Stuart Wyeth and—when he died in 1929—he left his fifty-five per cent of John Wyeth and Brother to Harvard University. The University accepted—but whishcd to scll its holdings. That was the end of John Wyeth and Brother as founded by John—but it was not the end of Wyeth. In fact it may be called a new beginning.

American Home Products Incorporated was interested and started negotiations in 1930. On June 24 in 1931, the business and good will of John Wyeth and Brother was sold to American Home Products Incorporated. Soon Wyeth was expanded. American Home was interested in expanding its pharmaceutical lines and brought several well known preparations under Wyeth management—Bovinine Company. Pctrogalar Laboratories. The S.M.A. Corporation. Bartos Inc. Gilliland Labs and Dr. H.M. Alexander Company. Now both Wyeth Laboratories and American Home Products Corporation have their new names. AHPC has under its banner some food firms plus housewares. Packaged medicines. And Prescription Drugs establishments, such as Ayerst Laboratories. Wyeth Laboratories. Ives Laboratories and Corometrics Medical Systems.

In 1942 Reichel Laboratories also became part of American Home. Since Reichel had developed a good method to dry blood plasma it could supply large amounts to the Armed Forces during World War II. This led to further collaboration with the United States Government—especially as regarded penicillin production and refinements. Thus the United States Office of Scientific Research and Development arrangcd for Wyeth to have priority for needed equipment. This enabled Wyeth's Biological Division to produce in the six month period between July 1943 to January 1944 over sixty per cent of the world's supply of penicillin.

After the war Wyeth developed tablet forms of penicillin. But also antacids. Preparations of infant formulas. Biologicals. Conception control products. And ataraxics. American Home is carrying on from where the second generation of the Wyeth family left off.

Deed of partnership between Silas M. Burroughs and Henri S. Wellcome : London 27 September 1880.

THE WELLCOME
FOUNDATION LIMITED

Henry Wellcome, pharmacist, entrepreneur, mentor of scientific research, philanthropist, collector, archaeologist, anthropologist, lives on today in the work of two organisations that bear his name.

The Wellcome Foundation Limited is one of the world's leading pharmaceutical companies, itself conducting research comparable to that of a university and engaged in the promotion of the health and hygiene of people and animals.

The Wellcome Trust is Britain's largest medical charity, applying all profits it receives from Wellcome's continuing and expanding business enterprise to the support of medical and allied research in universities and hospitals around the world.

In the words of "The Times" of London, "the Wellcome principle is a simple one: that all money made out of the company's operations in the relief of suffering and disease shall be used to further the relief of suffering and disease".

Henry Solomon Wellcome, who in 1910 was to become a British subject and in 1932 was to be knighted by King George V, was born on August 21, 1853 at Almond, Wisconsin. In 1861 the family moved still further westwards to Garden City, Minnesota, where the father's brother, a surgeon, owned a drugstore. Henry developed at an early age a healthy interest in making money. At 16 he began to bottle and sell a "Magic Ink".

In 1870 Henry left home to become a prescription clerk in Poole and Geisinger's Pharmacy at Rochester, Minnesta. Upstairs was the office of Dr. William Mayo, whose sons later founded the Mayo Clinic. Dr. Mayo encouraged Henry to fit himself for a professional career. So in 1872 he enrolled at the Chicago College of Pharmacy and obtained a job in Thomas Witfield's pharmacy there. After a year he moved on to the Philadelphia College of Pharmacy, and from there he graduated in 1874.

At the age of 23, whilst travelling as a salesman for the New York pharmaceutical house of McKesson and robbins, Wellcome made a special study of the cinchona forests of Peru and Ecuador, through which he passed on muleback, and published a paper on the subject.

In 1880 Wellcome sailed for England to form with Silas M. Burroughs, a friend from his Philadelphia student days, the firm of Burroughs Wellcome and Co., which at first acted as an agency to import Amemrican drugs. By 1882 the firm was making products of its own in a basement at Snow Hill, London.

In 1884 the firm registered the word "Tabloid", the name coined by Wellcome to describe its compressed tablets, which were gaining wide acceptance on acount of their accuracy of dosage.

Some of Wellcome's closest friends were explorers. Beginning with Sir Henry M. Stanley, practically every explorer of note has carried with him a Tabloid Medical Chest presented by Burroughs Wellcome. These chests went up the Amazon with Theodore Roosevelt and were part of the expedition that first scaled Mount Everest. They were carried by Shackleton, Scott, Aundsen and other polar explorers.

For cars and aeroplanes the firm produced light-weight aluminium first-aid kits. Wellcome was an early motor enthusiast and saw that King Edward VII received one of them. Louis Blériot, the first airman to fly the English Channel, took one with him. So did Charles Lindbergh when he flew across the Atlantic.

On February 6, 1895, Silas Burroughs died at Monte Carlo at the age of 48. In the following year, after negotiations with his heirs, Wellcome became the sole owner of the business, which nevertheless continued to use both their names.

After the death of Burroughs, Wellcome placed an emphasis on scientific research that was unkown in the commercial world. He established research laboratories in the 1890s and gave his scientific workers freedom of investigation in the broad field of experimental therapeutics. These concepts, far ahead of their time and firmly applied thereafter, were to be the cornerstone of the company's later development as a world-wide group of international repute.

In 1901 Wellcome visited the Sudan. Moved by the wretchedness of the natives, most of whom

275

suffered from malaria, he immediately established the Wellcome Tropical Research Laboratories at Gordon Memorial College in Khartoum. A steam tug was converted into a floating laboratory on the Upper Nile and named "Culex", after the mosquito. Pestridden Khartoum soon became one of the healthiest cities in Africa, and Wellcome developed an enduring interest in tropical problems.

From boyhood onwards Wellcome had always collected medical books and medical relics from all parts of the world. At the suggestion of Sir William Osler and others he exhibited some of his treasures at the XVII International Congress of Medicine in London in 1913. They attracted such attention that he was encouraged to establish the Wellcome Museum of the History of Medicine, still flourishing in London at the Science Museum in South Kensington.

The Wellcome Library for the History of Medicine, with which the museum is associated, contains Wellcome's collection of more than 250,000 printed books from the 15th century onwards, many of them rare and some unique. The library also possesses more than 10,000 manuscripts, both Western and Oriental, and about 75,000 autograph letters of famous doctors and scientists.

Sir Henry Wellcome became ill in 1935 but made a final visit to the United States in the spring of 1936, visiting the scenes of his youth at Garden City, Minnesota and undergoing treatment at the Mayo Clinic in Rochester. He returned to England and died at the age of 82 on July 26, 1936.

Henry Wellcome had brought together all his business interests under the name of The Wellcome Foundation Limited in 1924. When he died in 1936 he left his sole ownership of this company to the Wellcome Trust. This is the largest endowed charitable trust supporting medical research in the United Kingdom and plays a singificant role both in Britain and overseas, particularly in the tropics.

To consolidate and expand in the veterinary and agricultural field the Wellcome Foundation acquired the old-established British firm Cooper, McDougall & Robertson in 1959.

In 1979 Wellcome purchased the Jensen-Salsbery laboratories division of Richardson-Merrell Inc. Based in Kansas City, Missouri, Jensen-Salsbery now operates as the Wellcome Animal Health Division, manufacturing and selling animal health products which include biologicals, pharmaceuticals and surgical instruments.

The Wellcome Production Centre at Dartford in Kent is the principal technical and production centre for the whole of the group, and traces its origin to the earliest days of the Company. There are also Wellcome manufacturing centres in 26 of the 40 countries where the group has overseas subsidiaries.

The main centre for Wellcome research was established at Beckenham, Kent, in 1921, with a tradition going back for almost 30 years before that. Research at the Wellcome Research Laboratories in North Carolina is directed from here.

The American company, Burroughs Wellcome Co., at Research Triangle Park, North Carolina, is the largest wholly owned United States subsidiary of any British pharmaceutical company. In addition to carrying out research, it has large-scale manufacturing facilities at Greenville, North Carolina.

Fundamental scientific discoveries have been made on both sides of the Atlantic, the most recent of which are epoprostenol (prostacyclin), a naturally occuring hormone which may lead to new treatments of heart attack and stroke, and the antiviral acyclovir ('Zovirax'). Beckenham is also a centre for research into and production of the potential anti-cancer substance, interferon ('Wellferon').

The Foundation's medical products are known principally to the doctors who prescribe them, while some are the concern of specialists who use them under hospital conditions. They include 'Septrin', a broad-spectrum antibacterial, 'Lanoxin' for the treatment of heart failure, 'Zyloric' for gouty arthritis and 'Imuran' for suppression of the rejection of transplanted organs.

At Berkhamsted in hertsfordshire the Wellcome Research Laboratories continue and extend the Cooper tradition of worldwide expertise in chemicals for the control of internal and external parasites of livestock. The group's chemotherapy department in veterinary medicine is situated here, as are laboratories for the study of coccidiosis, general entomology and veterinary entomology. The laboratories at Berkhamsted are also a world centre for monitoring the resistance of cattle ticks to insecticides, and specimens are brought in for study from all over the world.

At Pirbright in Surrey, the Wellcome foot-and-mouth disease vaccine laboratory carries out research and production working with all seven types of foot-and-mouth disease virus. With seven other centres around the world, Wellcome is the world's major producer of foot-and-mouth disease vaccine.

276

The business which Sir Henry Wellcome owned continues to grow and prosper as The Wellcome Foundation Limited, whilst his benefactions and his work in the history of medicine have been maintained and extended by the Wellcome Trust. THus, by these two organisations, but one concept, the work of Sir henry Wellcome is still carried on.

Painting of the wellcome production. Centre at Dartford, Kent. 1890.

Corporate Headquarters and research laboratories of Burroughs Wellcome Co. at Research triangle Park, North Carolina.

Typical example of public advertising, end of nineteenth century. (Courtesy of Hoffmann La Roche and Co.).

BIBLIOGRAPHY

ANDRÉ-PONTIER (L.), *Histoire de la Pharmacie, Origines, Moyen Age, Temps modernes*, Paris, O. Doin, 1900, in-8°, XXI-729 p.

ADLUNG (A.) und URDANG (G.), *Grundriss der Geschichte der deutschen Pharmazie*, Berlin J. Springer, 1935, pp. 161-181.

ANTIDOTAIRE NICOLAS (L'), Deux traductions françaises de l'*Antiditarium Nicolai*, l'une du XIVᵉ siècle, l'autre du XVᵉ siècle, publiées d'après les manuscrits fr. 25327 et 14827 de la Bibliothèque nationale par le Dr Paul Dorveaux. Paris, H. Welter, 1896, in-8°, XXII-109 p.

BARIETY (Maurice) et COURY (Charles), *Histoire de la médecine*. Paris, Fayard, 1963, in-8°, 1 221 p.

BAUDERON (Brice), *La Pharmacie de Bauderon*, à laquelle... sont ajoutées de nouveau les remarques, corrections et compositions curieuses et nécessaires aux médecins, apothicaires, chirurgiens et autes. Lyon, B. Rivière, 1663, in-4°, VI-408-294-VI.

BAUME (Antoine), *Éléments de Pharmacie théorique et pratique*. Paris, Vve Damonneville et Musier fils, 1762, in-8°, XVI-854 p.

BLAESSINGER (Edmond), *Quelques grandes figures de la Pharmacie militaire*. Paris, Baillière, 1948, in-8°, 388 p.

BOUSSEL (Patrice), *Histoire illustrée de la Pharmacie*. Paris, Guy Le Prat, (1949), in-4°, 199 p.

BOUVET (Maurice), *Histoire de la Pharmacie en France des origines à nos jours*. Paris, éd. Occitania, 1937, in-8°, 447 p.

BOUVET (Maurice), *Les travaux d'histoire locale de la Pharmacie en France*. Paris, 1957, in-8°, 44 p.

BOVÉ (Frank J.), *The Story of Ergot*, Basel/New York Karger, 1970, pp. 297.

CASTIGLIONI (A.), *Histoire de la médecine*. Paris, Payot, 1931, in-8°, 781 p. *Centenaire de l'École supérieure de Pharmacie à l'Université de Paris*, 1803-1903. Paris, A. Joanin et Cie, s.d., in-4°, XXIII-407 p. *Cent cinquantenaire des Facultés et écoles de Pharmacie et de l'Académie de Pharmacie*. Séance solennelle tenue le 15 octobre 1953. Paris, Masson, s.d., in-8°, 51 p.

CHARAS (Moïse), *Pharmacopée royale galénique et chymique*. Paris chez l'auteur, 1976, in-4°, V-1060 p.

CYCLOSPORIN (A.), *The prototype of a new generation of immunosyppressive agents*, Basel International Sandoz Gazette, 27 March (1980).

DAGOGNET (François), *La raison et les remèdes*. Paris, P.U.F., 1960, in-8°, 351 p.

DAUMAS (Maurice), *Histoire de la science*. Paris, N.R.F., 1957, in-12, LI-1907 p.

DECHAMBRE (A.), *Dictionnaire encyclopédique des sciences médicales*. Paris, Asselin-Masson, 1864-1889, 100 vol., in-8°.

DELPHAUT (Jean), *Pharmacologie et psychologie*. Paris, A. Colin, 1961, in-12, 183 p.

HISTORY OF PHARMACY

DILLEMANN (Georges), *Jetons et médailles pharmaceutiques (Corporations, Sociétés, Écoles)*, Paris, Édit. de la Porte Verte, 1977, in-8°, 40 p.

Dispensatory of the United States U.S.D., Edited by OSOL (Arthur) and FARRAR (George E.), Philadelphia J.-B. Lippincott 24th Ed. 1947

DOMAGK (Gerhard), Manuscript Materials and Archive Documents from Bayer Leverkusen

DORVAULT (F. L. M.), L'*Officine*, 18ᵉ, édit. bis. Paris, Vigot frères, 1945, in-8°, 2345 p.

FABRE (René) et DILLEMANN (Georges), *Histoire de la Pharmacie.* Paris, P.U.F., 1963, in-8°, 128 p. *Figures pharmaceutiques françaises.* Notes historiques et portraits 1803-1953. Paris, Masson, 1953, in-4°, 277 p.

FLECHTENER (H. J.), Carl Duisberg – Eine Biographie, Manuscript and Documentary Materials from the Archives of Bayer A.G. Leverkusen.

FLÜCKIGER (Friedrich A.) and HANBURY (Daniel), Pharmacographia – A History of the Principal Drugs of Vegetable Origin London, MacMillan and Co., 2nd Ed., 1879, p. 803.

FOUGERE (Paule), *Grands Pharmaciens.* Paris, Corréa, 1956, in-12, 336 p.

FUCHS (Léonard), *Commentaires très excellents de l'hystoire des plantes, composez premièrement en latin par Leonarth Fuchs, et depuis, nouvellement traduictz en langue française par un homme sçavant et bien expert en la matière.* Paris, Jacques Gazeau, 1549, in-folio, 285 p.

GORIS (A.), *Centenaire de l'internat en pharmacie des hôpitaux et hospices civils de Paris. Histoire documentaire de la pharmacie dans les hôpitaux et hospices civils de Paris, de la Révolution à 1918.* Paris, impr. de la Cour d'Appel, 1920, in-4°, XIX-891-LXVII p.

GUITARD (Eugène-Humbert), *Deux siècles de presse au service de la Pharmacie et cinquante ans de « L'Union pharmaceutique ».* Paris, Pharmacie centrale de France, 1913, in-12, 316 p.

GUIBERT (Victor), *Histoire naturelle et médicale des nouveaux médicaments introduits dans la thérapeutique depuis 1830 jusqu'à nos jours.* 2ᵉ éd., Bruxelles, Paris, Londres, Madrid, 1865, in-8°, IV-XXI-681 p.

GUYBERT (Philibert), *Toutes les œuvres charitables de Philibert Guybert... rev., corr. et augm...* Paris, Estienne Loyson, 1660, in-8°, III-600-VII p.

HAHN (Dr A.) et DUMAITRE (Paule), *Histoire de la médecine et du livre médical.* Paris, O. Perrin, s.d., in-4°, 434 p.

HECQUET (Philippe), *La médecine, la chirurgie et la pharmacie des pauvres.* Paris, Vve Alix, 1740, 3 vol., in-12.

JULIEN (Pierre), *Catalogue de la collection d'anciens ouvrages de pharmacopée français et étrangers...* Paris, 1967, in-8°, 96 p.

KREMERS (E.) and URDANG (G.), *History of Pharmacy,* Philadelphia J.B. Lippincott Company, 1940.

LAIGNEL-LAVASTINE (Dr), *Histoire générale de la médecine, de la pharmacie, de l'art dentaire et de l'art vétérinaire.* Paris, A. Michel, s.d., 3 vol., in-4°.

LAURENT (Jean), *La Pharmacie en France, étude de géographie économique.* Thèse, Lettres, 1959, in-4°, 255 p.

LEFEBVRE (Gustave), *Essai sur la médecine égyptienne de l'époque pharaonique.* Paris, P.U.F., 1956, in-8°, XII-216 p.

LEMERY (Nicolas), *Traité universel des drogues simples, 2ᵉ éd.,* Paris, Laurent d'Houry, 1714, in-4°, VIII-922-XXXI p. *Pharmacopée universelle.* Paris, Laurent d'Houry, 1968, in-4°, VII-1050-XIX p.

LICHTENTHAELER (Dr Charles), *La médecine hippocratique.* Lausanne, Genève, 1948-1963, 4 vol., in-8°.

PHILLIPE (A.), *Histoire des apothicaires chez les principaux peuples du monde.* Paris, Publicité médicale, 1853, in-8°, VII-452 p.

POMET (Pierre), *Histoire générale des drogues simples et composées.* Paris, Étienne Ganeau, 1735, 2 vol., in-4°.

RENOU (Jean de), *Le grand dispensaire médical contenant cinq livres des Institutions pharmaceutiques, ensemble trois livres de la Matière médicale, avec une Pharmacopée ou Antidotaire fort accompli.* Traduict de latin et françois par Louys de Serres. Lyon, Pierre Rigaux et associés, 1624, in-4°, X-982-IX p.

REUTTER de ROSEMONT, *Histoire de la Pharmacie à travers les âges.* Paris, Peyronnet, 1931, 2 vol., in-8°.

RORDORF (Hartmann), Ueber die Erwicklund der chemisch – pharmazeutischen, Spezialitäten – Industrie in der Schweiz 1895-1925, Wohlen Aargan Schweiz Buchstruckerei, Kasimir Meyer's Söhne 1927, p. 53.

RUSK (Walter), 100 Jahre Deutsche Chemische, Gesellschaft Weinheim, Chemie Verlag., 1967, p. 260.

SCHMIDT (Albrecht), Die Industrielle chemie – Die pharmazeutischen Industrie, Berlin and Leipzig Verlag, Walter de Grazter & Co., 1934, pp. 153-171.

Scientific American, Industrial Microbiology, New York City Scientific American Inc., Vol. 245, No. 3, September 1981.

TATON (René), *Histoire générale des sciences.* Paris, P.U.F., 1957-1964, 4 vol., in-8°

VALETTE (G.), *Précis de pharmacodynamie.* Paris, Masson, 1963, in-8°, II-596 p.

VIEILLARD (C.), *Gilles de Corbeil.* Pais, H. Champion, 1903, in-8°, XIX-456 p.

ZEKERT (Otto), Berühmte Apotheker, Stuttgart Deutsche Apotheker Verlag, 1955, pp. 160.

CONTENTS

HISTORY OF PHARMACY

Printed in France
by Imprimerie Darantiere
Dijon-Quetigny
December 1982/January 1983

PHOTOS FROM:

Bibliothèque Nationale de Paris, Bibliothèque Universitaire de Bâle, Musée Pasteur, Musée Cantonal des Beaux-Arts de Lausanne, Musée Départemental des Vosges, P. Corson, R. Lalance, Chéret, P. Montbazet - Explorer -, Giraudon, laboratoires Abbott, Bayer, Sandoz, Hoffmann-La Roche, Eli Lilly, Schering, Squibb, Pr L. Ravies, Foreman Archive, Rietberg Museum.